ROCK MECHANICS DESIGN
IN MINING AND TUNNELING

Innovative design: Record-size tunnel boring. Robbins Tunnel Boring Machine, model 353-196, for hard rock, diameter 10.8 m. Photo courtesy of The Robbins Company, Seattle.

ROCK MECHANICS DESIGN
IN MINING
AND TUNNELING

Z.T.BIENIAWSKI

Professor of Mineral Engineering and Director
Mining and Mineral Resources Research Institute
The Pennsylvania State University

A.A.BALKEMA / ROTTERDAM / BOSTON / 1984

ISBN 90 6191 507 4 cloth edition
ISBN 90 6191 530 9 paper edition
© 1984 Z.T.Bieniawski

Published by A.A.Balkema, P.O.Box 1675, 3000 BR Rotterdam, Netherlands
Distributed in USA & Canada by: A.A.Balkema Publishers, P.O.Box 230, Accord, MA 02018
Printed in the Netherlands

Preface

*The essence of knowledge is, having acquired it, to
apply it.*

Confucius (450 B.C.)

Although mining and tunneling are the oldest engineering activities performed by man underground and current engineering technology in these fields has many great achievements to its credit, no design textbook exists to serve the graduate engineer specializing in rock mechanics design in mining and tunneling. In addition, there is a general lack of emphasis on the teaching of design in mining in spite of well established design courses in other engineering fields such as mechanical or civil engineering.

Granted that rock mechanics is a relatively new science, but this discipline forms the basis for the design of excavations in rock such as are found in mining and tunneling. Important projects in mining and tunneling have been made possible by accumulated practical experience, engineering judgment and often a trial-and-error approach by practitioners in underground excavation engineering. The actual design guidelines currently in use are essentially a collection of empirical rules. In essence, the construction of underground excavations has traditionally been an art rather than an engineering science.

The purpose of this book is to educate the student in the design process as applied to the rock mechanics aspects of underground mining and tunneling. These two engineering areas have purposely been chosen because they have a great deal in common, yet mining and civil engineers maintain insufficient contact. It is believed that much can be learned by interaction between mining and tunneling and by an exchange of ideas and experience between mining and tunneling engineers.

The specific objectives of this book are:

1. To instill into graduate students the vital role of engineering design as the culmination of all engineering courses.

2. To obtain an understanding of the engineering design process.

3. To determine the latest rock mechanics design approaches.

4. To apply current rock mechanics knowledge for the purpose of innovative design in mining and tunneling.

The book is thus aimed at mining engineers, civil engineers and geological engineers. It is hoped, too, that this book will provide a refreshing emphasis on the engineering design process for engineering educators and for the beginning engineers in industry as well as in consulting practice.

Since the book is aimed at graduate engineers, a basic knowledge of rock mechanics,

v

strength of materials and the theory of elasticity is assumed. There are a number of good introductory texts on rock mechanics, and these and other publications are listed at the end of Chapter 1.

This book is used for a two-term, four credit course for mining and civil engineering graduates at the Pennsylvania State University. The course is structured on three principles: i) the students have already covered the fundamentals of rock mechanics, ii) the book serves as the basic text for lectures but more outside class reading is prescribed; and iii) there is a practical design project involving 'real-life' situations that accompanies the course.

I wish to express my thanks to my colleagues and friends who have contributed significantly over many years to the ideas and developments described in this book. The general attitude towards high quality research and scholarship at the Pennsylvania State University has encouraged me greatly in the preparation of this volume. A number of persons have made significant contributions by discussions on specific topics and by reviewing the manuscript. Special thanks are due to Dr. Evert Hoek of Golder Associates, Vancouver; Dr. Don C. Banks of U.S. Army Waterways Experiment Station, Vicksburg, Mississippi; Prof. E. T. Brown of Imperial College, London; Prof. H. Reginald Hardy, Jr. of the Pennsylvania State University; Prof. Richard E. Goodman of the University of California, Berkeley; Prof. Fred H. Kulhawy of Cornell University; and Mr. Francis S. Kendorski of Engineers International, Inc., Chicago. The author's colleagues and graduate students at the Pennsylvania State University have also been most helpful, notably Professors Robert L. Frantz, R. V. Ramani, L. Saperstein, D. P. Gold and Messrs. Robert Belesky, Hasan Gercek, Christopher Mark, David Newman and Erdal Unal.

I am indebted to the following organizations for generously supplying photographs and illustrations: The Robbins Company; National Mine Service Company; U.S. Bureau of Mines, Spokane Research Center; Robert S. Mayo & Associates; U.S. Army Corps of Engineers; C.S.I.R., Pretoria; and Engineers International, Inc.

I am also very grateful to the sponsors of my research, especially the U.S. Department of Energy, Office of Advanced Research and Technology, and the U.S. Department of the Interior, Bureau of Mines and the Office of Surface Mining. In addition, university research funds were provided to me by Penn State's College of Earth and Mineral Sciences through the unfailing support of Deans Charles Hosler, Arnulf Muan and the late Dean Robert Stefanko.

My wife, Elizabeth, has contributed significantly to the chapter on historical perspective and was also most helpful in cross-referencing the bibliography and the index. My secretary, Carol Fee, has typed many manuscript versions of this book and through her patience and professional efficiency helped me succeed in meeting all the deadlines.

I gratefully acknowledge all the above contributions.

Z. T. Bieniawski

Contents

CHAPTER 1

Introduction

*Scientists explore what is; engineers create what has
never been.*

> Theodore von Karman (1911)

Engineers are designers and design is the goal of engineering activity. Although impressive progress has been made in the field of rock mechanics, particularly in the last two decades, the knowledge so accumulated has not been fully utilized for engineering design in mining and tunneling. While this situation may have been justified in the past, the pressing energy needs in the United States and in the world dictate an improved design philosophy for mining and tunneling engineering. This calls for a new breed of engineer-designers who will be able to assume the role of decision-makers and technical leaders.

Rock mechanics is an interdisciplinary field concerned with the study of the mechanical behavior of rock masses and, more appropriately, with the response of rock to the forces resulting from its physical environment.

ROCK MECHANICS APPLICATIONS

Currently, rock mechanics principles and methods of analysis find application in a variety of professional fields, namely, mining engineering, civil engineering, geological engineering, petroleum engineering, geology and geophysics. In engineering, rock mechanics is used from the stage of feasibility studies, through design and construction, to the maintenance of structures in rock. A recent report of the U.S. National Committee for Rock Mechanics (1981) on *Rock Mechanics Research Requirements* emphasizes the important role of rock mechanics in mineral resource recovery, construction and earthquake-hazards mitigation. Thus, rock mechanics finds applications in the design and construction of many structures, such as listed in Table 1.1. It can materially assist in building tunnels and other underground openings for civil and military purposes. In mining, it is an important aid in planning the layout of underground excavations, in the evaluation of support requirements and in the alleviation of mining hazards. Other principal fields for its application are in rock fragmentation studies leading to the design of improved tools and processes. Petroleum engineers use rock mechanics to understand how rock breaks and to develop more efficient drilling operations.

At present in the United States, rock mechanics is experiencing an unprecedented

Table 1.1. Some rock mechanics applications in mining and tunneling

Fields of application	Types of structures and design areas
Mining	Coal mining underground: room-and-pillar or longwall design, shafts
	Metal mining underground: drift and shaft design, cavability of ore, amelioration of rockbursts
	Surface mining: stability of slopes
Transportation	Highway tunnels, railroad tunnels, urban rapid transit (metro) tunnels and stations
Energy development (excluding petroleum)	Underground power stations (hydro-electric and nuclear), underground storage of oil and gas, energy storage (pumped storage or compressed-air storage), underground repositories for nuclear waste disposal, geothermal energy exploration
Petroleum development	Drilling processes, hydraulic fracturing, oil shale mining
Services	Water conveyance tunnels, industrial and municipal waste treatment, sanitation tunnels
Military	Deep basing of strategic missiles, underground chambers for invulnerable defense facilities
Housing	Underground or earth-sheltered homes, offices and warehouses
Emerging applications	Space exploration (e.g. use of Space Shuttle), earthquake prediction, remote control mining and in situ recovery, under-ocean tunneling for oil, very large underground chambers (100 m spans) for defense projects.

amount of activity due to the program of nuclear waste disposal in underground excavations (Smedes, 1982, Monsees and Munson, 1982) and deep basing of strategic missiles (U.S. National Committee on Tunneling Technology, 1982). The role of rock mechanics in engineering is changing, from providing solutions to isolated problems to giving positive assistance in integrated design procedures.

Historically, rock mechanics is a very young science. Following pioneering research in the United States on rock deformation by David Griggs in 1936, the National Academy of Sciences established the Committee on Experimental Deformation of Rocks in 1945. A year later, the Bureau of Mines published its specifications for standardized tests on mine rock. In 1950 active rock mechanics research was under way at the Colorado School of Mines while in 1951 the first annual Drilling, Blasting and Rock Exploration Symposium was held at the University of Minnesota. In Europe in the same year, the first Symposium on Rock Mechanics was organized by the Austrian Geomechanics Society in Salzburg and mining engineers gathered in Belgium for the first International Strata Control Conference.

The first annual U.S. Symposium on Rock Mechanics was held in 1956 and was sponsored by four mining schools: Colorado School of Mines, University of Minnesota, University of Missouri and the Pennsylvania State University.

In 1962, the International Society for Rock Mechanics was formed with its secretariat in Portugal and the 1st International Congress on Rock Mechanics was held in 1966.

In 1963, the President of the National Academy of Sciences appointed the Committee on Rock Mechanics to survey research and education in rock mechanics in the United States. The following definition was provided (Committee on Rock Mechanics, 1966):

> Rock mechanics is the theoretical and applied science of the mechanical behavior of rock and rock masses; it is that branch of mechanics concerned with the response of rock and rock masses to the force fields of its physical environment.

At present, the U.S. National Committee for Rock Mechanics – under the auspices of the National Research Council – plays an important role in coordinating rock mechanics activities in the United States. This committee represents the views of the American rock mechanics community to the International Society for Rock Mechanics.

No one can deny the improvements achieved by engineers in present times, in dealing with rock mechanics problems. In spite of its relatively short history, the discipline has developed into an all important engineering area. The application of its principles with increasing confidence and the further development of rational design procedures for excavations in rock are expected to enhance significantly the role of rock mechanics in the future.

SOURCES OF INFORMATION

Recent texts

Coates, D. F. *Rock Mechanics Principles*, Mines Branch Monograph 874, CANMET, Third Edition, Ottawa, 1980, 442 p.
Goodman, R. E. *Introduction to Rock Mechanics*, John Wiley & Sons, New York, 1980, 478 p.
Hoek E. and Brown, E. T. *Underground Excavations in Rock*, Institution of Mining and Metallurgy, London, 1980, 527 p.
Jaeger, J. C. and Cook, N. G. W. *Fundamentals of Rock Mechanics*, Chapman & Hall, London, Third Edition, 1979, 593 p.

Other notable texts

Brown, E. T. (Editor). *Rock Characterization, Testing and Monitoring-ISRM Suggested Methods*, Pergamon Press, Oxford, 1981, 211 p.
Muller, Leopold. *Der Felsbau*, Ferdinand Enke Verlag, Stuttgart, 1963, Vol. 1, 624 p.
Obert, L. and Duvall, W. I. *Rock Mechanics and the Design of Structures in Rock*, John Wiley & Sons, New York, 1967, 650 p.
Peng, S. S. *Coal Mine Ground Control*, John Wiley & Sons, New York, 1978, 450 p.
Roberts, A. *Geotechnology – An Introductory Text for Students and Engineers*, Pergamon Press, New York, 1977, 347 p.
Salustowicz, A. *Zarys Mechaniki Gorotworu*, Wydawnictwo Slask, Katowice, 1968, 196 p.
Spivak, A. I. *Mekhanika Gornych Porod*, Nedra, Moskva, 1967, 132 p.
Talobre, J. A. *La Mechanique des Roches*, Dunod, Paris, 1967, 442 p.

Important journals

International Journal of Rock Mechanics and Mining Sciences, Pergamon Press, Oxford
Rock Mechanics and Rock Engineering (formerly Rock Mechanics) Springer-Verlag, Vienna
Tunnels and Tunnelling, Morgan-Grampian Ltd., London
Engineering Geology – International Journal, Elsevier, Amsterdam

Underground Space, American Underground-Space Association, Pergamon Press, New York
Journal of Geotechnical Engineering, American Society of Civil Engineers, New York
Mining Engineering, Journal of the Society of Mining Engineers of AIME
Mining Magazine, Institution of Mining and Metallurgy, London
Gluckauf Translation, Verlag Gluckauf, Essen

Major international conferences and dates relevant to rock mechanics design

1951	First International Conference on Rock Pressure and Support (later called Strata Control in Mines) Liege, Belgium (2nd: 1956, Germany; 3rd: 1960, France; 4th: 1964, USA; 5th: 1972, Great Britain; 6th: 1977, Canada; 7th: 1982, Belgium)
1951	First Annual Drilling Symposium, Minneapolis, USA
	First Geomechanics Colloquium in Salzburg, Austria
1956	First U.S. Symposium on Rock Mechanics at the Colorado School of Mines (held annually since then)
1958	International Bureau of Rock Mechanics formed (agency of the World Mining Congress)
1962	International Society for Rock Mechanics founded
	First Canadian Symposium on Rock Mechanics
1966	First International Congress on Rock Mechanics, Lisbon, Portugal (2nd: 1970, Yugoslavia; 3rd: 1974, USA; 4th: 1979, Switzerland; 5th: 1983, Australia)
1972	First Rapid Excavation and Tunneling Conference, Chicago, USA (2nd: 1974, San Francisco; 3rd: 1976, Las Vegas; 4th: 1979, Atlanta; 5th: 1981, San Francisco; 6th: 1983, Chicago)
1974	International Tunneling Association formed
1976	International Tunneling Symposium, London, (2nd: 1979; 3rd: 1982)
	Symposium on Exploration in Rock Engineering, Johannesburg
1984	Symposium on Design and Performance of Underground Excavations, Cambridge, Great Britain

REFERENCES

Committee on Rock Mechanics. *Rock Mechanics Research : A survey of United States Rock Mechanics Research to 1965, with a Partial Survey of Canadian Universities*, National Academy of Sciences, Washington, DC, 1966, 82 p.

Griggs, D. T. Deformation of rocks under high confining pressures. *J. Geol.*, Vol. 44, 1936, pp. 541–577.

Monsees, J. E. and Munson, D. E. Design considerations for a nuclear waste repository. *Tunneling Technology Newsletter, U.S. National Committee on Tunneling Technology, No. 37*, March 1982, pp. 1–12.

Smedes, H. The national program for isolating high-level nuclear waste. *Underground Space*, Vol. 6, No. 5/6, April 1982, pp. 220–228.

U.S. Department of Energy. *National Plan for Siting High-Level Radioactive Waste Repositories and Environmental Assessment*, DOE/NWTS-4, DOE/EA-151, Washington, DC, 1982.

U.S. National Committee for Rock Mechanics. *Limitations of Rock Mechanics in Energy-Resource Recovery and Development*. National Academy of Sciences, Washington, DC, 1978, 67 p.

U.S. National Committee for Rock Mechanics. *Rock Mechanics Research Requirements for Resource Recovery, Construction and Earthquake-Hazard Reduction*, National Academy of Sciences, Washington, DC, 1981, 222 p.

U.S. National Committee on Tunneling Technology. *Design and Construction of Deep Underground Basing Facilities for Strategic Missiles*. National Academy of Sciences, Washington, DC, 1982, 68 p.

CHAPTER 2

Historical perspective

*No man belongs only to his own time: he is the heir to
the past and the maker of the future.*

D. Perkins & G. C. VanDuesen

Among the few books on the history of engineering fields, processes or materials, the text by Stephen P. Timoshenko (1953), professor of engineering mechanics at Stanford University, is truly outstanding. Entitled *History of the Strength of Materials*, it was the first book directed to students who had already completed the courses in strength of materials and, by studying the history of the subject, could obtain a better appreciation of the field, a better perspective and motivation for future developments. Engineers in general can learn much from the history of their fields and feel justifiably proud of past engineering achievements. Furthermore, in these days of high technology, one tends to forget the miseries and challenges faced by our forefathers and we take for granted the many engineering achievements of the present day. It is in the spirit of enhancing our knowledge of the past and learning to respect the present that this chapter is presented.

Not many centuries ago, the word 'engineer' was exclusively a military term. Civil, that is civilian, engineering had been invented by the French in the mid-18th century. The origin of the term 'engineer' does not lie in the term engine, as is so popularly believed. It is derived from the French word genie meaning 'ingenious'. Hence, ingenuity, creativity and innovation should be the aspiration of all engineers.

The engineer's ingenuity and inventiveness is well demonstrated by a brief historical overview of mining and tunneling.

ANCIENT MINING AND TUNNELING

From time immemorial, men have chiselled and hammered their way into the Earth's rocky surface: to bury their dead; to take their enemies by surprise; to mine its minerals and precious metals; to transport men or vital natural resources, such as water, by more direct and therefore cheaper routes. Always they have had to contend with the tunneler's twin nightmares – fire and water – added to which (as tunnels became longer and deeper) were lack of air and high temperatures. Mother Nature, as the tunneler encounters her, could be more murderous than motherly!

The oldest known mine in the world, Bomvu Ridge in Swaziland in southern Africa, was in operation before 40,000 B.C. Here Neanderthal Man mined hematite, literally 'blood stone', which because of its color was much prized for burial rites and personal decoration. The technique was of the brute-force variety: bones, sharp stones and his bare hands were all he had. Burrowing, rather than mining, would be a more accurate description.

Following the revolutionary discovery of flint (e.g. 'Grime's Graves' in Norfolk, England) in the New Stone Age, primitive picks and hammers, with handles of bone and flint cutting edges, were invented and put to use to mine more flint from chalk and limestone deposits in England, Belgium, France and Sweden, and salt at Halstatt near Salzburg in Austria and at Wieliczka near Cracow in Poland – vital commodities for a civilization becoming increasingly settled and agrarian in character. Flint, however, was brittle and soon blunted. These stone tools were replaced in time by copper, then bronze and finally iron chisels.

While salt has been mined at Halstatt since 2500 B.C., the Magnum Salalias Wieliczka salt mine region in Poland is the oldest in Europe with salt manufacturing installations discovered dating back to the Middle Neolithic period (3500 B.C.– 2500 B.C.). The salt deposits at Wieliczka mined continuously since the early 13th century provide today not only salt but also a rich mining heritage admired by some 700,000 visitors annually. The tourists can inspect an impressive museum, an underground post office, as well as an underground church excavated in salt and two chapels containing altars and ornaments. A labyrinth of chambers and passages totals about 100 km, with many chambers carved in salt and decorated with statues. Today the mine employs 1,000 men and produces over 60,000 tons of salt annually.

The art of copper smelting was highly developed among the Sumerians by 4000 B.C. and was probably introduced into Egypt by them. By 2900 B.C. Egypt began to build stone pyramids of blocks hewn and shaped with copper chisels. This copper was mined at Wadi Maghara in the Sinai Peninsula. Science was augmenting brute force. Holes were cut around large blocks, wedges were then driven in to loosen the blocks, or wooden plugs were inserted. Soaked in water these swelled and caused the rock to fracture. Fire setting, alternately heating the rock by building a fire against the face, then contracting it with buckets of cold water, or better still, vinegar, was used.

The Egyptians applied their tunneling expertise to carve out tombs for the pharaohs, the longest of which is the tomb of Seti having a total length of some 215 m. Large underground caverns were excavated to store water. The gold that was found in King Tutankhamun's tomb was probably mined at Coptos, in the area between the Nile and the Red Sea. The deepest mine in this region was 90 m and extended 460 m along the vein. The roof was supported by wooden props and the principal tool used was a stone hammer. Emerald mines near the Red Sea had workings at a depth of 240 m. Life in an Egyptian mine has been likened to Dante's Inferno. Half suffocated from smoke and lack of air, choking on the fumes of vinegar or worse, if the ore body contained sulphur or arsenic, miners did not have a long or happy life. They were all slaves and regarded as expendable.

Fire must have been a frequent hazard. Military sappers knew how to turn this to their advantage. The trumpet blast that 'caused' the walls of Jericho to fall was probably a signal to the troops who had undermined the fortifications to fire the timber and evacuate the tunnel. Robbed of support, the roof collapsed, bringing down the walls in the resulting subsidence.

Like the Egyptians, the Greeks and Romans in their search for precious metals were forced to mine at ever greater depths. The silver mines at Laurium near Athens reached a maximum depth of 117 m – they dared not mine below sea level. Although the shafts were large, 1.2 m by 1.8 m in section, underground drifts were very narrow, slaves often working in a crouched position. As little timber was available, pillars of ore were left to support the roof – an early example of room and pillar mining! Silver from these mines paid for the fleet that defeated the Persians under Xerxes at the battle of Salamis in 480 B.C. and supported a leisure class who gave us the art and philosophy of the Golden Age. Silver too, this time from the mines in the Sierra Morena in Spain, paid the Roman legions, bastions of the Pax Romana. Ore bodies here were worked to a depth of 200 m, with drifts extending 900 m into the ore body, using fire-setting and iron tools.

Drainage was by means of slave-operated waterwheels or cochleas, a device invented by Archimedes. Each of these could raise water between 2 m to 3 m, depending on the circumference of the wheel, and had to be linked in series. One such arrangement in the Rio Tinto mine could raise 70 liters a minute a distance of 30 m – a miniscule amount by modern standards! Even with slave labor these drainage devices were too expensive to install and operate in any but the richest mines.

Proper alignment of tunnels was a problem right up to Roman times. King Hezekiah in 715 B.C., fearing the Assyrians would besiege Jerusalem, built a tunnel connecting the Pool of Virgins with the Pool of Siloam outside the walls. Although the two were only 350 m apart, the tunnel zigzagged for a 'thousand and two hundred cubits', approximately twice the required length. The tunnelers were guided as to depth and direction by noise made on the surface!

The Romans were experts in tunneling for a wide variety of purposes such as military, transportation, water supply and drainage. Many of the Roman tunnels are still in use for example, the aqueduct tunnel built in Athens by the Emperor Hadrian 1,800 years ago. The Romans took some of the guesswork out of tunneling. A number of shafts were dug and work proceeded in headings from each shaft. Plumb lines were dropped down neighbouring shafts and primitive leveling devices were used.

The Fucinus Tunnel completed A.D. 41 to drain Lake Fucino was 5.6 km long, 6 m high, and 2.7 m wide. Forty shafts were dug for access and ventilation, some as deep as 120 m. It took 11 years to complete and required the labor of 30,000 slaves under a constant replacement system. The average advance per working face was 7 cm per week!

Obviously, only successful conquerors with large numbers of expendable slaves were able to accomplish much tunneling. Mines for precious metals and salt were also excavated by slaves and usually being sent to the mines was synonymous with a death sentence. The fragmentation of Europe into small city-states and dukedoms which followed the collapse of the Roman Empire led to a decline in the demand for minerals and, worse still, no exchange of information to advance knowledge and expertise in mining and tunneling. This trend was reversed by the agglomeration of states under the aegis of the Holy Roman Empire and by the crusading zeal of these emperors. Money and weapons were again in demand. Gone, however, were the slave miners, to be replaced by skilled medieval craftsmen, complete with an emblem, the crossed hammer and maul; and a patron saint, Saint Barbara [see box]. Trained probably in Saxony, or Bohemia, possibly even in the famous Rammelsberg Mine, the only mine in the world worked continuously for over 1,000 years from 968 A.D., the miner took his skills across Europe to Britain and thence to the New World.

THE LEGEND OF SAINT BARBARA

Saint Barbara is the Patron Saint of miners and tunnelers and her feast is widely celebrated in Europe every December 4. No new mine or tunnel is started unless a dedication to St. Barbara has first taken place and her statue placed in a prominent place.

Saint Barbara lived in the third century in the Middle East in a region known as Nicomedia, in present-day Turkey. She was the daughter of Dioscuros, a prominent pagan ruler, who was alarmed at the spread of Christianity in his lands and had his 17-year daughter removed to a secure tower residence where she would not come in contact with teachers of the new religion. Despite his precautions Barbara received instruction and was baptized. She ordered the workers to cut two new windows in her tower room, making three in all, and when her father asked the meaning of it, she explained: 'Grace comes to us through three channels, the Father, the Son and the Holy Spirit.' Realizing his daughter's conversion, her father beheaded her with his own sword. The legend has it that, instantly, from a cloudless sky, a bolt of lightning struck him dead. The precise year of St. Barbara's death is unknown – some sources say it was 303 A.D. while others give an earlier year (235).

Based upon ancient devotion to the girl-martyr, Saint Barbara was named as Patroness of all in danger from thunder, lightning, fire, storms at sea and explosions. She is best known as the Patroness of miners and tunnelers (explosions and fire) but also of seafarers, artillerymen and firemen.

Miners and tunnelers in Germany, Poland, France, Italy and other countries celebrate each year the feast of St. Barbara as an official holiday, complete with parades, music in the parks, dancing and partying.

The city of Santa Barbara in California is named after her. In December 1602 when Spanish voyager Viscaino was sailing up the present California coast, his ship was engulfed in a sudden tempest. The sailors sought the intercession of Saint Barbara and were delivered from shipwreck on her feast day, December 4. In thanksgiving, they named the channel in her honor from which the city was given her name in 1782.

MIDDLE AGES

Mining practice in Saxony and Bohemia is well documented by Georg Bauer (1556), writing under the latinized form of his name 'Agricola', in *De Re Metallica*.* The 'hot tunneling method' he describes differs little from the fire-setting practiced by the Egyptians 4000 years ago. This was the primary method of rock shattering until the 13th century. The invention of black powder in the 14th century did eventually speed up the rock-breaking process. Blasting holes, however, were drilled by hand right up to 1849.

Agricola's book, which served as the only handbook on the subject for 350 years, could disseminate knowledge to many as a result of the rapid spread of the art of printing following Gutenberg's invention which deserves some special attention.

The invention of the printing-press by Johann Gutenberg in about 1450 was an interesting case study of the nature and morphology of design. There were, in essence, four elements which Gutenberg had to combine so as to produce a successful printing press – each of them well known before his time. These were the press, paper, ink, and

*The English translation of Agricola's work was undertaken by Herbert Clark Hoover and his wife Lou. Hoover was U.S. President (1928–1932) and also a mining engineer.

movable type. The press had already been in use in Europe for centuries. Paper – invented in China in about 150 AD – had found its way into Europe by the middle of the 12th century and was already replacing parchment and vellum. Ink was well known from antiquity and separate type had long been used by book-binders for titles in books.

What Gutenberg did was to synthesize these four elements into an effective device designed to achieve a specific objective. Firstly, he had to adapt his press for printing on paper. Secondly, he devised a means of casting his movable type in an adjustable mold so that it could be easily assembled and clamped together. And thirdly, he developed an oil-based ink so as to avoid the running which occurred on his metal type with the water-based inks then in use. What can be seen here is an example of the identification of a need or an opportunity followed by a creative synthesis of known elements coupled with experiment or analysis to produce a desired end result – in essence a description of the design process.

Returning to medieval mining and tunneling, water was obviously a major problem and Agricola described very sophisticated drainage devices. No fewer than six different types of pumps operated by men, horses or a surface waterwheel are described. All were of the 'rag and chain' variety in which bundles of rags or hollow balls attached to a continuous chain dipped into a sump, were raised to the surface and emptied into a reservoir. A highly elaborate system in use in a mine near Schemnitz in Slovakia consisted of three units in series, each unit comprising 32 horses in groups of eight, working four hour shifts with a twelve hour rest period, that is 96 horses in all!

Lift pumps, with pistons operating in cylinders, which sucked water from the mine were first used at Joachimsthal in 1550 and at the Rammelsberg Mine in 1566. A mine map of 1661 showing underground workings in the Harz Mountains in Saxony shows a drainage adit with a series of piston-pumping installations activated by waterwheels. One particular mine at Zellerfeld had six waterwheels on the surface and eighteen underground!

As mines became progressively deeper and wetter, some better method had to be found. Here the cross-fertilization of ideas paid off. Cornishmen who had learned their trade from the miners of Schemnitz invented and perfected the Newcomen steam engine. Thomas Newcomen built his first engine in 1712. Before he died in 1729 his engines were in use in Hungary, France, Belgium, Austria and Sweden, but they relied heavily on coal. Improvements by Smeaton and later Watt and Boulton cut consumption considerably. Watt engines were also used in Pennsylvania coal mines. Further improved by Trevithick and Woolf, they were remarkable for their simplicity and reliability. Starting out as a device to dewater mines, the steam engine ventually powered the Industrial Revolution, driving looms, furnaces and, of course, trains. The latter gave a tremendous impetus to tunneling.

As trade revived at the end of the Middle Ages, transportation presented a serious problem. The Roman roads were in ruins or infested with robbers. Rivers presented the obvious and immemorial answer. Could goods go all the way by water and avoid lengthy portages? So canals were built linking the great European rivers. There was still the snag of different levels. Locks could overcome this but they were expensive to build and maintain and terribly time consuming. Why not go 'under' rather than 'over' or 'around'?

The big first in canal tunnels was on the Canal du Midi which connected France's

Atlantic coast with the Mediterranean Sea. First of its kind, it was also the first tunnel excavated by gunpowder. It also marked a trend – tunnels primarily for transportation. Situated at Malpas and completed in 1681 after two years' work, the tunnel is 157 m long, 6.7 m wide and 8.2 m high.

MODERN TIMES

In America, the early nineteenth century saw a rash of tunnels, first for canals and then – the wave of the future – for railroads (Mayo, 1982). The Erie Canal, opened in 1825, started the American transportation era. The first American tunnel was the 137 m long, 6 m by 5.5 m cross-section, Auburn Tunnel in Pennsylvania, built during 1818–1821, on the Schuylkill canal. It was followed in 1826 by the 183 m long Lebanon Tunnel, on the Union Canal, which is now a national monument. The Allegheny Portage Railroad Tunnel (275 m long) was completed near Altoona, Pennsylvania, in 1833. More ambitious by far was the project to build a railroad through the Hoosac Mountain in Massachusetts. Known as the 'Great Bore', this tunnel commenced in 1851 at a contract price of $3.88 million and was only completed in 1875 at a final cost of $17.3 million. The first tunneling machine on record, built by John Wilson in 1856, was tested in this tunnel. With its European sisters, two Alpine tunnels, the Mont Cenis 1857–1870, and the Saint Gotthard 1872–1881, the Hoosac Tunnel taxed human endurance and ingenuity to the utmost and marked a revolution in tunneling technology (Brierley, 1976).

In the first 30 years, up to 1850, there were 48 tunnels completed in the United States for both canals and railroads. By 1875, some 300 tunnels for railroads alone, were listed (Mayo, 1982).

In 1849, Jonathan Couch of Philadelphia patented the first power drill. Using several of his drills powered by steam and mounted on a platform, work on the Hoosac commenced but was abandoned after only 3 m had been excavated. Six years later Germain Sommeiller, the engineer in charge of the Mont Cenis project, devised a method for compressing air to drive the nine power drills mounted on his 'corps de bellier'. Raymond Leschot invented the diamond drill in 1864 specifically for use in the Mont Cenis Tunnel and the rate of advance increased ten-fold reaching 4.5 m per day in 1870.

Meanwhile in America, work on the Hoosac had recommenced in 1856. The 7.6 km long tunnel was to be 7.3 m wide and 6.7 m high. At first progress was slow but finally compressed air drilling allied to Thomas Doane's daring experimentation with a new blasting agent – nitroglycerine – and better management, saw the completion of the tunnel in 1875. It was the first project in the U.S. that employed compressed air drilling and the first one in tunneling utilizing nitroglycerine (Brierley, 1976).

Encouraged by these successes, work on the Saint Gotthard was started in 1872. Working conditions were appalling. In all, 311 died and 877 were rendered invalids from silicosis, bronchitis, pneumonia and 'miners' anaemia' caused by the parasitic worm ankylostome. However, it too saw tremendous technological advances. Blasting gelatin, a mixture of 92% nitroglycerine and 8% nitrocellulose, developed by Nobel in 1875, was used and the 15.2 km St. Gotthard tunnel was completed in 1881, after only nine years. Compare this with thirteen years for the 12.6 km Mont Cenis! Note that the

St. Gotthard tunnel had no ventilation and, after a half hour train ride through the tunnel, passengers had to disembark so that the carriages could be aired and the windows washed.

Paralleling developments in tunneling in the 1860's and '70's, mining engineers were experimenting with coal-cutting machinery powered first by steam (not very successfully) and later by compressed air. The first compressed air cutter was used in a Lancashire (England) coalfield in 1868. This was a circular disc set horizontally, with hardened pick points mounted on the periphery, which undercut coal. Bar-type machines, better suited to the cutting of soft seams, were also introduced in the 1860's. Both types became very popular in America where more regular and thicker seams presented ideal conditions for mechanical cutting. American engineers developed a chain-type cutter from the bar-type in the early 1870's.

Virginia City, in Nevada, situated as it was on the famous silver-mining Comstock Lode, became a center for experimentation with new techniques in these years. This was an extremely wet mining area – so wet that a drainage adit, the Sutro Tunnel, was driven into the mountain beneath the ore body to drain the mines to a depth of 670 m. To support the walls of the large stopes on the Ophir Mine, Philip Deidesheimer designed special 'square sets', a system of modular timber support. Rock-breaking was speeded up by compressed air drilling, diamond drills, and the use of dynamite. From Virginia City these techniques spread to other mines in the western states.

Major developments in tunneling

The late 19th century has been called the Golden Age of Tunneling and is typified by such great projects as the 20 km-long Simplon Tunnel through the Alps and the Moffat Tunnel through the Rockies. Nothing succeeds like success. In less than 50 years three Alpine tunnels were completed; each one longer and deeper than its predecessor; each at the limits of man's imagination in design and ingenuity in execution; each a proving ground for new developments and a challenge to find ever faster, more economic and safer methods of construction.

Consider the economic and social effects of these tunnels. Distances in Europe were telescoped and with the completion of the Simplon none of the major European capitals was more than a day or so away by train – a jet age in miniature.

Alfred Brandt, chief engineer on the Simplon, had designed a rock drill in 1876 which embodied a completely new concept. Earlier mechanical drills were percussive, mimicking the manual hammering action, this drill bored into the rock. Consisting of a hallow drilling stem with a bit fitted with four teeth and driven by water, not compressed air, it was capable of drilling to a depth of 1 meter in 15 minutes. This was the beginning of 'wet drilling' which was to be a boon to deep level mining. First used in the Arlberg Tunnel on the railway line between Vienna and Paris, it increased the rate of advance to 8 m a day.

Mindful of the ventilation problems encountered in the Saint Gotthard, Brandt adopted a novel design – two parallel single track tunnels 17 m apart at their centers. Both headings were driven simultaneously with cross-cuts connecting them at 200 meter intervals. Large electric fans installed at the portal of one heading pushed air in. It was then diverted by doors into the cross-cut and back out. For every cubic meter of air supplied to the Saint Gotthard, 25 were supplied to the Simplon.

AMERICAN METHOD OF TUNNELING

Heading-and-Bench Method, about 1840. Four crews drilling with Double-Jacks while the Muck Gang loads out. Black Powder was the only explosive. (Courtesy of Robert S. Mayo).

Three Brandt drills were used at a time, each drilling four holes in the space of two hours. Gelatin, far more powerful than dynamite, was used for blasting. The complete cycle of drilling, charging, detonating and mucking took about five hours and the average daily rate of advance was 5.5 m.

Numerous problems were encountered, those involving water being most severe. On the Swiss side, the water was hot and as the heading advanced became hotter, reaching a scalding temperature of 60°C. The surrounding rock at 55°C was too hot to touch and, ironically water had to be pumped into the tunnel – icy mountain water to cool the rock. Due to the great depth of the tunnel, over 2134 m below the surface, and the resulting rock pressure, timbering was often crushed and special steel supports had to be used – 40 cm thick with 15 cm flanges, bolted onto massive timber beams 50 cm square. In places the lining of the completed tunnel was 1.7 m thick!

The Simplon Tunnel was opened in 1906. The error in direction between the two headings was only 20 cm and that in level 9 cm – remarkable in a tunnel 20 km long. Due to the difficulties encountered, the toll in lives was 96 workers.

While at Simplon care was taken not to repeat the nightmare of the St. Gotthard, even greater care characterized the construction of the Moffat Tunnel, the first piercing of the Rockies.

Trains crossing the Continental Divide had to climb to over 3500 meters. It took five special locomotives to haul a train up some gradients and one stretch of 145 km was so

Beton lined tunnel – Erie Railway. The first American Tunnel to be concrete lined, probably 1875. Built 1855-1861 through the Palisades at Jersey City, 4,400 feet in length. In those days the Erie RR was 6-ft gauge; the third rail was for standard gauge equipment. (Reprinted by Elgood-Mayo Corp., Lancaster, PA).

hazardous that it took fourteen hours to traverse. The idea of building a tunnel originated with David Moffat, builder of the Denver Northwestern and Pacific Railroad, but work only commenced in 1923 after his death. It was to serve a double purpose – as a water tunnel too. A design similar to that of the Simplon was adopted. A pilot tunnel would be driven parallel and simultaneously with the main tunnel, but always slightly in advance of it so that the nature of the ground could be determined. Subsequently the pilot tunnel would be broken out to form a circular water conduit 3.7 m in diameter. The main tunnel was to be 4.0 m wide by 7.3 m high with a length of 9.6 km.

Facilities at the portals included housing, schools, shops, even a fully equipped hospital. Similar attention was paid to health and safety underground. Geological reports had been fairly optimistic predicting hard rock with some soft patches. In fact some 5.6 km of soft ground were encountered. Softened by water and under high pressure, the rock simply 'flowed'. To combat this, George Lewis, general manager of the project, invented what became known as the Lewis Girder. It consisted of an enormously strong cantilevered bar that held steel wall plates in position supporting some 27 m of roof. Below this bar the tunnel was excavated to full size and the permanent lining put in, then the whole system advanced to the next section. Cantilever support bars were not new, but the method of advancing the whole structure, without dismantling and rebuilding it, was. An added bonus was that the Lewis Girder actually cut the cost of excavation from $3.61 to $2.24 per cubic meter. In February 1928 the first train from Salt Lake City steamed through the tunnel en route to Denver completing in twelve minutes a journey which had previously taken seven hours. This 9.6 km tunnel had taken only five years to construct at a cost of $18 million.

The advent of the automobile added a new parameter to tunnel design – ventilation. Clifford M. Holland, chief engineer of the Holland Highway Tunnel (1920–1927) under the Hudson River, the first tunnel designed especially for heavy motor traffic, devised the so-called 'vertical transverse flow' method of ventilation. Ventilation buildings at the portals pumped fresh air into the tunnel, which issued from vents at curb level. As this mixed with the exhaust gases, it rose, to be sucked out by fans in the roof.

One would think that by this time technological advances had taken the danger and discomfort out of tunneling. Not so. The Tecolote Tunnel, a 10.4 km long water tunnel through the Santa Ynez Mountains in California, built in the 1950's, was hot, wet and smelly. In one section water poured in at a rate of 35,000 liters a minute and at a temperature of 47°C. To alleviate this Turkish bath atmosphere the men rode to the face in 'bathtubs', skips filled with cold water. Adding insult to injury, evil-smelling sulphurated hydrogen seeped through the seams. When at last it was holed through, the party was held, appropriately, in nearby Santa Barbara!

The two Alpine road tunnels – the 5.6 km long Great Saint Bernard and the 11.2 km long Mont Blanc tunnels (both completed in 1962) were a repetition of the earlier rail tunnels. 'Spalling', or rockbursts, in which chunks of rock released from the pressure of the mountain would suddenly fly across the heading, killing or seriously injuring anyone in their path, was a serious problem. Rock bolts were used to stabilize the rock burst-prone strata. In other areas the granite crumbled like rotten wood and had to be held in place by wire-netting and steel pins. In the heart of the mountain forty-one hours had to be spent on mucking-out and supporting the roof after each shot-firing. The introduction of tungsten carbide drill bits – tungsten had been developed during World War II by the Germans for machining gun barrels – did speed up this part of the cycle. The Atlas Company (later Atlas Copco of Stockholm) devised drill steels with tungsten carbide bits brazed to their tips. Mounted on their lightweight, self-rotating, piston-feed rock drills, they were capable of withstanding the heavy shock loads of hard-rock drilling.

Major developments in mining

As mechanical coal-cutters became widely accepted in the early 20th century, logically the next step was to combine cutting and loading operations. Joseph Joy produced his brainchild in 1921, a prototype cutter-loader capable of drawing coal on to a conveyor with the help of two steel grabbers that moved forward and back. In an era of cheap labor there was no demand for such a machine and his company narrowly averted bankruptcy. About the same time, McKinlay brought out his 'entry-driver'. Some 20 of these were sold. One of them, installed in the New Orient Mine, caught the imagination of Harry Treadwell, vice-president of the Chicago, Wilmington and Franklin (C. W. and F.) Coal Company, which owned the mine. Although the machine was breaking down, he recognized its potential and had the resources to make modifications.

Coal operators in the late 1940's were on the brink of disaster. Wages had risen, production had fallen, gas and oil were taking over as energy sources. Prices had to be

First Hudson River Tunnel, 1889: 19′ 6″ O.D. 18′ o″ I. D. 35 psi. (Reprinted by Elgood-Mayo Corp., Lancaster, PA).

reduced. The miracle arrived in the form of a new machine – a continuous miner. No fewer than four machines came on the market between 1948–1950. The Joy Continuous Miner was the first machine of this kind which in 1948 was successfully applied at the Mathies Mine in Pennsylvania. The Colmol Continuous Miner (Jeffrey Manufacturing Company) and the Marietta Miner followed. The BCR (Bituminous Coal Research) machine was designed by the coal industry but never put into production.

John L. Lewis, a union leader, convinced that it was a choice between mechanizing or lower wages, began a campaign to convince operators to buy the new machines. He has been called 'the best salesman Joy Company ever had'. The dream of a continuous miner had never been abandoned by the company and in 1947 they bought the patent of a machine which was seen operating in a Colorado mine. Twenty-five prototypes were built at a cost of nearly $1,000,000. To overcome the skepticism of the operators these machines were installed in a variety of mines of differing conditions at a nominal cost to the mine. To sweeten the deal still further, Joy undertook to make any necessary modifications free of charge. Teething problems were overcome. These early machines produced two tons of coal per minute. A Joy model brought out in 1968 with rotary drum cutters produced up to 12 tons per minute.

The Colmol machine was the work of three men, Vincent McCarthy, an inventor of drilling machines, Clifford Snyder and Arnold Lamm, both of the Sunnyhill Coal Company of Pittsburgh. Observing the large quantity of rock debris produced by horizontal drilling in his strip mining operation, Snyder approached McCarthy and Lamm and together they converted a drilling machine into a continuous miner. By 1948 they had spent $750,000 on development and were amenable to a fifty-fifty offer from the Jeffrey Manufacturing Company.

In 1965–67, the Jeffrey Manufacturing Company began producing the 'Jeffrey Heliminer', very similar in design to the Joy Company model which came out in 1968. The Heliminer has a helical cutting head almost 3.3 m wide and a 93 cm diameter drum and can produce 15 tons per minute from seams up to 3.5 m in height.

The Marietta Miner was the offspring of the McKinlay Entry Driver and Harry Treadwell's interest in it. Gathering a group of engineers around him he set them the task of designing a new machine, based on the McKinlay, but with the modifications he had seen to be necessary. Among those engineers was James S. Robbins, who – as will be seen later – started a leading tunnel boring company. The Marietta Miner proved very successful. Eleven machines were installed shortly after its introduction in 1950. Recent models are little changed from the original in concept.

The Lee-Norse Company introduced their 'Koal-master' in 1951. In 1964 the company became a subsidiary of Ingersoll Rand and is currently producing both oscillating head type machines and fixed head miners. Some Lee-Norse machines can cut seams as low as 76 cm. These low chassis machines may be remotely controlled by radio or electric cable.

The Bureau of Mines estimated that in 1980 there were about 3100 continuous miners in use in the United States, producing 2/3 of the country's underground coal production and leading the world in productivity.

Developments in longwall mining followed similar lines. In 1933 the Meco-Moore Cutter Loader was tested at Chiswall Hall Colliery in Britain and found wide acceptance. In operation, it cut the coal seam at the bottom and again about halfway up. At the same time vertical slits were cut at intervals. As British coal mines are deep and the coal is under considerable pressure, introducing these shear lines caused the coal to 'slab' off the face.

The Goodman Manufacturing Company produced a longwall coal-cutter in America in 1900 but found no market for it in an industry using room and pillar mining. Beginning in 1951 longwall mining was introduced in West Virginia. By 1980, there were 112 longwall operations in the USA (93 of them using shield support) accounting for about 3% of all coal mined or some 10% of the coal mined underground. Joy Manufacturing Company produced the first American-developed longwall equipment installation in 1978. The current rate of growth in America is seven longwall faces per year.

Recently, there has been much interest in the United States in the next generation of continuous miners, which incorporate a roof bolter, and in remotely controlled continuous miners.

The automated extraction system (AES) is a new concept combining the functions of cutting and loading with continuous mining, roofbolting, face ventilation and dust collection – all achieved by semiautomatic operation with semi-remote control capabilities in seam heights of 1.7 m to 3 m. A prototype of such a machine underwent field trials in 1978, aiming at mining rates of 4–6 tons/minute (King, 1982). The second generation AES design is under construction by the National Mine Service Co. and is scheduled for underground testing during 1983 (Sprouls, 1982).

Radio control systems which enable the operator to control the machines from up to 15 m distance are now available. Remote control mining is one of many systems emerging from research into innovative mining methods in the United States (Ramani and Frantz, 1983, Chironis, 1983).

From the mid-1940's, rock bolting revolutionized the mining industry in America, particularly in coal mining. Although the first known use of bolts for 'pinning' loose rock is lost in history, E. M. Thomas was instrumental in promoting the widespread use of systematic roof bolting in the USA. Today, some 120 million bolts are used annually in U.S. mining (in over 7000 mines), featuring mechanized 'roof bolters' in coal mines. The next largest user, South Africa, employs about $8\frac{1}{2}$ million bolts yearly.

Moving towards mechanization

Tunneling from the fifties onward has become increasingly scientific and automated leading to the greatest development of them all – the TBM (tunnel boring machine). Blasting, which cracked and weakened the rock around the excavation, has largely been superseded by machine-tunneling, with such advantages as up to 40% saving in labor, continuous operation to replace the conventional drill-blast-muck out and support cycle; and a smooth bore. Custom built for major operations, TBM's are capable of high advance rates but require a certain minimum tunnel length to be economically viable. They are also not suited to all conditions.

Although the first TBM on record was made in the U.S. by John Wilson in 1856 for the Hoosac tunnel, the first successful TBM was developed in England by Colonel Beaumont in the early 1880's (2.15 m diameter). However, for the modern era of TBMs, one name stands out: James S. Robbins of Seattle. After working on the Marietta Miner, James Robbins became a consultant to the Goodman Company. When they were approached in 1952 by F. K. Mitry with a request for a machine to be used in excavating a tunnel in soft shale at Oahe Dam in South Dakota, Goodman suggested Mitry discuss it with Robbins. From their collaboration came the history-making tunnel borer, the 7.9 m diameter 'Mitry Mole.' It broke all existing records by advancing 18.6 m in one 8 hour shift and 49 m in one day (Thon, 1982). Other machines such as Hughes Tool Co. 'Betti 1', and Jarva have also made important contributions.

Various problems were encountered and more or less satisfactory solutions have been found. In hard rock, dust tended to clog the bearings – dust accumulators were added. In wet ground, bucket blockages slowed the clearing of debris – shields were added. In poor rock, the TBM could be locked in the heading – cutting arms were made reversible or retractable. Today, TBMs have established a sound reputation and most tunnels in the USA utilize machine boring.

The latest TBM technology is prominently in evidence at the largest current tunneling project in the world – the Chicago Tunnel and Reservoir Plan (TARP). Featuring 211 km of tunnels when complete, this $11 billion project incorporates the largest TBMs ever built: 10.8 m diameter Robbins machines for boring 13.6 km of hard dolomite limestone and shale (see photograph on the face plate). Since the project calls for tunnels of various sizes, 5 Robbins TBMs and 7 Jarva TBMs are in use. The current

TARP record was achieved in a 9.14 m diameter tunnel where a Jarva TBM had the best month (22 work days) of 751.33 m. The best week stands at 223.72 m with a best day at 52.43 m. The best 8-hr shift was 20.42 m. The TBMs availability at TARP is over 80% but utilization works out at some 40–50% due to other stoppages.

On other projects, American TBMs have claimed these world records: Robbins TBM in hard granite, mica and gneiss: 240.5 m/week; Jarva TBM in mica shist and amphibolite rock (110–180 MPa strength): 4 m/hr, 58 m/day, 345 m/week (7 days), 1261 m/month – tunnel diameter 3.5 m. A 3.2 m diameter tunnel in shale featured a Robbins TBM boring a record 128 m in a day and 2087 m in one month.

The typical TBM in use on today's tunnel projects (Leonard, 1981) uses 40 cm diameter cutters at a nominal pressure of 310 MPa (45,000 psi). The cutterhead rotates at a speed of 400/D revolutions per minute where D is the cutterhead diameter in meters. The typical machine operates about 50% of the time. Delivery of a new machine takes 12 to 15 months.

A new development in TBM technology is an extruded tunnel lining system (ETLS). Developed by Foster-Miller Associates under contract to the U.S. Department of Transportation, the ETLS should reduce ground support costs in machine-bored tunneling by slip-forming the final concrete lining directly behind the TBM (Qunanian et al., 1981). Large-scale tests are currently planned to demonstrate the system in a 3 m diameter steel 'tunnel'.

Today, there is a machine suitable for most tunnels, but not all, as the history of the Straight Creek Tunnel, now designated as the Eisenhower Memorial Tunnel, shows.

The Eisenhower Memorial Tunnel is located approximately 100 km west of Denver on Interstate 70 crossing the Rocky Mountains. It is the world's highest mechanically-ventilated tunnel. To move up to 85,000 m^3 of rarefied air requires one of the largest tunnel cross-sections attempted anywhere. This 2.7 km long tunnel consists of dual, two-lane vehicular tunnels, each 14.5 m wide by 13.5 m high (excavated 17 m wide and 20 m high). It passes beneath the Continental Divide at an altitude of 3,383 m. As it falls within the general area of the Loveland Fault, extensive mapping was carried out by the U.S. Geological Survey. The maximum cover of 442 m made it difficult to predict more than the major geologic features. So a 3 m wide pilot tunnel was dug in 1963–64 along the alignment of the future South Tunnel. In situ and laboratory tests were carried out. Tunnel technology did not, however, permit successful extrapolation of rock support problems from a 3 m pilot tunnel to a 17 m wide final excavation. A tunnel this large had never before been constructed in such geologic conditions. The material encountered was as predicted but its behavior was worse then expected. This resulted in great difficulties necessitating major changes in the excavation and support techniques employed.

The tunnel was divided into five zones numbered consecutively from the west portal to the east. Work commenced in December 1967 and by September 1969 zones 1, 3 and 4 had been excavated using a top heading and bench method. Zone 2, the most heavily faulted area, was to have been excavated full face using a shield. This zone included some 580 m of bad ground of which 45 m was known to be 'squeezing ground'. After only 23 m into the zone, the shield was abandoned and another method was adopted, the multiple-drift excavation. Depending on the quality of rock, the projected bore was ringed with anything from five to thirteen small tunnels or drifts, filled with concrete, and then excavated within this shell.

The Eisenhower Tunnel, completed in 1973 (first bore), took two years longer to complete than anticipated and cost twice as much as bid – $108 million. The second tunnel bore was completed in 1979 within schedule.

Looking into the future

Recent tunneling projects in the USA, such as nuclear waste disposal in underground repositories (Schmidt, 1981), deep basing of strategic missiles (USNC/TT, 1982) and excavations of very large underground cavities at the Nevada Test Site (span 91.4 m) (Kipp et al., 1979), all point out many design challenges for rock engineers. Other new developments studied in the USA and in Britain include plans for under-ocean tunneling for oil (Walton, 1980). Finally, bids have been advertised for a novel construction (by 1986) of the Mt. Baker Ridge road tunnel in Seattle: to be bored for a 19.2 m (63 ft) inside diameter! This 460 m long highway tunnel in soft ground will incorporate 5 lanes of traffic plus bicycle and pedestrian paths. It will be constructed by the multiple-drift method employing 3 m diameter tunnels bored on its circumference (Parker, 1982).

From 7 cm a week with 30,000 slaves in the Fucinus Tunnel, to 3 m per week with hand-drilling and black powder shooting, to 60 m per week with well managed power drilling and gelatine powder blasting, to 345 m a week with one tunnel boring machine, tunneling has made tremendous advances. But there is no substitute for engineering judgment and each new tunnel is still a challenge to the perseverance and ingenuity of the men who built it.

In mining, expected demand for more coal will provide new challenges to design engineers for increased productivity and safer mining (President's Commission on Coal, 1980). It is estimated that in the United States alone, the 1982 production will reach an all-time high of 880 million tons of coal – 9.7% over 1981 and 46% above the 1974 level. The National Coal Association predicts U.S. coal production at 987 million tons by 1985 and 1,235 million tons by 1990.

What will the future bring? One thing is obvious that more high-technology developments can be expected. Since each of the past four decades has been categorized by a major technological development: 1940s – radar, 1950s – transistors, 1960s – computers, 1970 – microprocessors, will the eighties by distinguished by gene slicing or remote-control fully automated mining and tunneling?

However, one may ask when high-technology arrives, what will be the demand for mining and tunneling projects? Again, the future looks bright. According to the U.S. National Committee on Tunneling Technology, Subcommittee on Demand Forecasting, (1981) in the next 10 years (1982–1992) over 1,680 km of civil engineering tunnels with cross-sections over 10 m^2 can be expected in the USA. This figure excludes tunneling for strategic petroleum reserve, nuclear waste disposal and defense. The mineral industry in America is expected to construct a total of 34,180 km of tunnels annually by the year 1990, made up as follows: 317 km annually in metal mines, 65 km annually in non-metal mines and 33,800 km annually in coal mines. The current coal production per kilometer of tunnel is 10,500 metric tons. The projected total tunnel demand for the year 2000 is 42,075 km of tunnels in U.S. mines.

The U.S. Bureau of Mines monitors closely the supply and the demand in the United States for strategic minerals (Morgan, 1982) which in the $2,900 billion economy in

1981 required $236 billion domestic non-fuel minerals and $29 billion imported non-fuel minerals. In 1981, U.S. energy sources comprised of: 27% domestic petroleum, 16% imported petroleum, 27% natural gas, 22% coal, 4% hydroelectricity and 4% nuclear power. This quest for strategic minerals and energy resources will place mining and tunneling in great demand for decades to come. Most of all, however, the quest for improved safety – particularly in underground coal mining – will continue to present many design challenges. In spite of major improvements in coal mine safety since implementation of the Coal Mine Health and Safety Act of 1969, i.e. an 80% reduction in fatality incidence by 1974, underground coal mining is still the most hazardous occupation in the United States. It is twice as dangerous as manufacturing and three times more dangerous than surface mining (President's Commission on Coal, 1980). In 1979, 58% of the 115 fatal injuries in underground coal mines resulted from the collapse of mine roofs and walls.

A design engineer must be appropriately prepared for the challenges of the future. After all, it has been dramatically stated that technology has advanced as much in the last 40 years as in the previous 4,000!

What lessons can a design engineer learn from this historical overview of mining and tunneling? There are probably many, but some deserve special attention, namely:

1. Mining and tunneling have moved from an art into an engineering science as the complexity of projects increased and engineering has been transformed from an empirical art to a profession.

2. The great advances made were due to team efforts but often depended on the initiative of a single man.

3. The engineer's ingenuity has been amply demonstrated but there is a tremendous potential for further improvement and innovation.

4. A designer must be aware of the social and environmental factors of his engineering activities.

LANDMARK DATES IN THE HISTORY OF MINING AND TUNNELING

B.C.

41000	Hematite mined for ritual paint in Swaziland, Africa
18000	Fine leaf shaped spearheads made from flint found in Spain and Southern France
3500	First evidence of copper tools and wheeled vehicles in Egypt and the Near East
3000	Copper mined on the island of Cyprus
2000	Earliest known metal working in prehispanic America evidenced in gold foil found in Peru
1000	Iron tools and weapons; the beginning of the Iron Age
983	King Solomon's mines
450	The flowering of civilization in Greece. The mining of silver was in part responsible for the wealth of Athens
100	The Roman Empire at its height, serviced by a network of extraordinary roads, bridges, aqueducts and tunnels

A.D.

77	Pliny wrote five books on earth, metals, stones and gems
122	Coal used by the Romans in the area now known as Britain

303	Saint Barbara, the patron of miners and tunnelers, put to death by sword at Nicomedia in Bithynia (now Turkey). The feast of Saint Barbara, December 4, is the annual day of celebration by miners and tunnelers in Europe, especially in Poland, Germany, France and Italy
800	Charlemagne began extensive renovation of the Roman mines in Lombardy (now Italy)
1225	Salt mined in Wieliczka, Poland, in remarkable underground chambers; active mining still in progress today
1238	First collieries established in Newcastle, Britain
1324	The use of the cannon spells the doom of armor and castles and indeed of feudalism itself. It also spurs interest in metallurgy and surveying
1450	Gutenberg's printing press is a major factor in disseminating the 'new learning' of the Rennaissance
1502	On his fourth voyage, Columbus found indications of gold on the coast of Central America starting a search for gold in the New World
1550	Slump in European mining following entry of rich ores from the Americas
1550	Coal industry began in Britain
1556	Agricola published *De Re Metallica*
1600	The date usually given as the beginning of the era of modern science. This is the century of Galileo, Copernicus, Leibniz, and Newton
1627	Explosives (black powder) first used in mines in Slovakia
1627	First use of drilling and blasting at the Oberbieberstollen mine at Schemnitz, Hungary
1646	First successful blast furnace in North America built in Saugus, Massachusetts
1679	Friar Hennepin discovered coal on the banks of the Illinois River near the present town of Ottawa, Illinois
1762	Charles University at Prague established the first major department of mining
1783	Ecole des Mines founded in Paris, France
1785	Famous underground chapel carved in salt in Wieliczka, Poland
1786	Rhode Island College offered first U.S. course in Mineralogy
1789	Bituminous coal fields of Richmond, Virginia were the first deposits to be developed extensively, shipping to New York, Philadelphia, and Boston
1812	The earliest use of mechanical haulage underground when George Stevenson altered an engine to make it haul cars up an incline plane to the shaft
1815	Davy safety lamp introduced
1818	The first record of blasting in American coal mines
1821	Anthracite stripping began at Summit Hill, Pennsylvania continuing into the mid 1970's
1828	The first American gold rush occurred in the state of Georgia
1839	Invention of the steam shovel which was instrumental in the growth of mechanization of stripping in the United States
1842	Employment of women and children forbidden underground in Britain
1844	Copper mining commenced in upper Michigan
1848	Discovery of gold in California (gold rush)
1851	Royal School of Mines founded in London, England
1852	American Society of Civil Engineers founded
1855	The Pennsylvania State University founded
1857	Polytechnic College of Pennsylvania in Philadelphia the first U.S. institution to offer a degree in mining engineering
1859	The first American oil well (Titusville, Pennsylvania)
1860	Discovery of gold and silver in Nevada and discovery of gold in Rocky Mountains (Central City, Colorado)
1863	Alfred Nobel invented dynamite
1864	First school of mines in the United States was Columbia College (Columbia School of Mines)
1867	Diamond mining began at Kimberley, South Africa

1868	First dynamite in the U.S. manufactured by the Giant Powder Company under A. Nobel's patent
1868	First successful coal cutter introduced
1871	American Institute of Mining Engineers (AIME) founded in Wilkes-Barre, Pennsylvania
1874	Colorado School of Mines established. Gold discovered in South Dakota
1878	Discovery of copper in Montana and in Arizona
1886	Gold discovered near Johannesburg, South Africa
1890	Department of Mining Engineering (School of Mines) established at The Pennsylvania State University
1910	U.S. output of bituminous coal and lignite reaches 417 million tons produced by 555,000 men at 3.46 tons per man per shift at an average value of $1.12/ton from 8,018 mines
1910	U.S. Bureau of Mines established
1934	The working day in U.S. coal mines was reduced from eight hours to seven, wages rose from $4.60 to $5.00/hr
1937	Joy Manufacturing Company invented the shuttle car, the first was battery powered
1946	First diesel engine installed in the U.S. underground coal mine
1947	British coal industry nationalized under management of National Coal Board
1948	Continuous miner machine introduced for underground coal mining in the USA
1950	Tungsten carbide hard compound introduced for drill bits
1954	Lowest modern era production of U.S. bituminous coal and lignite at 392 million tons for the year
1955	Blasting agents introduced (to replace dynamite)
1960	First regular use of AnFo explosives in a major underground mine at Stanrock Uranium Mines
1960	Modern longwall mining in the U.S. began at Eastern Associated Coal Corp. in West Virginia
1969	America's first man on the moon selects lunar rock samples for testing.
1969	Federal Coal Mine Health and Safety Act enacted by U.S. Congress
1970	U.S. output of bituminous coal and lignite reaches 603 million tons produced by 140,000 men at 18.84 tons/manshift at an average value of $6.26/ton from 5,601 mines
1972	First Landsat space craft launched by NASA for earth resource remote sensing
1976	U.S. output of bituminous coal and lignite reaches 678,685,000 tons produced by 202,280 men at 14.46 tons/manshift, an average value of $20/ton from 6,200 mines
1977	Surface Mining Control and Reclamation Act passed by U.S. Congress
1978	Mining and Mineral Resources Research Institutes established in 20 states in the United States. Subsequently, another 11 institutes were added
1980	Total U.S. production of bituminous and lignite coal exceeded 800 million tons. Underground coal mining share of total production decreased to 39%.

REFERENCES

Agricola Georgius, *De Re Metallica*, 1556. Translated from Latin by Herbert Clark Hoover and Lou Henry Hoover, Dover Publications, New York, Second edition, 1950, 638 p.

Armstrong, E. L. Underground excavation – status and potential. *Proc. Rapid Excav. & Tunnel. Conf.*, AIME, New York, 1974, Vol. 1, pp. 17–27.

Beaver, P. *A History of Tunnels*. Peter Davies, Ltd. London, 1972, 155 p.

Brierley, G. S. Construction of the Hoosac Tunnel: 1855–1876. *J. Boston Soc. Civ. Eng.*, ASCE, Vol. 63, No. 3, October 1976, pp. 175–208.

Bronner, F. E. The soldier digs through history. *Proc. Rapid Excav. & Tunneling Conf.*, AIME, New York, 1979, Vol. 2, pp. 1411–1445.

Chironis, N. P. Bureau takes lead in 1983 R & D. *Coal Age*, February 1983, pp. 56–64.

Florman, S. *The Existential Pleasures of Engineering*. St. Martin's Press, New York, 1976, 160 p.

Gregory, C. E. *A Concise History of Mining*, Pergamon, New York, 1980, 259 p.

Harding, H. *Tunneling History and My Own Involvement*. Golder Associates, Toronto, 1981, 258 p.

King, R. H. Production potential of AES-type machines. *Mining Engineering*, August 1982, pp. 1248–1252.

Kipp, T. R., Cording, E. J., Merritt, A. H. and Kennedy, R. Feasibility evaluation for the excavation of large hemispherical cavities at the Nevada Test Site. *Proc. Rapid Excavation & Tunneling Conf.*, AIME, New York, 1979, Vol. 2, pp. 1446–1465.

Leonard, J. M. TBM's-US: Where are we – What can we do about it? *Proc. Rapid Excavation & Tunneling Conf.*, AIME, New York, 1981, pp. 535–543.

Mayo, Robert S. Early tunnels in America. *Tunnels and Tunneling*, December 1982, pp. 14–16.

Mayo, Robert S. and Richardson, H. W. *Practical Tunnel Driving*. McGraw-Hill Book Co., New York, 1975, 447 p.

Morgan, J. D. Future demands of the United States for strategic minerals. *Proc. Conf. on Strategic Minerals and International Economic Assistance*, U.S. Bureau of Mines, University of Delaware, Wilmington, December 1982.

National Coal Board. *Mining Beyond 2000 AD*. A Consideration of Possible Devices and Techniques. Mining Research and Development Establishment, London, 1977, 68 p.

National Research Council. *Rapid Excavation – Significance and Opportunities*. National Academy of Sciences, Publication No. 1690, Washington, DC, 1968, 48 p.

Parker, H. Baker Ridge Tunnel-technical design. *Underground Space*, Vol. 7, December 1982, pp. 175–181

Plattes, Gabriel. *A Discovery of Subterraneal Treasures*. 1638. Reproduction by Institution of Mining and Metallurgy, London, 1980, 60 p.

President's Commission on Coal. *Recommendations and Summary Findings*. U.S. Government Printing Office, Washington, DC, 1980, 27 p.

Qunanian, D. W., Boyce, J. S. and Maser, K. Development of an extruded tunnel lining system. *Proc. Rapid Excavation and Tunneling Conf.*, AIME, New York, 1981, Vol. 2, pp. 1333–1351.

Ramani, R. V. and Frantz, R. L. Development of new underground coal mining system. *Proc. ASCE Spring Convention, Session: Innovations in Energy Development*, American Society of Civil Engineers, Philadelphia, May 1983, pp. 15–28.

Schmidt, B. Design problems for underground nuclear waste disposal in basalt. *Proc. Rapid Excavation & Tunneling Conf.*, AIME, New York, 1981, Vol. 2, pp. 1229–1250.

Sprouls, M. W. The wave of the 80's: New approaches for continuous miners, *Coal Mining & Processing*, March 1982, pp. 38–41.

Stack, B. *Handbook of Mining and Tunneling Machinery*, John Wiley & Sons, New York, 1982, 742 p.

Thon, J. G. Tunnel-boring machines. *Tunnel Engineering Handbook*, Ed. Bickel & Kuesel, Van Nostrand Reinhold Co., New York, 1982, pp. 235–278.

Timoshenko, S. *History of the Strength of Materials*, McGraw-Hill Book Co., 1953, 452 p.

U.S. National Committee on Tunneling Technology. *Demand Forecast of Underground Construction and Mining in the United States*, National Academy Press, Washington, DC, 1981, 25 p.

U.S. National Committee on Tunneling Technology. *Design and Construction of Deep Underground Basing Facilities for Strategic Missiles*, Academy of Sciences, Washington, DC, 1982, 68 p.

Walton, B. Tunneling for oil: The system and its construction. *Tunnels and Tunneling*, September 1980, pp. 40–43.

Wilson, A. J. *The Pick and the Pen/History of Mining Journalism*. Mining Books, Ltd., London, 1979, 309 p.

Mont Cenis Tunnel: 1857–1870. The first Trans-Alpine Tunnel, 8 miles long, connecting France and Italy. Masonry lined; 26–ft. x 24–ft. Pneumatic drills and nitroglycerin were introduced in 1861: progress at each end then jumped from 1.5 ft. to 6 ft. per day. (Reproduced by Mayo Tunnel & Mine Equipment, Inc.).

CHAPTER 3

The design process in engineering

Science is built up with facts as a house is with stones.
But a collection of facts is no more science than a heap
of stones is a house.

Henri Poincare

The engineer's genie or his creative ability manifests itself in one word: design. It is design which makes engineers out of applied scientists and it is design that represents the culmination of all engineering training. Although impressive progress has been made in the field of mining and tunneling, the knowledge accumulated has not been fully utilized in rock engineering design. This situation can be improved by a better understanding of the design process.

The Engineers' Council for Professional Development (ECPD) made this definition in 1975:

Engineering design is the process of devising a system, component, or process to meet desired needs. It is a decision-making process (often iterative), in which the basic sciences, mathematics, and engineering sciences are applied to convert resources optimally to meet a stated objective. Among the fundamental elements of the design process are the establishment of objectives and criteria, synthesis, analysis, construction, testing and evaluation. Central to the process are the essential and complementary roles of synthesis and analysis. In addition, sociological, economic, aesthetic, legal and ethical considerations need to be included in the design process.

It is clear from the above definition that the solution to any real engineering problem is never merely technological.

The teaching of design is a demanding and particularly challenging task. There are three primary reasons why design is sometimes taught poorly or not at all: i) professors are better at analysis than at design; ii) design is difficult to teach, teaching analysis is easier; iii) in spite of all the discussion about design, it is not considered in some quarters to be very important in terms of its 'academic value'.

In essence, the engineering design process, which is iterative in character, consists of the following relatively distinct stages: identification of a need or an opportunity; selection or creation of a method, concept or model; analysis and/or experimentation; decision; development and implementation. The design process is concerned with the methodology of problem-solving.

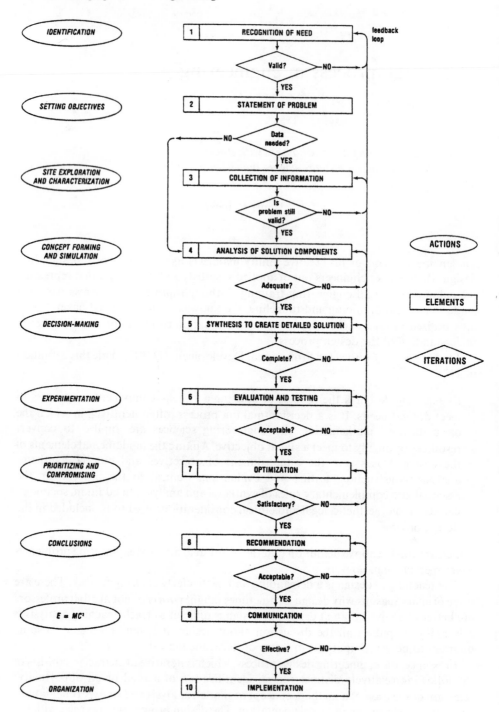

Figure 3.1. The engineering design process.

DESIGN STAGES

The following are the various distinguishable stages of the design process (see Figure 3.1 and Rallis, 1973):

1. *Recognition of a need or a problem*
The existence of a problem must be recognized before any attempt can be made to solve it. This is not as easy a task as one would imagine. It requires the rather rare ability of asking the right kind of question and calls for a clear recognition of the problem to be solved. In design-type situations, it involves the recognition of a genuine social need, a want or an opportunity.

2. *Statement of the problem*
Having established that a problem exists, it is then necessary to define it. This may involve a list of specifications or criteria. These must be stated clearly and concisely. A poorly formulated problem cannot be expected to produce a good solution. In rock engineering, this means the setting of objectives in terms of stability, safety and economy.

3. *Collection of information*
This phase involves the gathering, investigation, processing and screening of information to determine the specific characteristics of the problem. It invariably results in a clearer and more detailed statement of the problem. In rock engineering, collection of information includes site exploration, featuring geological and geophysical investigations, laboratory and field testing to establish the characteristics of the rock strata, and evaluation of field stresses and the applied loads.

4. *Search for method, theory, model or hypothesis – analysis of solution components*
Depending on the nature of the problem, either a search is conducted for the most promising method of solution or a hypothesis is selected or invented. Design approaches at this stage may involve mathematical and numerical analyses, physical model studies, observations and monitoring, or empirical analyses based on experience. Intuition, imagination and innovation should be utilized in a manner not unlike that of a genuinely creative artist. The choice and approximations made must take into account the accuracy required, the time available for a solution, and the costs involved.

5. *Synthesis to create a detailed solution*
All the options having been considered and, with the analysis of the individual components completed, all design is directed to create detailed alternative solutions. This stage should comprise any or all of the following: design calculations and specifications, performance predictions, cost estimates, scheduling procedures, experimental results or the like.

6. *Evaluation of ideas and solutions*
The solution proposed must now be interpreted and compared with the original hypothesis, specifications, facts, assumptions, requirements or constraints. This calls for a clear understanding of all the pertinent interacting factors; that is, for the exercise

of engineering judgment. The duty of the design engineer is to produce a balanced design involving all the factors which interact.

If, as is frequently the case, such an evaluation shows up deficiencies or suggests more promising alternatives, some or all of the foregoing stages must be repeated. The number of iterations carried out once again calls for judgment – based on the accuracy required and the time and money available.

7.   Optimization

Most engineering situations do not have a unique solution. Reconsideration of the solution may then be necessary in an attempt to approach a feasible compromise between the generally conflicting requirements and resources. The effectiveness of any optimization process depends directly on the clarity with which criteria are stated.

8.   Recommendation

Conclusions and recommendations are the essence of the entire design process. They provide a concise restatement of the answer to the problem, point out limitations or restrictions and indicate the direction to be followed in implementing the solution.

9.   Communication

The ultimate purpose of all the foregoing is the production, construction or initiation of a course of action. Achievement of this objective requires the engineer to communicate or 'sell' his findings. Unless he can persuade his associates, client or society of the merit of his ideas they are essentially stillborn. Effective communication requires that all pertinent facts be properly presented. If a mathematician were to sum up these thoughts, he might well do so by the equation (with apologies to Alfred Einstein):

$$E = MC^2$$

where E equals effectiveness, M equals mastery of the subject matter and C equals communication.

The designer must recognize that the efficient transfer of his knowledge and findings is an essential part of his task. Hence, the ability to convey thoughts concisely and clearly and to transmit technical knowledge effectively must be acquired by design engineers.

10.   Implementation

This entails putting the plan into action, and generally involves a high order of organizational skill as well as knowledge and experience of costs, labor, law and equipment. This is the phase which occupies the bulk of the time and energy of most practicing engineers.

Discussion

To summarize, engineering design may be considered as that socio-economic activity by which scientific, engineering and behavioral principles, together with technical information and experience, are applied with skill, imagination, and judgment, in the creation of functional, economical, aesthetically pleasing, and environmentally accept-able devices or systems for the benefit of society. The design process embraces all those activities and events that occur between the recognition of a social want, need, or opportunity, and the detailed specification of an acceptable solution. The designers' responsibilities continue throughout the designed life of their creation – and generally beyond it.

The overall objective of design is to ensure that a desired goal and quality will be achieved within the time and cost required. While most sponsors know what they think they want, they usually need a great deal of help to refine their vague initial ideas into a feasible compromise. The designer will usually be their guide and this will be one of his or her creative challenges.

ETHICS AND PROFESSIONALISM IN DESIGN

Thorstein B. Veblen (1857–1929), a brilliant American social philosopher and economist, believed that 'the engineers comprised the indispensable General Staff of the industrial system' without whose guidance industry would come to a grinding halt.

In 1921, Veblen's *The Engineers and the Price System* was published and had a considerable impact on economics and social thinking during the Great Depression. However, the engineers never fulfilled the 'revolutionary' role he had assigned them. Had the engineers taken over the industrial system, it was asked by one Veblen critic, philosopher Max Lerner, what kind of society would it have meant for America? Lerner wrote: 'No group can take over a technology without setting it down again in a framework of political and moral values. A corps of engineers might well run our society more efficiently, but whether they would run it more humanely is another question.'

The above discussion is highly relevant in the context of the engineering design process. It emphasizes the importance of engineers in our society but it also directs our attention to the fact that engineers have certain responsibilities to society. These responsibilities should be met by engineering professionalism and ethics.

Sociologists regard professionalism as one of the important characteristics of industrial societies. A profession may be defined in terms of its traits. For example, professional status is attained by the acquisition of considerable theoretical knowledge and its acquisition can make strenuous demands on intelligence and time. It is the acquisition of theoretical knowledge that distinguishes a profession from a craft.

The authority of a profession stems from the demonstration that the practitioner alone has the knowledge and skills needed by the client. By claiming a monopoly of competence for its members, a profession confers a sense of security on the client. For example, confidence in a practitioner is particularly important in the medical field.

The standing of a profession ultimately depends upon the confidence and respect of the public. This is reflected by the degree to which a profession regulates its own affairs – such as conditions of entry and qualifications – in the public interest. Professionalism generally implies a code of ethics, giving a profession a public image.

Code of ethics

Grinter (1955) details the following attributes of the well-educated engineer:

He must be not only a competent professional engineer but also an informed and participating citizen, and a person whose living expresses high cultural values and moral standards. Thus, the competent engineer needs understanding and appreciation in the humanities and the social sciences as much as in his own field of engineering. He needs to be able to deal with the economic, human and social factors of his professional problems. This facility with, and understanding of, ideas in the fields of humanities and social sciences not only provide an essential contribution to his professional engineering work, but also contribute to his success as a citizen and to the enrichment and meaning of his life as an individual.

The author suggests that, to fulfill the above attributes, engineers would benefit from reading a stimulating text by Florman (1976).

A code of engineering ethics appeared as early as 1918 and now there are almost as many different codes as there are engineering societies.

The majority of the engineering societies in the United States have endorsed the following ethical professional standards (ASCE, 1980):

Fundamental principles
Engineers uphold and advance the integrity, honor and dignity of the engineering profession by:

1. Using their knowledge and skill for the enhancement of human welfare
2. Being honest and impartial and serving with fidelity the public, their employers and clients
3. Striving to increase the competence and prestige of the engineering profession; and
4. Supporting the professional and technical societies of their disciplines.

Fundamental canons
1. Engineers should hold paramount the safety, health and welfare of the public in the performance of their professional duties.
2. Engineers shall perform services only in areas of their competence.
3. Engineers shall issue public statements only in an objective and truthful manner.
4. Engineers shall act in professional matters for each employer or client as faithful agents or trustees, and shall avoid conflicts of interest.
5. Engineers shall build their professional reputation on the merit of their services and shall not compete unfairly with others.
6. Engineers shall act in such a manner as to uphold and enhance the honor, integrity, and dignity of the engineering profession.
7. Engineers shall continue their professional development throughout their careers, and shall provide opportunities for the professional development of those engineers under their supervision.

REFERENCES

American Society of Civil Engineers. Code of Ethics, *ASCE Official Register*, New York, 1980, pp. 279–283.
Dallaire, G. The engineer: what role in the development of civilization? *Civil Engineering*, American Society of Civil Engineers, October, 1977, pp. 64–70.

Dixon, J. R. *Design Engineering: Inventiveness, Analysis and Decision-Making.* McGraw-Hill Book Company, New York, 1966.

Florman, Samuel C. *Engineering and the Liberal Arts.* McGraw-Hill Book Co., New York, 1968, 278 p.

Florman, Samuel C. *The Existential Pleasures of Engineering,* St. Martin's Press, New York, 1976, 160 p.

Grinter, L. E. Report of the Committee on Evaluation of Engineering Education. *J. Engineering Educ.*, Vol. 46, 1955, pp. 26–52.

Krick, B. V. *An Introduction to Engineering and Engineering Design,* second edition. John Wiley & Sons, 1965.

Lynn, W. R. Engineering and society programs in engineering education. *Science,* Vol. 195, 1977, pp. 150–155.

Rallis, C. J. Design—the goal of engineering activity. *S. Afr. Mech. Engr.*, April 1973, pp. 62–71.

Roadstrum, W. H. *Being Successful as an Engineer,* Engineering Press, Inc., San Jose, 1978, 246 p.

Veblen, Thorstein B. *The Engineers and the Price System,* However Press, New York, 1921.

Walker, E. A., Pettit, J. M. and Hawkins, G. A. *Goals of Engineering Education,* American Society for Engineering Education, Washington, DC, January 1968, 74 p.

Wassell, H. J. H. The objectives of design, *J. Inst. Mechanical Engineers,* September 1965, pp. 105–107.

Wilde, D. J. *Globally Optimal Design.* John Wiley & Sons, New York, 1978, 288 p.

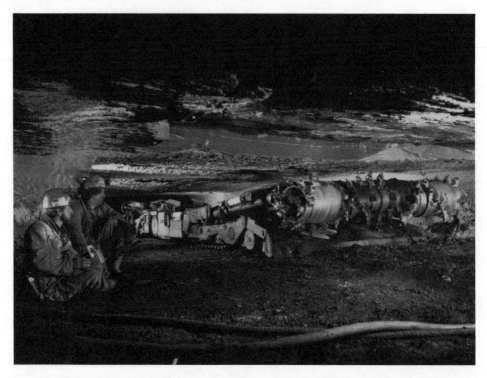

Innovative Design: Remote Control Mining Marietta Drum Miner model 2460 for continuous mining of low coal seams. (Photo courtesy of National Mine Service Company).

CHAPTER 4

Design approaches for excavations in rock

Imagination is more important than knowledge.

Albert Einstein

Obert (1973) emphasized rightly that compared with the time that man has been mining underground, the concept of designing an underground opening is a relatively recent innovation. One reason for this situation is that the problem of designing a mine or a tunnel is different from that of designing a conventional structure such as a building or a bridge.

In a conventional engineering design, the external loads to be applied are first determined and a material is then prescribed with the appropriate strength and deformation characteristics, following which the structural geometry is selected. In rock mechanics, the designer deals with complex rock masses and specific material properties cannot be prescribed to meet design requirements. Furthermore, the applied loads are not as important in rock masses as the forces resulting from the redistribution of the original stresses, i.e. those existing before the excavation was made. Also, a number of possible failure modes can exist in a rock structure so that determination of the 'material strength' is a major problem. Finally, the geometry of a structure in rock may depend on the configuration of the geological features. Hence, the design of an excavation in rock must include a thorough appraisal of the geological conditions and especially of possible geological hazards.

Clearly then, any design approaches for excavations in rock call for close cooperation between rock mechanics engineers and engineering geologists. In fact, a new breed of geological engineers (not to be confused with engineering geologists) has emerged in America combining skills in engineering design, rock mechanics, soil mechanics, geology and geophysics.

Does this mean that the engineering design process discussed in the previous chapter cannot be applied in rock mechanics design? Certainly not! It does mean, however, that the design of excavations in rock requires extra considerations involving the special geotechnical conditions. In this respect an excellent design philosophy was offered by E. Hoek (Hoek, 1981, Hoek and Brown, 1980, Hoek & Londe, 1974):

The basic aim of any underground excavation design should be to utilize the rock itself as the principal structural material, creating as little disturbance as possible during the excavation and adding as little as possible in the way of concrete and steel support. In their intact state and when subjected to compressive stresses, most hard

33

rocks are far stronger than concrete and many are of the same order of strength as steel. Consequently, it does not make economic sense to replace a material which may be perfectly adequate with one which may be no better.

A good engineering design is a balanced design in which all the factors which interact, even those which cannot be quantified, are taken into account. The duty of the design engineer is not to compute accurately but to judge soundly.

In essence, rock mechanics design in mining and tunneling incorporates such aspects as planning the location of structures, determining their dimensions and shapes, their orientations and layout, excavation procedures (blasting or machine boring), support selection and instrumentation. The rock mechanics engineer studies the original in situ stresses, monitors the changes in stress due to mining or tunneling, determines rock properties, analyzes stresses, deformations and water conditions (pressure and flow) and interprets instrumentation data.

Unfortunately, the application of geotechnical design in mining and tunneling has not progressed at the same rate as for other engineering works. The result has been excessive safety factors in many aspects of underground projects. It is believed that an increasing demand for more realistic safety factors as well as the recognition of the money-saving potential of rock mechanics will lead to greater application of rock mechanics design in mining and tunneling. Nevertheless, while extensive research is being conducted in rock mechanics today, there still seems to be a major problem in 'translating' the research findings into innovative and concise design procedures.

DESIGN METHODS IN MINING AND CIVIL ENGINEERING

There are many practical considerations which are different when designing tunnels in mining and in civil engineering. Muir Wood (1979) believes that differences in practice arise more from tradition, from acceptable standards and from regulation than from reason. Nevertheless, there are some essential differences in the design of mining and civil engineering tunnels: (1) most civil engineering tunnels are virtually permanent (e.g. underground railways, water tunnels, etc.) while mining tunnels are temporary, although, of course, some mining tunnels can have a service life of several decades; (2) civil engineering tunnels serve mainly the general public whereas mining tunnels are used only by trained miners; (3) the total length of tunnels in mines exceeds manyfold the length of tunnels excavated for civil engineering purposes and it is not surprising, therefore, that more exacting standards are employed in civil engineering than are in mining engineering (for example in site exploration, in excavation, in support, etc.); (4) ground conditions in mining are better known because of the mining activities over a number of years while civil engineering structures are usually placed in ground needing detailed site exploration; (5) civil engineering structures are generally at shallow depths (less than 500 m below surface) with the influence of the field stress being frequently neglected and the absence of a well-developed compressive stress field giving rise to the dominant effect that geological factors have in civil engineering – in mining the stress field is of paramount importance; (6) since mining is a dynamic process, mining excavations are subjected to changing stress conditions and this necessitates different rock reinforcement than for static stress situations – civil engineering tunnels, in general, do not experience changing stress conditions; (7) mining aims at increasing profits and funds are less freely available for design investigations than in civil engineering; (8) civil engineering sites can be often selected for their superior rock conditions, whereas in mining the ore location dictates the site.

Bieniawski (1977) compared design investigations for mining and civil engineering chambers and, similarly, Muir Wood (1979) stressed the benefits of mining-civil engineering interaction. While mining has passed to civil engineering the use of yielding supports, rockbolting and doweling, civil engineering has extended some of the soft-ground tunneling methods into mining by modification, in particular, of lining methods for circular tunnels – for example, as used in the Belgian coalfields. The special area where mining has made most significant progress concerns the maximum economic extraction of ore or coal compatible with acceptable criteria for stability.

The design methods which are available for assessing the stability of mines and tunnels can be categorized as follows:
  a) Analytical methods;
  b) Observational methods;
  c) Empirical methods.
In addition, two other approaches are also utilized, namely, geological techniques and compliance considerations (mining or tunneling regulations).

Analytical methods utilize the analyses of stresses and deformations around openings. They include such techniques as closed form solutions, numerical methods (finite elements, finite difference, boundary elements), analog simulations (electrical and photoelastic) and physical modeling.

Observational methods rely on actual monitoring of ground movement during excavation to detect measurable instability, and on the analysis of ground-support interaction. This includes the New Austrian Tunneling Method and the Convergence-Confinement method. Although considered as separate methods, observational approaches are the only way to check the results and predictions of the other methods.

Empirical methods assess the stability of mines and tunnels by the use of statistical analyses of underground observations. Engineering rock mass classifications are the best known empirical approach for assessing the stability of underground openings in rock (Hoek & Brown, 1980, Goodman, 1980). They have received increasing attention in recent years (Einstein et al., 1979) and in many tunneling projects this approach has been utilized as the only practical basis for design. In mining, recent applications include metal mining (Kendorski et al., 1983) and coal mining (Bieniawski et al., 1980, Ghose, 1981).

All the methods require geological input and consideration of statutory safety regulations.

Geological techniques are utilized to identify geological structures and other features affecting structural stability (Ealy et al., 1979). For this purpose, core drilling, geological mapping, isopach mapping, aerial photography, lineament analysis, and satellite imagery are employed. More recently, a method of 'hazard analysis' has been developed (Ellison and Thurman, 1976). The latest major breakthrough in exploration technology in the USA is geological remote sensing from the space shuttle 'Columbia' (Taranik, 1982).

Compliance considerations must be included because regardless of the results of the design methods, the designers must comply with the mining or tunneling regulations and/or other underground limitations, e.g., ventilation, transportation, etc.

A recent research effort has been directed to developing a design approach for mining and tunneling (Bieniawski et al., 1981). This is illustrated diagrammatically in Figure 4.1. An important observation to be made is that no rock engineering design may be considered final until the construction of the structure is complete. The typical costs of design investigations compiled by the author are depicted in Figure 4.2.

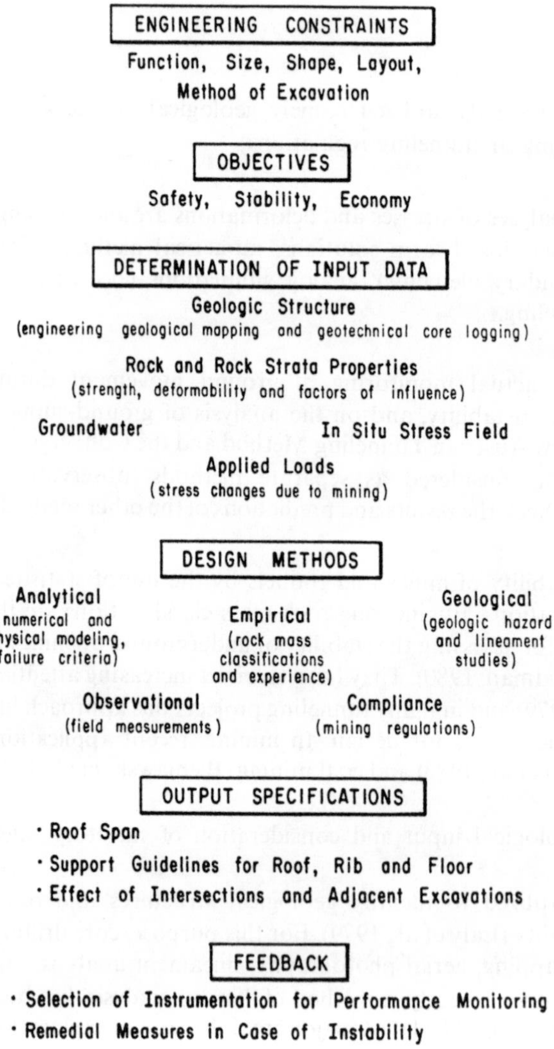

ENGINEERING   CONSTRAINTS

Function, Size, Shape, Layout,
Method of Excavation

OBJECTIVES

Safety, Stability, Economy

DETERMINATION OF INPUT DATA

Geologic Structure
(engineering geological mapping and geotechnical core logging)

Rock and Rock Strata Properties
(strength, deformability and factors of influence)

Groundwater   In Situ Stress Field

Applied Loads
(stress changes due to mining)

DESIGN   METHODS

Analytical	Empirical	Geological
(numerical and physical modeling, failure criteria)	(rock mass classifications and experience)	(geologic hazard and lineament studies)

Observational   Compliance
(field measurements)   (mining regulations)

OUTPUT SPECIFICATIONS

· Roof Span
· Support Guidelines for Roof, Rib and Floor
· Effect of Intersections and Adjacent Excavations

FEEDBACK

· Selection of Instrumentation for Performance Monitoring
· Remedial Measures in Case of Instability

Figure 4.1. Simplified design chart for mining and tunneling.

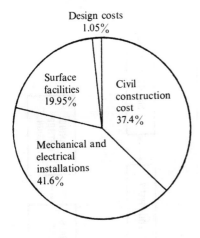

Distribution of costs on Project 1

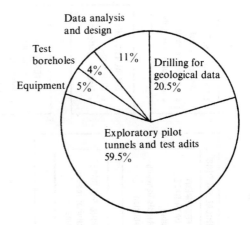

Details of design costs on Project 1

Costs in thousand $	Project 1	Project 2	Project 3	Project 4	Project 5	Project 6
Construction cost*	119,700	63,840	31,425	1,500,000	200,000	885
Design cost (incl. site characterization)	3,353	1,968	2,515	12,000	2,940	11
Total cost	$123,053	65,808	33,940	1,512,000	202,940	896
Design cost as % of total cost	2.72%	2.99%	7.41%	0.80%	1.45%	1.23%
Remarks	22 m span machine hall for power station	24 m span machine hall for power station	7.5 m dia 3 km long undercity tunnel	Very large tunneling project	Long water conveyance tunnel	Mining hoist chamber in good rock

*Construction cost does not include mechanical and electrical installations such as incurred on civil engineering underground hydro-electric projects. For example, for Project 1, the mechanical and electrical costs were $133 million plus the cost of one dam and access roads of $63.8 million. The overall cost of the project was thus: $319.85 million. The cost of design investigations as a percentage of this overall cost was thus 1.05%.

Figure 4.2. Costs of design investigations for underground excavations in rock, in 1980 U.S. dollars.

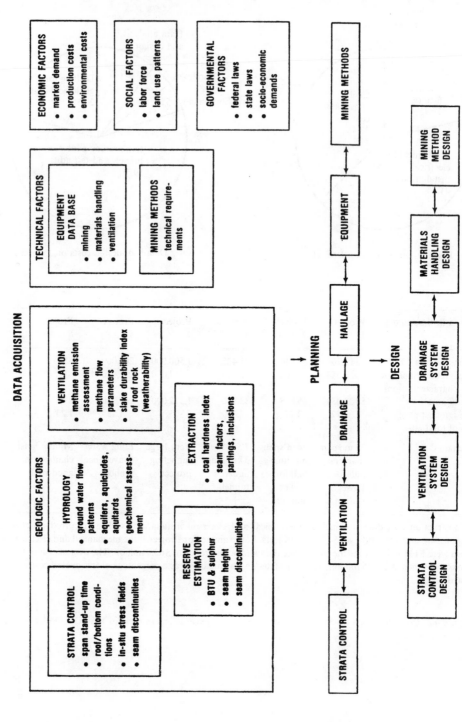

Figure 4.3. Interaction of various factors in mine design (modified after Luxbacher and Ramani, 1980).

It should be noted that designing a mine or a tunnel involves the design of many systems besides those involved in rock mechanics design. A good treatment of this aspect for mining was provided by Luxbacher and Ramani (1980) and is depicted in Figure 4.3. In the case of tunneling, Muir Wood and Sauer (1981) discussed the interactions in the decision-making processes. They emphasized that actions taken and decisions made in early design phases must, for successful outcome, take account of their consequences at later stages. Other interesting studies in this respect were performed by Hoek and Brown (1980), Selmer-Olsen and Broch (1977), Nicholas and Marek (1981) and Hoek (1982).

The principal factors affecting the stability of mines and tunnels are:

a) The stress fields to which an underground excavation is subjected especially those caused by mining in its vicinity;

b) The interaction between adjacent excavations;

c) The strength and other properties of the rock strata through which the excavation passes;

d) The ground water conditions;

e) The method and quality of excavation;

f) The support of the rock strata.

A very detailed but self-explanatory chart of design procedure for rock tunnels is depicted in a series of diagrams given in Figures 4.4 through 4.9.

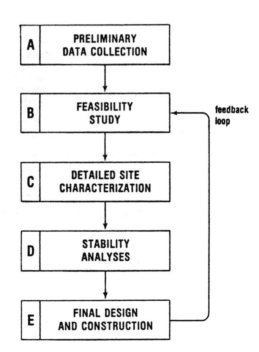

Figure 4.4. Detailed design procedure for rock tunnels.

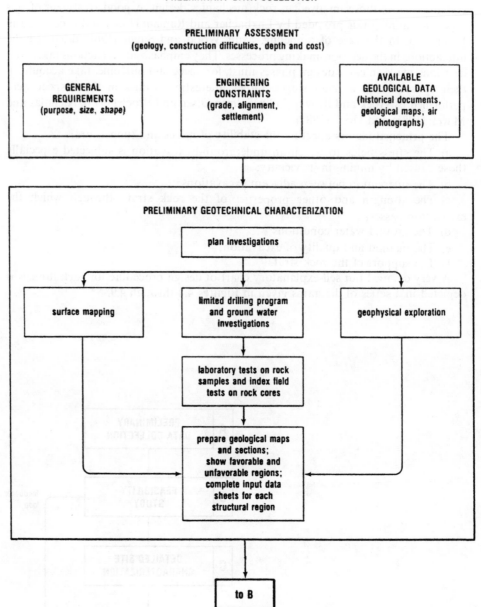

Figure 4.5. Diagram A of the design procedure.

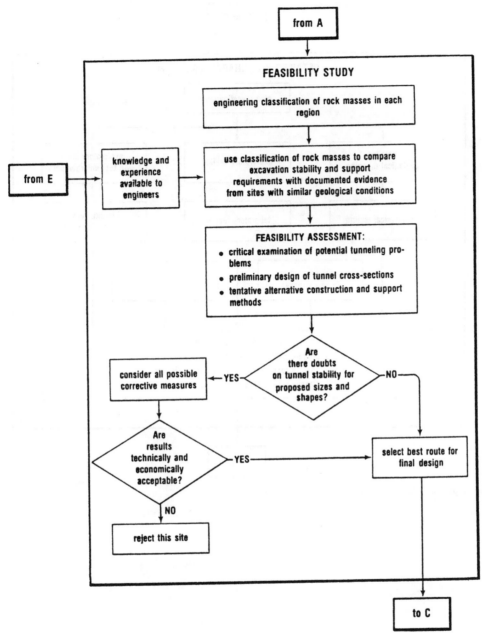

Figure 4.6. Diagram B of the design procedure.

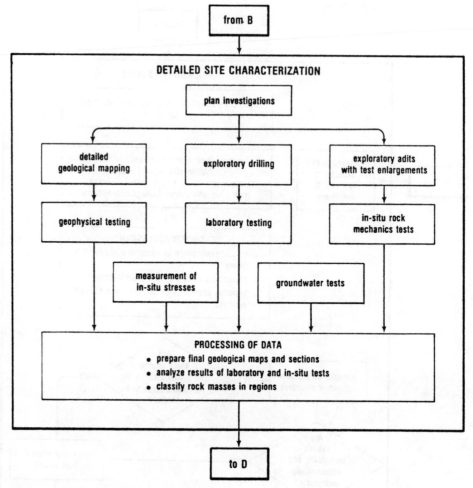

Figure 4.7. Diagram C of the design procedure.

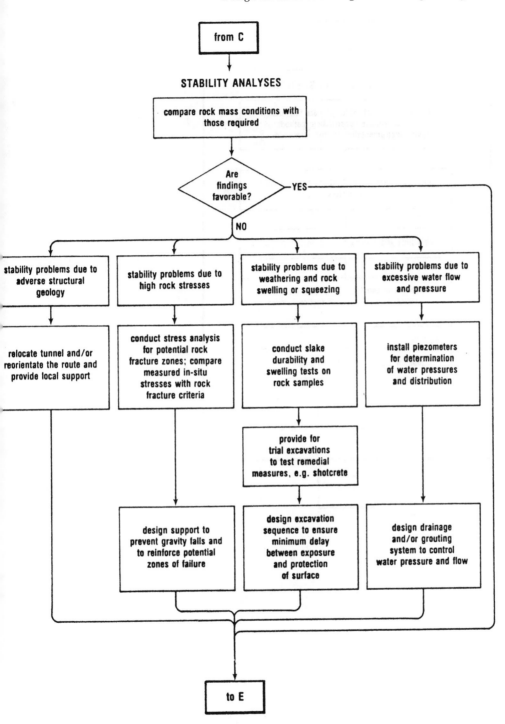

Figure 4.8. Diagram D of the design procedure.

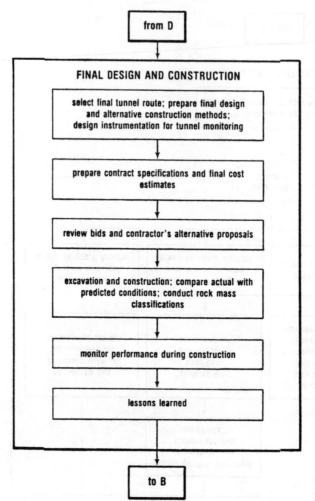

Figure 4.9. Diagram E of the design procedure.

CONTRACTING AND PROJECT MANAGEMENT

Successful completion of major tunneling and mining projects depends not only on careful engineering design and construction procedures, but also on good project management and, most of all, sound contractual provisions. An efficient design may not materialize into a successful project if problems arise in contracting matters. The contracting practices governing any construction project involve the most basic considerations of professional responsibility, equity, and financial compensation. In underground construction, one of the most controversial questions that persistently arises is that of the risk involved and of how the responsibility should be divided.

In recent years, it has become apparent that contractual practices in underground projects could be improved substantially throughout the world and hence lead to better design and construction technology. Accordingly, a special study of the U.S. National Committee on Tunneling Technology was initiated in 1976 to prepare recommendations on better contracting for underground construction. In the United Kingdom, the Construction Industry Research and Information Association (CIRIA) proposed in 1978 improved contract practices for tunneling. In addition, the International Tunneling Association has established a working group to study contractual practices throughout the world. Most recently, Hoek (1982) discussed geotechnical considerations in tunnel designs and in preparation of contracts.

These studies were necessitated by the trend toward large claims and litigation in many countries which has brought both the owners and contractors to the point where nobody gains and everybody loses. A prominent U.S. construction-industry attorney, speaking to a national audience, said 'the last place you ever want to be is in court. I will be the only person who is going to make money as a result of your litigation.'

USNCTT recommendations for better contracting

In December 1974, the U.S. National Academy of Sciences published the results of an intensive research effort by the U.S. National Committee on Tunneling Technology (USNCTT), *Better Contracting for Underground Construction*. This intensive study included the following:

1. Personal interviews with 39 leaders in U.S. underground construction, representatives of contracting agencies, construction firms and consulting engineers.

2. A detailed questionnaire sent to 178 public works organizations.

3. A national workshop conference.

4. Interviews with 108 owners, contractors, engineers, and lawyers in seven European countries.

The results of this research effort have produced a number of recommendations for improving contractual practices. These recommendations will provide substantial benefits not only to owners and contractors but also to the general public. The recommendations are as follows:

Group 1. To share construction risks:

a) Inclusion of changed-conditions clauses. Contracts for underground construction should include changed conditions clauses, permitting the owner to assume the risk for unknown sub-surface conditions and reducing the need for large contingencies in contractors' bids;

b) Disclosure of geological data and interpretations. The greatest possible use should be made of modern geological technology, and all subsurface data should be made available to bidders, along with professional interpretations;

c) Elimination of disclaimers. Contracts should not contain disclaimers as to the accuracy of subsurface data provided to bidders;

d) Provision for water problems. Contracts should include provision for the cost of coping with unexpected water problems;

e) Responsibility for support system. Contracts should include plans for necessary tunnel support systems, as designated by the owners and for which the owner accepts responsibility.

Group 2. To share financial risks:

a) Bid pricing. Bidding schedules should be structured in such a way as to reduce the necessity or desire of contractors to engage in unbalanced bidding;

b) Inclusion of escalation clauses. Contracts should include escalation clauses covering inflation and permitting owners and contractors to share the increased cost of labor, installed equipment and construction materials;

c) Contractor financing requirements. Contracts should contain provisions intended to reduce the contractors' financing needs, including prompt payment for the cost of modernization, for materials when delivered to the site, and for progress payments at appropriate intervals;

d) Cost-reimbursement contracts. Cost-reimbursement contracts should be explored as a possible solution to present-day problems of undue risk in underground work and unpredictable inflation.

Group 3. To expedite handling of claims:

a) Provision for change negotiations. Contracts should contain procedures under which owners and contractors could negotiate contract changes, without costly delays to work, when differences arise;

b) Provision for arbitration. Contracts should contain provision for arbitration, if necessary. Public agencies prohibited by law from submitting disputes to binding decisions may find nonbinding arbitration an acceptable alternative. Plans should be developed for the formation of a large panel of experienced arbitrators under the sponsorship of the American Arbitration Association.

Group 4. To stimulate innovation in construction:

a) Consideration of alternative bids. The merits of permitting alternative bids should be explored;

b) Encouragement of value engineering programs. The incentive system, 'value engineering', should be adopted more widely with owners and contractors sharing the cost savings equally.

Group 5. To assure award to qualified contractors:

a) Prequalification of bidders. The feasibility of a prequalification system should be explored by public agencies rather than determining if the low bidder is responsible after the bids have been opened.

Group 6. To realize other cost savings:

a) Advance acquisition of right-of-way. Right-of-way and necessary permits should be obtained by owners in advance of construction;

b) Wrap-up insurance. Wrap-up insurance is an overall, coordinated insurance program, provided and administered by the owner, with respect to all the construction contracts awarded for a project. The decision of whether to use wrap-up insurance should remain the prerogative of the owner;

c) Publication of engineers' estimate. Present practices controlling disclosure of engineers' estimates should be respected. However, if an owner has a fixed limit on funds available for the project, this sum should be disclosed in the bid invitation.

It is difficult to estimate the dollar value of good contracting practices. Investigations indicate that improvements such as those recommended above may produce savings of up to 10% to contractors and owners.

CIRIA recommendations for better contracting

The British Construction Industry Research and Information Association (CIRIA) recommended that a set of reference conditions be established by the engineer and, after discussion with, and modification by the contractor, these be used as a basis for settlement of disputes. These reference conditions should cover one or more of the following: geological description of the rock strata in terms of engineering geology, method of construction, behavior of the ground in response to tunneling, and rate of advance.

A major factor in establishing reference conditions and agreeing on these conditions with the contractor, before tunneling commences, is the extent to which geological information and interpretation is disclosed (Hoek, 1982, Waggoner, 1981, D'Appolonia, 1981). Rock mass classifications systems, which will be discussed in later chapters, represent a major attempt to collect together relevant geological and geotechnical data and to organize these into a rational system for predicting tunnel behavior and estimating tunnel support requirements. These systems can provide an effective basis for establishing reference conditions and for subsequent discussions between engineers and contractors (Hoek, 1982).

An important development in this respect in the United States is the requirement that a design firm or agency produce a report *Geotechnical Basis for Design and Construction Specifications* (Deere, 1978). This practice has been successfully used on the Washington Metro as a result of the discussions between the owners, general designers and consulting board of the Washington Metropolitan Area Transit Authority.

Such a report, generally called the Geotechnical Report, sets forth the regional and local geology, the significant engineering geological features which would influence the design and construction and essentially would give the geotechnical basis for the design and construction specifications. The report explicitly states what tunneling conditions are anticipated; the types of initial support and final lining that were considered, and which were finally adopted, including the loading conditions and design analysis, and the importance of certain construction specifications (such as rockbolting within 1 meter of the face and within 2 hours, etc.). Another feature of the geotechnical report is that it forces cooperation among the various specialists – the engineering geologists, the rock mechanics engineers, the structural design engineers, and the construction management engineers. This aspect in itself has resulted in better designs and specifications. The report is included as part of the contract documents and is given to all the contractors who wish to tender on the job.

Types of contract

Construction contracts may be grouped together into two large categories. One category includes those contracts for which the contractor is selected on the basis of competitive bidding. The second category consists of those that result from direct owner-contractor negotiations. Almost all public construction contracts, as well as a large proportion of private work, are in the competitive bid category.

Crack, Ramani and Frantz (1982) discussed the breakdown of the contracts into various sub-groups, each group representing a distinct form of contract as depicted in Figure 4.10. In Table 4.1 their listing of the various types of contracts is given together with a description of each contract and associated advantages and disadvantages.

A full discussion of the types of contracts can also be found in the U.S. National Committee on Tunneling Technology report (1974) and the British CIRIA report (1978). The U.S. report also contains a particularly useful appendix summarizing tunnel contracting practices in Britain, France, Italy, Norway, Sweden, Switzerland, and West Germany.

One contract type which could more equitably take into account the great risk of the unknown in tunnel construction, is the 'target estimate' type of contract with penalty and bonus clauses. This type of contract was recently awarded in the USA for two cooling water tunnels. Because of the possible risk involved with potential water inflow problems and with the use of a tunnel boring machine in hard meta-sedimentary

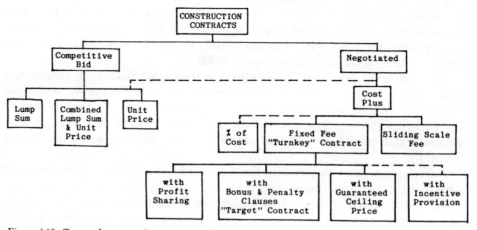

Figure 4.10. Types of construction contracts (Crack et al., 1982).

Type of contract	Method of paying contractor	Description	Advantages	Disadvantages
Competitive bid 1) Public works construction 2) Contract to lowest qualified bidder	Lump sum	When types of construction are standardized and when variety of operations are involved	1) Owner knows in advance cost of work 2) Promotes contractor speed and efficiency	1) Requires detailed plans and specs 2) Changes and extra work orders are expensive
3) Anyone can submit bid	Unit price	When work requires large quantities of relatively few types of work or where quantities cannot be determined in advance	1) Contractor not forced to gamble 2) Limits of plans and specs may be somewhat indefinite 3) Reduces number of formal change orders	1) Engineers estimates must be reasonably accurate 2) Owner does not know cost in advance 3) May promote 'unbalanced' bids
	Combined lump sum & unit price	When work contains items, details of which may be broken down into units but which are indefinite as to quantities (e.g., building construction)	Combines advantages of lump sum and unit price; e.g, in building construction, foundation work by unit price and superstructure by lump sum	
Negotiated bid 1) Awarded to selected contractor after study of qualifications of candidates	Lump sum, unit price or combination of these	See above	See above	See above
	Cost + % of cost	Oldest form of negotiated type. Not recommended for general use	1) Permits starting work before plans completed 2) Easy to change plans during construction	1) Contractors profit is increased by increasing cost, therefore no incentive to economize 2) Project cost not known in advance
2) Private works (forbidden by law for most public works)	Cost + sliding scale fee	Contractor's fee increased by fixed amounts for various increments of cost	1) and 2) same as above 3) Promotes economy	1) Project cost not known in advance
	Cost + fixed fee	Amount of fee determined from consideration of character and scope of work and its estimated cost	1) Permits starting construction before plans are completed 2) No incentive for contractor to inflate construction costs	1) Requires good estimate of cost by engineer 2) Actual cost of project not known in advance

schists, gneisses and quartzites with intruded granite, it was decided to share the risk with the contractor so that realistic bids could be achieved (Deere, 1978).

Hoek (1982) summarized the situation well: 'Flexibility in both contract nego- tiations and in dealing with on-site problems is the key to successful tunneling. If one or more of the parties involved approaches the contract negotiations with preconceived and rigidly held attitudes, it is unlikely that the project will be completed without disputes, claims and perhaps long and costly litigation. Worse still, these preconceived views and rigidly held attitudes can extend to technical matters and can result in a lack of on-site technical cooperation and even the use of incorrect remedial measures when technical problems arise.'

Better management of mining and tunneling projects

The need for flexibility and cooperation in contract negotiations and in technical activities can best be realized if mining and tunneling projects feature good management practices. This matter has been treated in detail by the U.S. National Committee on Tunneling Technology (1978) in a report entitled *Better Management of Major Underground Construction Projects*.

For use in mining, the Pennsylvania State University has published important guidelines for mineral management (Frantz and Ramani, 1982). A listing of factors that must be taken into consideration by traditional management and those factors that are unique to mineral management, is given in Table 4.2.

Table 4.2. Management concerns (after Frantz and Ramani, 1982)

Traditional management concerns

Objectives	Relations with	Tasks	Techniques
Return on investment	Owners	Planning	Scientific management
Development of people	Employees	Organizing	Decentralization
Social impact	Customers	Staffing	Personnel management
Community	Government	Controlling	Manager development
responsibility	Community		Managerial accounting

Additional concerns unique to mineral management

Geological site constraints	Sequential operations	Optimum resource recovery	Total land-use planning
Fixed locations	Exploration	Extraction sequence	Resource characteri- zation
Remote locations	Development	Minimization of unrecoverable minerals	Sequential land-use planning
Different cultures	Extraction	Quality consideration	Pre-mining uses Concurrent-with-mining uses
Adverse climatic conditions	Waste management		Post-mining uses

REFERENCES

Bennett, R. D. *Tunnel Cost-Estimating Methods.* U.S. Army Corps of Engineers, Waterways Experiment Station, Technical Report, GL–81–10, October 1981, 238 p.

Bieniawski, Z. T. Design investigations for rock chambers in South Africa. *Proc. Rockstone '77 Symp.*, ITA, Stockholm, 1977, Vol. 3, pp. 107–112.

Bieniawski, Z. T. Tunnel design by rock mass classifications. *U.S. Army Corps of Engineers, Waterways Experiment Station*, Report RM-123, Vicksburg, Mississippi, 1979.

Bieniawski, Z. T., Cincilla, W. A. and Unal, E. A design approach for coal mine tunnels. *Proc. Rapid Excavation and Tunneling Conf.*, San Francisco, AIME, New York, 1981, pp. 147–163.

Bieniawski, Z. T., Rafia, F. and Newman, D. A. Ground control investigations for assessment of roof conditions in coal mines. *Proc. 21st U.S. Symp. Rock Mech.*, University of Missouri, Rolla, 1980, pp. 523–535.

Brady, B. T. Basic requirements for the design of mine openings. *U.S. Bureau of Mines Information Circular*, IC 8585, 1973, pp. 8–21.

Brierley, G. Controlling Tunnel Lining Costs – Tips for Owners and Designers. *Civil Engineering – ASCE*, American Society of Civil Engineers, July 1978, pp. 51–53.

Budavari, S. Rock mechanics aspects of the design of underground mine workings. *Australian Mining*, Vol. 66, No. 10, October 1974, pp. 15–27.

Choi, D. S. and McCain, D. L. Design of longwall systems. *SME AIME 1979 Annual Meeting*, Mini-Symposium No. 79–07, 1979, pp. 15–26.

Coates, D. F. and Gyenge, M. Incremental design in rock mechanics. *Mines Branch Monograph 880*. Canada Department of Energy, Mines and Resources, 1973, 79 p.

Construction Industry Research and Information Association. *Tunneling – Improved Contract Practices.* CIRIA Report #79, London, 1978, 70 pp.

Cook, N. G. W. The sitting of mine tunnels and other factors affecting their layout and design. *Pap. Disc. Assoc. Mine Mgrs. S. Afr.*, May 1973, pp. 199–215.

Crack, F. G., Ramani, R. V. and Frantz, R. L. Professional project management in mine construction. *Mining Engineering*, July 1982, pp. 801–805. Also in: *SME-AIME Annual Meeting*, Dallas, 1982, Preprint No. 82–70.

Cundle, R. D. Panel design problems, *U.S. Bureau of Mines Information Circular*, IC 8630, 1974, pp. 14–21.

D'Appolonia Consulting Engineers. *Geotechnical Investigation and Design Guidelines; Mining : Surface and Underground.* Rocky Mountain Energy Co., January 1976.

D'Appolonia, E. Relationship between design and construction in geotechnical engineering. *Tunneling Technology Newsletter*, U.S. National Committee on Tunneling Technology, Washington, DC, No. 19, September 1977, pp. 1–5.

D'Appolonia, E. Contact Methods not Technology Restrain U.S. Underground Development. *Underground Space*, Vol. 6, No. 3, 1981, pp. 138–140.

Dahl, H. D. and Schonfeldt, von H. A. Rock mechanics elements of coal mine design. *Monograph on Rock Mechanics Applications in Mining* (from 17th U.S. Symposium on Rock Mechanics), AIME, New York, 1977, pp. 31–39.

Deere, D. U. Current Tunnel Design, Construction and Research in the U.S. *Proc. Int. Tunnel Symp. on Tunneling Under Difficult Conditions*, Japan Tunneling Association, Tokyo, 1978, pp. A–8–1:6.

Dendrou, B., van Dillen, D., and Sennett, R. E. A programmatic study of a discontinuous rock medium and its effects the design of an underground structural support. *Proceedings of the 20th Symposium on Rock Mechanics*, University of Texas, Austin, 1979, pp. 525–534.

Duvall, W. I. General principles of underground opening design in competent rock. *Ibid*, pp. 101–111.

Ealy, D. L., Mazurak, R. E. and Laugrand, E. L. A geological approach for predicting unstable roof and floor conditions in advance of mining. *Mining Congress Journal*, Vol. 65, No. 3, 1979, pp. 17–22.

Einstein, H. H. and Bischoff, H. Design of tunnels in swelling rock. *Design Methods in Rock Mechanics* (Proceedings of the 16th U.S. Symposium on Rock Mechanics), ASCE, New York, 1977, pp. 185–196.

Einstein, H. H., Steiner, W., and Baecher, G. B. Assessment of empirical design methods for tunnels in rocks. *Proc. 4th Rapid Excavation Tunneling Conf.*, AIME, New York, 1979, Vol. 1, pp. 683–706.

Ellison, R. and Thurman, A. G. 'Geotechnology: an integral part of mine planning.' *Coal Exploration*, ed. W. Muir. Miller-Freeman, San Francisco, 1976, pp. 324–372.

Feld, J. Relationship of Owner, Engineer and Contractor in Tunnel Work. *Proc. Rapid Excav. and Tunnel. Conf.*, San Francisco, Vol. 2, 1974, pp. 1421–1444.

Frantz, R. L. and Ramani, R. V. Mineral Management – Its Unique Aspects. *Earth and Mineral Sciences Bulletin*, The Pennsylvania State University, Vol. 52, No. 1, 1982, pp. 1–4.

Ghose, A. K. and Raju, N. M. Characterization of rock mass vis-a-vis application of rock bolting-modeling of Indian coal measures. *Proc. 22nd U.S. Symp. on Rock Mech.*, MIT, Cambridge, Mass., 1981, pp. 422–427.

Goodman, R. E. *Methods of Geological Engineering*, West Publishing, St. Paul, 1976, 472 p.

Goodman, R. E. *Introduction to Rock Mechanics*, John Wiley & Sons, New York, 1980, 478 p.

Haimson, B. Design of underground powerhouses. *Proc. 16th U.S. Symp. on Rock Mech.*, ASCE, New York, 1977 pp. 197–204.

Heuze, F. E. Geotechnical studies for room-and-pillar mine design. *SME-AIME 1978 Fall Meeting*, Mini-Symposium No. 78–1, 1978, pp. 1–15

Heuze, F. E. Design optimization for multiple rock caverns. *Proc. 16th U.S. Symp. on Rock Mech.*, ASCE, New York, 1977, pp. 267–276.

Hoek, E. Geotechnical design of large openings at depth. *Proc. Rapid Excavation & Tunnel. Conf.*, AIME, New York, 1981, Vol. 2, pp. 1032–1044.

Hoek, E. Geotechnical Considerations in Tunnel Design and Contract Preparation. *Trans. Inst. Min. Metall.*, Vol. 91, 1982, pp. A101–109.

Hoek, E. and Brown, E. T. *Underground Excavations in Rock*, Institution of Mining and Metallurgy, London, 1980, 527 p.

Hoek, E. and Londe, P. The design of rock slopes and foundations. *Proceedings of the 3rd International Congress of Rock Mechanics*, ISRM, Denver, 1974, Vol. 1A, General Report, pp. 613–752.

Hooker, V. A method of evaluating room and pillar or panel design. *U.S. Bureau of Mines Information Circular*, IC 8630, 1974, pp. 33–38.

Johnson, L. P., Haycocks, C., Neall, G. M. and Townsend, J. M. Geological factors in longwall design. *SME-AIME 1977 Annual Meeting*, Preprint No. 77–F–56.

Karwoski, W. J., McLaughlin, W. C. and Cockle, A. R. Design of drift supports in block caving operations. *SME-AIME 1979 Fall Meeting*, Preprint No. 79–302.

Kendorski, F. S. Caving operations drift support design, *Design Methods in Rock Mechanics* (Proc., 16th U.S. Symposium on Rock Mechanics), ASCE, New York, 1977, pp. 277–286.

Kendorski, F. S., Cummings, R. A., Bieniawski, Z. T. and Skinner, E. H. A rock mass classification for the planning of caving mine drift support. *Proc. Rapid Excav. and Tunneling Conf.*, AIME, New York, 1983, Vol. 1, pp. 191–223.

Ko, K. C. and Ferguson, D. A. Geotechnical and mine design considerations in multiple seam mining. *SME-AIME 1978 Fall Meeting*, Mini-Symposium No. 78–1, 1978, pp. 21–32.

Kovari, K. Basic considerations on the design of underground openings. *Int. Assoc. Bridge and Structural Engineering Surveys*, No. S–10/79, August 1979, pp. 1–23.

Kuesel, T. R. Faults in Swedish and American Tunneling Practices: A Fable. *Civil Engineering – ASCE*, American Society of Civil Engineers, January 1979, pp. 74–75.

Lama, R. D. Principles of underground coal mine design – an approach. *Colliery Guardian*, July 1977, pp. 375–378.

Lindberg, H. E., Schwer, L. E., and Senseny, P. E. Reinforcement design for underground protective cavaties. *Proc. Rapid Excavation and Tunneling Conf.*, AIME, New York, 1979, Vol. 1, pp. 641–650.

Luxbacher, W. G. and Ramani, R. V. The interrelationship between coal mine plant and ventilation system design. *Proc. 2nd Intern. Mine Ventilation Congress*, AIME, New York, 1980, pp. 73–82.

Mathews, R. E. Design of underground mining layouts. *Underground Space*, Vol. 2, No. 4, June 1978, pp. 195–209.

Megaw, T. M. and Bartlett, J. V. *Tunnels – Planning, Design, Construction*, Ellis Horwood Ltd., Chichester, 1981, 284 p.

Muir Wood, A. M. Ground behavior and support for mining and tunneling. *Tunnels and Tunneling*, June 1979, pp. 47–51.

Muir Wood, A. M. and Sauer, G. Efficacy and equity of the management of large underground projects. *Proc. Rapid Excav. and Tunnel. Conf.*, AIME, New York, 1981, Vol. 2, pp. 1032–1044.

Nicholas, D. E. and Marek, J. M. The feasibility study – selection of a mining method integrating rock mechanics and mine planning. *Proc. Rapid Excav. and Tunnel. Conf.*, AIME, New York, 1981, Vol. 2, pp. 1018–1031.

Obert, L. A. Philosophy of Design. *U.S. Bureau of Mines Information Circular*, IC 8585, 1973, pp. 6–7.

Panek, L. A. Bureau of Mines approach to ground control aspects of mine design. *U.S. Bureau of Mines Information Circular*, IC 8585, 1974, pp. 5–13.

Pariseau, W. G. Limit design of mine pillars under certainty. *Design Methods in Rock Mechanics* (Proceedings of the 16th U.S. Symposium on Rock Mechanics), ASCE, New York, 1977, pp. 287–302.

Pariseau, W. G. and Sorensen, W. K. 3D mine pillar design information from 2D FEM analysis. *Int. J. Numerical and Analytical Methods in Geomechanics*, Vol. 3, 1979, pp. 145–157.

Rose, D. C. Influence of Geologic Logs and Descriptions on Tunnel Design and Costs. *Tunneling Technology Newsletter*, U.S. National Committee on Tunneling Technology, No. 35, September 1981, pp. 12–16.

Selmer-Olsen, R. and Broch, E. General design procedure for underground openings in Norway. *Proc. Rockstore '77*, Stockholm, 1977, ITA, Vol. 3, pp. 219–226.

St. John, C. M. and Hardy, M. P. Geotechnical models and their application in mine design. *SME-AIME 1978 Fall Meeting, Mini-Symposium*, Preprint No. 78–1, 1978, pp. 43–52.

Taranik, J. V. Geological remote sensing and Space Shuttle. *Mining Congress Journal*, July 1982, pp. 18–44.

U.S. National Committee on Tunneling Technology. *Better Contracting for Underground Construction*. National Academy of Sciences, Washington, DC, 1974, 143 p.

U.S. National Committee on Tunneling Technology. *Better Management of Major Underground Construction Projects*. National Academy of Sciences, Washington, DC, 1978, 151 p.

Waggoner, E. B. Construction Claims – Spurious and Justified. *Bulletin of Association of Engr. Geologists*, Vol. 18, 1981, pp. 147–150.

Waldeck, H. G. The design of large underground chambers at depth in gold mines of South Africa. *Proceedings of the 4th International Congress of Rock Mechanics* ISRM, Montreux, A. A. Balkemea, Rotterdam, 1979, Vol. 1, pp. 565–570.

Wardell, K. and Eynon, P. Structural concept of strata control and mine design. *The Mining Engineer*, London, August 1968, pp. 633–645.

Wells, H. M. Optimization of mining engineering design in mineral valuation. *Mining Engineering*, December 1978, pp. 1676–1685.

Wheby, F. T. Parametric Estimates of Costs for Tunneling in Rock. *Tunneling Technology Newsletter*, U.S. National Committee on Tunneling Technology, No. 12, December 1975, pp. 1–6.

White, D. H. Analysis of rock mass properties for the design of block caving mines. *SME-AIME 1979 Fall Meeting*, Preprint No. 79–309.

Whittaker, B. N. and Pye, J. H. Design and layout aspects of longwall methods of coal mining. *Proc. 16th U.S. Symp. on Rock Mech.*, ASCE, New York, 1977, pp. 303–314.

Whittaker, B. N. and Singh, R. N. Design and stability of pillars in longwall mining. *Mining Engineer*, Vol. 139, No. 214, July 1979, pp. 59–72.

An underground power station – machine hall excavated in hard rock. (Courtesy of Dr. E. Hoek, Golder Associates).

CHAPTER 5

Input parameters for design

If you can measure what you are speaking about, and
express it in numbers, you know something about it.

Lord Kelvin (1824–1907)

Provision of reliable input data for engineering design of structures in rock is one of the most difficult tasks facing engineering geologists and design engineers. It is extremely important that the quality of the input data matches the sophistication of the design methods. It has been contended often that some design methods such as numerical techniques, have outpaced our ability to provide the input data necessary for the application of these methods. Obviously, it must be realized that if incorrect input parameters are employed incorrect design information will result. Speaking in computer jargon, the following expression would be appropriate: 'garbage in, garbage out'.

The input information needed for design purposes generally includes geological characterization of the rock masses, evaluation of the virgin ground stresses and the mechanical properties which characterize the rock mass in its natural state. Whatever procedures and techniques are employed to obtain the input parameters, it is necessary to emphasize that any such procedures and techniques should only be used if they can be fully justified for the purposes of a given project. In other words, measurements and investigations should be carefully planned and matched with the purpose of a project, full justification being given for any investigations and tests performed. It may come as a surprise to some that on a number of projects throughout the world extensive investigations have been conducted, the results of which had little bearing on the subsequent design of the excavations in rock. Thus, much money and effort was wasted.

Furthermore, determination of the input parameters for design should be so planned that as much quantitative data as possible is obtained rather than relying on qualitative descriptions.

In essence, the following three important messages emerge:

1. The eventual quality of the engineering design is directly proportional to the quality of the input parameters.

2. Any procedures or methods employed in providing the input data should be fully justified and carefully planned.

3. Quantitative rather than qualitative information is required for design purposes.

Determining the input parameters for rock engineering design will be of prime concern both to the design engineer and the engineering geologist. It is therefore essential that both these persons work closely as members of the same team. Moreover, two principles should be observed: 1) the design engineer should clearly state his requirements so that the engineering geologist can understand the need for specific input parameters and 2) the engineering geologist should provide the data in such a way that they can be employed directly for design purposes by the engineer.

The determination of the input data for design, involving geological site characterization, ground stress conditions, ground water conditions and mechanical properties of rock masses is a wide subject which in itself could well be the topic of a separate textbook. Accordingly, the purpose of this chapter is only to highlight the most important concepts for obtaining input parameters for design while actual detailed information on individual methods and techniques will be found in the literature cited at the end of this chapter. In particular, see Goodman (1976), Hoek and Brown (1980), Hansen and Lachel (1980) with special reference to mining, and Merritt (1981).

GEOLOGICAL SITE CHARACTERIZATION

When the design engineer is confronted with rock, he must visualize the rock mass as an assemblage of intact rock blocks separated by different types of geological discontinuities. He must therefore consider the characteristics of both the intact material and the discontinuities.

The question immediately arises as to how the strength of the rock material is related to the strength of the rock mass. In answering this question one must note, first of all, that the importance of the properties of intact rock material will be generally overshadowed by the properties of the discontinuities in the rock masses. However, this does not mean, that the properties of the intact rock material should be disregarded when considering the behavior of jointed rock masses. After all, if discontinuities are widely spaced or if the intact rock is weak and altered, the properties of the intact rock may strongly influence the gross behavior of the rock mass. Furthermore, a sample of a rock material sometimes represents a small scale model of the rock mass since they both have gone through the same geological cycle. Nevertheless, in general, the properties of the discontinuities are of greater importance than the properties of the intact rock material.

The interaction of the various testing approaches and the parameters needed for engineering design is listed in Table 5.1. It will be seen that the testing approaches are divided into categories of field testing, in-situ testing, and laboratory testing. Their purpose is to establish the needed design parameters characterizing the rock material, the rock mass, the in-situ stress field, and other conditions.

Initial site characterization

'The first fact which must be recognized when planning a site investigation program is that there is no such thing as a standard site investigation' (Hoek, 1982). This statement applies equally well to both stages of site characterization, namely, a preliminary site investigation and the final site investigation. The scope of a preliminary geological investigation has been outlined in Figure 4.5 of the previous chapter while the scope of the final site exploration is outlined in Figure 4.7 of Chapter 4.

The purpose of the initial site investigation is to establish the feasibility of the

Table 5.1 Recommended rock mechanics observations and measurements for site characterization

Property or data / Test or activity	Rock material	Rock mass	In-situ stress field	Modulus of deformation	Empirical design data
Field testing					
Geotechnical surveys and integral sampling	Detailed engineering geological description of rock strata				Input data for engineering classification of rock masses
Point-load test	Strength index from rock pieces				
Direct sheer test–portable shear box		Friction and cohesion of joints from cores			
In situ testing					
Overcoring cells & small flat jacks			Magnitude & directions of stresses	Deformation parameters	
Plate bearing tests & borehole jack		Effect of joints on strength of rock mass		Deformation parameters	
Seismic/sonic measurements (petite sismique)	Sonic velocity data on laboratory rock specimens			Longitudinal and shear wave velocities and dynamic moduli	
Convergence monitoring & borehole extensometers			Stress redistribution	Time-dependent rock mass movements around excavations	
Piezometers in boreholes		Data on water inflow, pressure and permeability of rock mass			

Table 5.1 (continued)

Rockbolt and other support trials; pullout tests					Rock support data: spacing, length, etc.
Laboratory testing					
Uniaxial compression tests	Uniaxial compressive strength and strength anisotropy			Elastic modulus and Poisson's ratio of rock specimens	
Triaxial compression tests	Friction and cohesion of rock material and Mohr's envelope				
Density, porosity, water content, swelling and slake durability	Density and porosity data, water content influence on material strength				Weatherability and swelling parameters

project. In essence, the initial site assessment involves the discovery, correlation and analysis of geological data such as:

1. Rock types to be encountered,
2. Depth and character of overburden,
3. Macroscopic scale discontinuities such as major faults,
4. Groundwater conditions,
5. Special problems, such as weak ground or swelling rock.

The initial site assessment can utilize a number of sources of information of which two are particularly relevant:

a) Available geological maps, published literature and possibly local knowledge;
b) Photogeological images (aerial photographs) of the area.

The photogeological study is of particular importance and its benefits may even justify procuring new aerial photographs if those available are inadequate. The benefits of the photogeological study include information on topography, drainage, lithology, geological structures and discontinuities.

One of the purposes of the initial site exploration is to determine the regional geology of the vicinity of the project. This aspect is fully treated by Fisher and Banks (1978).

While determination of the regional geology is based mainly on studies of reports, maps and publications involving the geological history of the area as well as studies of information derived from local knowledge and aerial photography, some limited investigations may also be conducted. These would include mapping of the surface outcrops, physical exploration, and a limited program of drilling and groundwater investigations. Some laboratory tests on rock samples and index field tests on rock cores may also be performed. Based on these investigations, preliminary geological maps and sections should be prepared showing favorable and unfavorable regions in the rock mass. These maps and sections are important for planning the next stages of the site characterization program.

Where outcrops and geological structures are not easily deduced by either photogeological or ground investigations, geophysical methods may be used to locate large discontinuities such as faults. The most effective means of doing this would be by seismic or resistivity methods. These geophysical methods are discussed fully by Farr (1979) and Lytle (1978), as well as by Hoek and Brown (1980), Bell (1980) and Griffiths and King (1981).

New developments in geological remote sensing emerged from the availability of the Space Shuttle 'Columbia' as a global reconnaissance platform (Taranik, 1982). This may constitute a major breakthrough in exploration technology. The launching of the Sky Lab and the Landsat satellites provided a new source of aerial photography for a decade. Campbell et al. (1975), and Dunham et al. (1976) discussed techniques of lineament analysis using black-and-white, color and infrared satellite photography. A good discussion of fracture mapping and lineament analysis using satellite and aerial photography is presented by Rinkenberger (1977).

Final site investigation

Based on an initial site exploration, the final site investigation will be conducted once the feasibility of the project has been established. This stage of site characterization will include detailed exploratory drilling, geological mapping, geophysical surveys, and rock mechanics testing.

Drilling investigations
The purpose of a drilling investigation is to:
    1. Confirm the geological interpretations,
    2. Examine cores and boreholes to determine the quality and characteristics of the rock mass,
    3. Study groundwater conditions, and
    4. Provide cores for rock mechanics testing and petrographic analyses.
As the object of drilling is to obtain rock cores for interpretation and testing, it is essential to obtain as near 100% core recovery as possible. To ensure a successful drilling operation the following aspects should be remembered:
    1. The cost of a drilling investigation for geotechnical purposes is much higher, sometimes by a factor of two, than the cost of drilling for mineral exploration purposes. Geotechnical drilling necessitates good quality equipment and extra care but it can provide high quality information.
    2. The drilling equipment should feature diamond core drilling facilities permitting

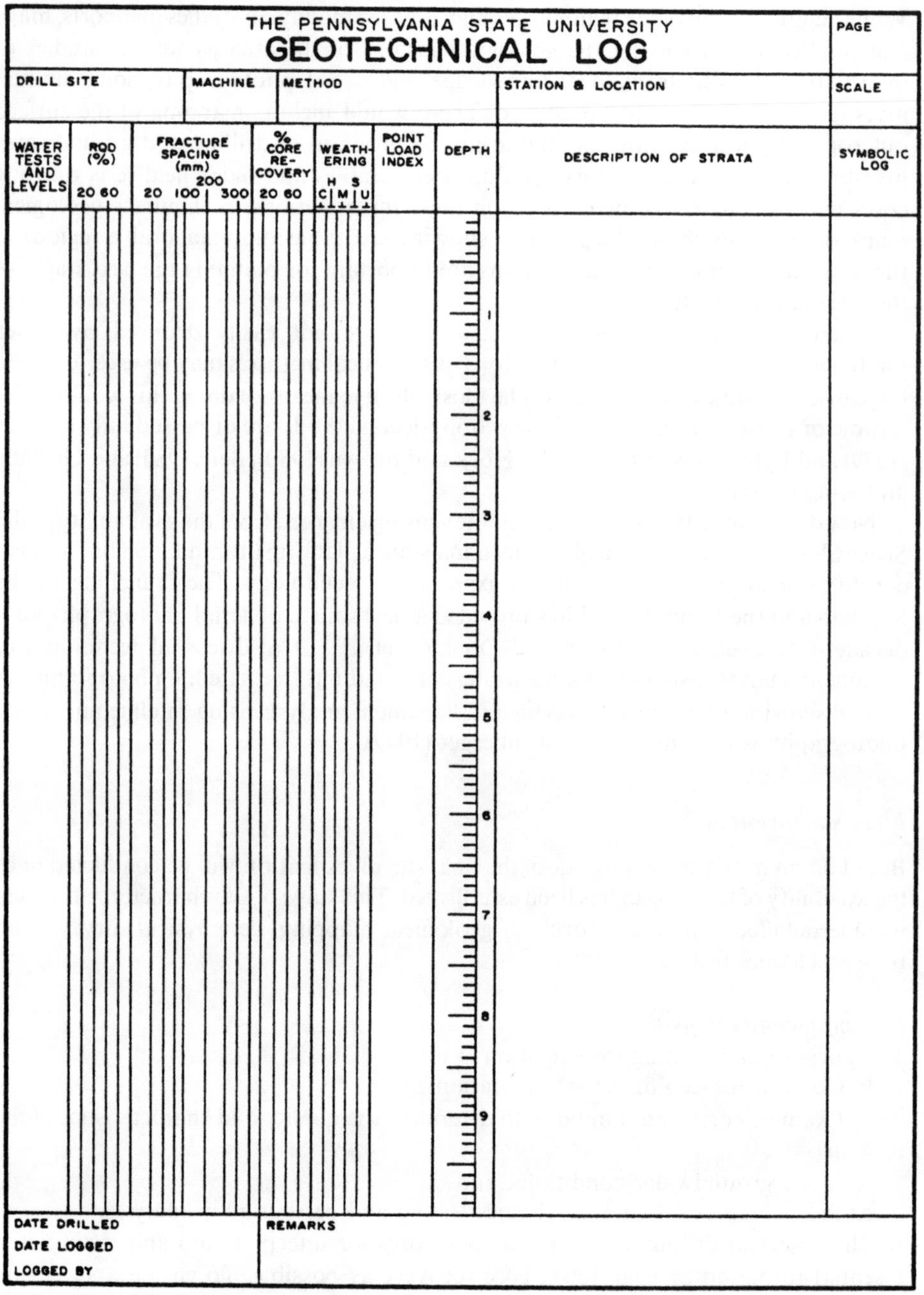

THE PENNSYLVANIA STATE UNIVERSITY GEOTECHNICAL LOG								PAGE	
DRILL SITE		MACHINE	METHOD				STATION & LOCATION		SCALE

WATER TESTS AND LEVELS	RQD (%) 20 60	FRACTURE SPACING (mm) 200 20 100 300	% CORE RE- COVERY 20 60	WEATH- ERING H S C M U	POINT LOAD INDEX	DEPTH	DESCRIPTION OF STRATA	SYMBOLIC LOG
						1		
						2		
						3		
						4		
						5		
						6		
						7		
						8		
						9		

DATE DRILLED	REMARKS
DATE LOGGED	
LOGGED BY	

Figure 5.1. Geotechnical core log.

core of at least NX size (54 mm diameter) and featuring split double-tube core barrels to minimize drilling vibrations. Also included should be equipment for performing water pressure tests.

3. The purpose of the drilling investigation is to obtain not only the core logs but also the logging of the borehole itself. Hence, examination of the borehole walls by borehole cameras or by other systems should also be considered (Barr and Hocking, 1976).

4. For meaningful interpretation of the orientation of the geological features, core orientation procedures may be employed during geotechnical drilling. A number of techniques are available for that purpose (Hoek and Brown, 1980). Boreholes should be angled so that vertical discontinuities could be sampled.

5. In cases where poor rock conditions are evident and yet 100% core recovery is desirable, a technique known as the integral sampling method may be employed (Rocha, 1967) in shallow holes.

6. Good care should be taken of the core recovered from the boreholes. This means that the cores should be photographed as soon as possible, should be carefully marked, placed in protective wrapping in the core boxes, and stored in properly provided storage sheds. Core samples removed for testing should be appropriately marked in the core boxes.

A systematic method should be used for geotechnical logging of the rock cores. There is a difference between a geological core log for general purposes and a geotechnical core log for engineering purposes. The geotechnical core log provides a format to record both the geological and engineering characteristics of the rock core and the results of any field tests. The log of core should systematically record all the information available from the core. An example of a geotechnical core log is given in Figures 5.1. It should be noted that there is no rigid standard format for a geotechnical core log and the amount of detail used will depend on the actual purpose of the project.

Engineering geological mapping
The purpose of engineering geological mapping is to investigate the significant features of the rock mass, especially the discontinuities such as naturally occurring joints. It is also important to determine the geological structure especially in stratified rock which may have been subjected to faulting. Detailed procedures for engineering geological mapping have been described in a number of publications, notably by Dearman and Fookes (1974), Kendorski and Bischoff (1976) and the Geological Society of London (1970).

It should be noted that while engineering geological mapping is fairly frequently found on tunneling projects, this is not the situation on mining projects. Engineering geological mapping in underground coal mines is a fairly recent innovation and an example of a mapping conducted in a coal mine is depicted in Figure 5.2.

Finally, one should emphasize that one of the purposes of engineering geological mapping is to provide input data for a rock mass classification to be used at the site for estimating the stability of underground structures and support requirements. Clearly, engineering geological mapping will provide the most reliable input data for a rock mass classification although it is also possible to obtain reasonable data from interpretations of the borehole and core logs.

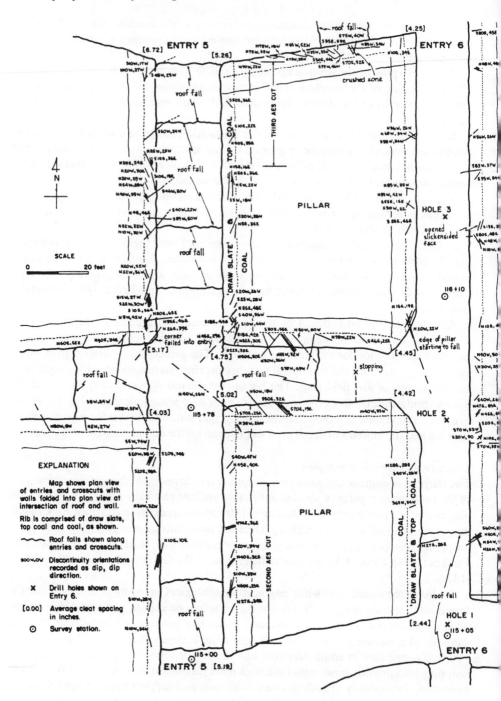

Figure 5.2. Engineering geological mapping in a coal mine (after Newman, 1981).

Geophysical investigations

Geophysical techniques involving seismic refraction and reflection, electrical resistivity, gravimetric and magnetic measurements form an accepted part of
engineering-geological investigation procedures (Lytle, 1978, Farr, 1978). Detailed
descriptions of these methods, together with their applications, limitations, accuracy
and costs, may be found in many textbooks and articles as listed at the end of this
chapter (see specifically Hoek and Brown, 1980, Griffiths and King, 1981). It should be
emphasized that the results of geophysical surveys should always be checked by
diamond drilling investigations. Alternatively, geophysical measurements may be used
to provide geological information about regions of a rock mass positioned between two
boreholes.

Geophysical investigations may be conducted either by surface geophysical
investigations or by geophysical exploration in boreholes.

Of the geophysical techniques applicable to rock mechanics, the seismic refraction
method is the most popular and useful for the purposes of rock mass characterization.
This method may be used either on the surface or in boreholes.

It should be emphasized that for rock engineering purposes, seismic methods should
be directed to provide data needed for the design of rock excavations rather than broad
qualitative data. Hence information leading to estimating the modulus of deformation
of rock masses is more important than general information on the velocity of wave
propagation in a rock mass.

Seismic refraction techniques. Seismic refraction utilizes measurements of the time delay
involved between the generation of seismic waves and the subsequent detection of their
'first arrivals' at a distance from the wave source. Generation of both longitudinal
(compressional) or P-waves and shear (transverse) or S-waves is performed by the use of
a sledge-hammer, sparked device or explosive charge. Velocities of longitudinal waves
vary considerably with the type of rock materials involved, the degree of weathering
and fracturing, the in-situ stress situation and groundwater conditions. A representative selection of typical longitudinal wave velocities is given in Table 5.2.

The magnitude of the velocities of shear or transverse seismic waves is about one-
half of the longitudinal or compressional waves. Efficient recording of shear-wave
velocity can be rendered difficult since the 'first arrivals' of these waves are masked by
later refracted wave arrivals of longitudinal waves. However, the use of various
electronic filtering devices built into the seismic equipment, together with special
geophones can do much to facilitate their recognition.

The squared ratio between the longitudinal seismic wave velocity as measured in the
field (V_F) and the sonic wave velocity measured in the laboratory (V_L) has been used as
an index of rock quality. The ratio is squared to make the velocity index equivalent to
the ratio of the dynamic moduli. The difference in these two velocities is caused by the
structural discontinuities in the rock mass. For a high quality massive rock mass
containing only a few joints, the velocity ratio (V_F/V_L) should approach unity. As the
degree of jointing and fracturing becomes more severe, the velocity ratio will be reduced
to values lower than unity. Table 5.3 below illustrates the relationship between the
velocity index and rock mass quality (after Coon and Merritt, 1970).

Determination of the longitudinal (P-wave) and transverse (S-wave) seismic

Table 5.2. Typical longitudinal wave velocities through different materials

Rock type	Velocity (m/s)
Sandstone	1400–4500
Shale	1200–3500
Slate	4500–5000
Limestone: Soft	1700–4200
Hard	2800–6400
Dolomite	3500–6900
Granite	4600–7000
Diabase	5800–6000
Gabbro	6400–6700
Basalt	3600–6400
Schist	4200–4900
Gneiss	3500–7500
Coal	800–1300
Clay	900–2500
Sand	200–2000
Water	1450
Air	335

Table 5.3. Velocity index and rock mass quality

Velocity index $(V_F/V_L)^2$	Rock mass quality
< 0.2	Very poor
0.2 to 0.4	Poor
0.4 to 0.6	Fair
0.6 to 0.8	Good
0.8 to 1.0	Very good

velocities enables the dynamic (seismic) modulus of deformation (E_d) and Poisson's ratio (v) of a rock mass to be computed. The relationships are given below:

$$V_p = \left[\frac{E}{\rho} \frac{1-v}{(1+v)(1-2v)} \right]^{1/2} \tag{5.1}$$

$$V_s = \left[\frac{E}{\rho} \frac{1}{2(1+v)} \right]^{1/2} \tag{5.2}$$

$$\left[V_p/V_s \right] = 2 \frac{(1-v)}{(1-2v)}$$

hence

$$E_d = \rho V_p^2 (1-2v)(1+v) = 2 V_s^2 \rho (1+v) \tag{5.3}$$

$$v = \frac{(V_p/V_s)^2 - 2}{2[(V_p/V_s)^2 - 1]} \tag{5.4}$$

where

V_p = velocity of longitudinal wave (m/s);
V_s = velocity of shear wave (m/s);
ρ = density of rock material (kg/m^3).

The value of the dynamic modulus of deformation has been found to be greater in magnitude than the in-situ static modulus determined from a variety of in-situ large scale tests such as plate bearing or pressure chamber tests. This difference has been attributed to the very short duration of the seismic pulse and the small values of the stress levels associated with the seismic pulse which give rise to an entirely elastic type of behavior of the rock mass.

Attempts have been made to use the velocity index to estimate the ratio of the static modulus of the rock mass to the laboratory modulus of the rock material. However, Coon and Merritt (1970) concluded that the velocity index is not reliable for predicting directly in-situ rock mass deformability. This index has too many uncertainties because of the different sensitivities of the seismic and sonic waves as well as difficulties in generating and identifying elastic waves in rock masses and rock materials.

Petite sismique. As a result of the uncertainties involved in determination of the static in-situ modulus of rock masses, a new geophysical technique called 'petite sismique' was proposed in France by Schneider in 1967. While the conventional seismic techniques utilize mainly seismic wave velocities, the petite sismique method involves the measurement of the following seismic parameters of the shear wave: frequency, velocity, attenuation and half-wave length. Schneider introduced three findings (see Figure 5.3):

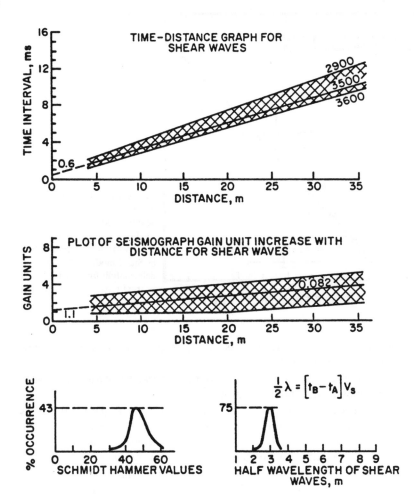

Figure 5.3. Rock mass identification by 'petite sismique' (after Schneider, 1967).

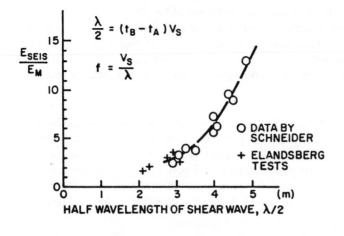

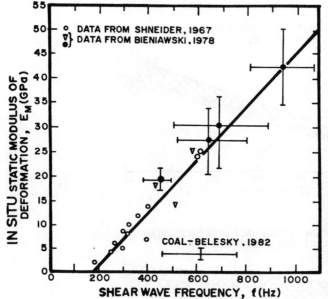

Figure 5.4. Petite sismique correlations: a) Ratio of seismic modulus to in situ modulus of deformation versus shear-wave half-wave length, b) Static modulus of deformation from plate-bearing tests versus shear-wave frequency.

1. An identification profile of the rock mass can be established as based on shear-wave velocity and attenuation trends.

2. A relationship exists between the wave-length of the shear-wave and the ratio of the field seismic modulus to the static in-situ modulus.

3. A correlation is apparent between the transverse shear-wave frequency and static modulus of deformation, as shown in Figure 5.4. Roussel (1968) offered a theoretical explanation for this correlation based on a rheological rock mass model.

The petite sismique technique has not been used extensively due to difficulties in obtaining clear shear waves on seismic records. However, the advent of signal enhancement seismorgraphs that store and add signals on a record while possibly reducing random noise has given a new impetus to the use of this method. In addition, directional geophones may be used which take advantage of the shear wave polarity characteristics. Accordingly, studies involving the petite sismique method have recently been performed by Bieniawski (1978), Heuze (1980) and Belesky (1981). While promising, the technique is still in the stage of development and more information and data are needed before its use for reliable determination of the modulus of deformation could be accepted.

Geological data presentation
If determination of geological data for site characterization is a difficult problem, presentation of these data for engineering purposes is sometimes even more difficult. Communication between the engineering geologist and the design engineer would be greatly enhanced if the format for data presentation could be established in the early stages of an engineering project. The following suggestions are useful:

1. Borehole data should be presented in well executed geotechnical logs.
2. Mapping data derived from joint surveys should be presented as spherical projections such as of the Schmidt or Wolff type (Goodman, 1976, Hoek and Brown, 1980).
3. A summary of all the geological data including the groundwater conditions should be entered in the input data sheets for rock mass classification purposes, such as presented in the last section of this chapter.
4. Longitudinal and cross-sections of structural geology at the site should form an integral part of a geological report.
5. Consideration should be given to constructing a geological model of the site.

Hazard analysis
Several researchers, for example, Overby et al., 1973, Dunham et al., 1976 and Ealy et al., 1979, incorporated various geological factors into hazard analysis maps. This technique, particularly used in coal mining, involves the plotting of topography, drainage patterns, lineaments, faults, changes in lithology, sandstone channels, roof falls, floor heaves, the extraction ratio and areas of potentially high water bed on the overlays of a mine property. The location and interaction of potential geological hazards in relation to existing and planned underground excavations are clearly presented in the overlays. The hazard analysis map is used to predict the occurrence of potentially unstable areas. A similar technique was devised by Hylbert, 1978 in which various roof rock lithologies were classified according to their relative stability. The results of borehole logs were used to delineate potentially unstable areas.

In summary, the following geological parameters are considered important in the stability of underground excavations and should be included in a site characterization report:

1. Orientation of discontinuities in the rock mass.
2. Spacing of discontinuities in the rock mass.
3. Condition of discontinuities, including roughness, separation, continuity, weathering and infilling (gouge).
4. Groundwater conditions.
5. Major faults.
6. Properties of intact rock material.

In essence, for the solution of practical engineering problems, the designer needs to know: the geological conditions at the site under investigation, the in-situ stress field (boundary conditions for analyses) and the mechanical properties of the rock masses (in-situ deformability and strength).

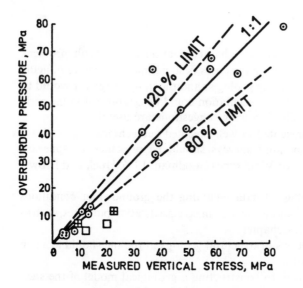

Figure 5.5. Correlation between calculated and measured vertical stresses.

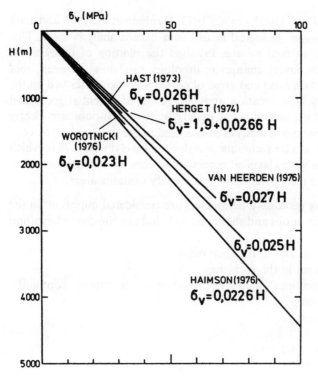

Figure 5.6. Plot of vertical stresses versus depth below surface.

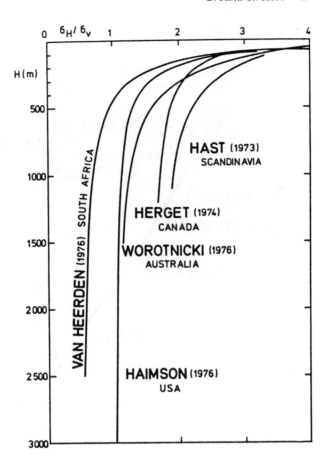

Figure 5.7. Variation of ratio of average horizontal stress to vertical stress with depth below surface.

GROUND STRESSES

When an excavation is made in a rock mass, the initial in-situ stresses are disturbed and redistributed in the vicinity of the excavation. Ground stresses can therefore be categorized into the virgin (original) stresses and induced (due to excavation) stresses. These two types of stresses combine into, what is known as, the field stresses.

The virgin stresses can be of gravitational, tectonic or residual type. They are defined as follows:

Gravitational stress – is due to the effect of gravity on the overburden rock.
Tectonic stress – is due to previous or present-day straining in the earth's crust, e.g. regional faulting.
Residual stress – is the stress remaining after the cause has been removed, e.g. thermal stresses or stresses caused by swelling or heat.

Rock stress measurements featuring a variety of techniques have been conducted throughout the world. These techniques may involve either overcoring methods, flat jack techniques, or the hydrofracturing method. Full details of these methods may be

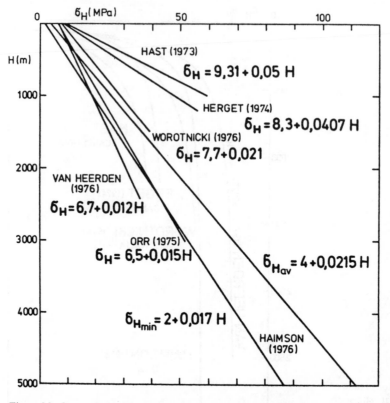

Figure 5.8. Comparison of the relationship proposed for the variation of the horizontal stress component with depth.

found in the extensive literature on the subject (Lindner, 1978, Haimson, 1978, Hoek and Brown, 1980).

Figures 5.5 and 5.6 show the accumulated results of stress measurements obtained in certain parts of the world featuring a variation of the vertical stress with depth. A clear trend in the data is apparent in Figure 5.6. However, there is little consistency if a similar figure is constructed featuring the change of the horizontal stress with depth. As depicted in Figure 5.7, there is no unique correlation between the ratio of the horizontal to vertical stresses and depth. It can also be seen that at a depth of about 450 meters, the horizontal stresses are greater than the vertical stresses. This is a world-wide phenomenon but a difference of opinion exists as to the actual relationship governing the horizontal stresses. This is shown in Figures 5.8 and 5.9. A conclusion that can be reached from this discussion is that while the vertical stresses may be predicted on the basis of the depth of the overburden with an accuracy sufficient for engineering purposes, no simple method exists for estimating the horizontal stresses. Consequently, in situations where such stresses are of great importance, stress measurements should be conducted. Note that Aggson (1978), Haimson (1978) and Lindner (1978) compiled information on the principal stress magnitudes and directions in the United States.

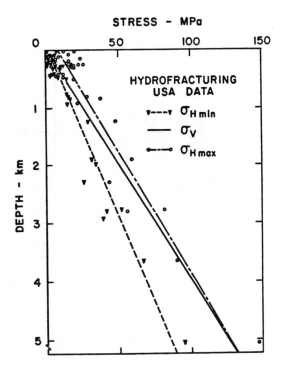

Figure 5.9. Hydrofracturing stress measurements data from the USA (after Haimson, 1978).

STRENGTH AND DEFORMABILITY OF ROCK MASSES

As said earlier, the design engineer in rock mechanics is confronted with rock as a rock mass, that is an assemblage of blocks of rock material separated by various types of geological discontinuities such as joints, bedding planes, shears and faults. Consequently, the engineering properties of both intact rock and rock masses must be considered.

Properties of rock materials

The behavior of rock is best presented in a stress-strain curve, an example of which is given in Figure 5.10.

It will be noted that initially, deformation increases approximately proportionally with increasing load. Eventually a stress level is reached at which fracture is initiated, that is, minute cracks which are present in almost any material, start to propagate. With increasing deformation, the crack propagation is stable, that is, if the stress increase is stopped, the crack propagation also stops. Further increasing the stress, however, leads to another stress level called critical energy release at which the crack propagation is unstable, that is, it continues even if the stress increase is stopped.

Next, the maximum load bearing capacity is reached, called strength failure and this is in fact the strength of the rock material. Most rocks characterized by brittle fracture fail violently at this stage when tested in a conventional (soft) loading machine. In such

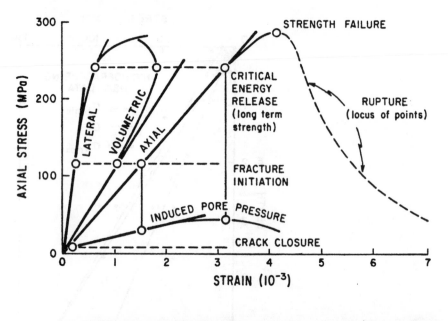

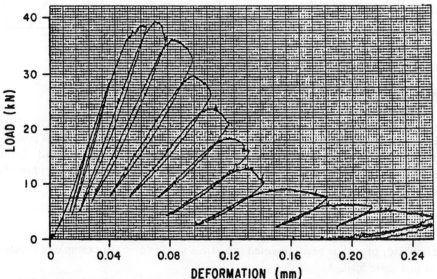

Figure 5.10 Representation of brittle fracture mechanism for quartzite in uniaxial compression.

a case, the specimen machine system collapses and strength failure coincides with rupture, i.e. complete disintegration of rock specimen. If, however, the stiffness of the testing machine is increased, the stress decreases with increasing strain. This stage is characterized by the negative slope of the stress-strain curve and the material is now in a fractured state. This is important since it shows that even cracked, fractured material can offer resistance to loads applied to it. An excavation may be such that it will not collapse although the rock material surrounding such a structure has failed by exceeding its material strength. Thus, the rock surrounding an excavation may be fractured while the excavation is still stable. Indeed, fractured rock may even be desirable since it will not lead to sudden and violent strength failure. Practical applications of this concept to mining and tunneling and its significance for rock support considerations are dealt with in detail by Jaeger and Cook (1981).

Stress-strain curves such as those given in Figure 5.10 serve as the source for obtaining the modulus of elasticity and Poisson's ratio of rock materials. A great variety of different types of stress-strain curves has been recorded. Since most rock types do not exhibit an elastic behavior it is more appropriate to use the term modulus of deformation instead of modulus of elasticity in these cases. Table 5.4 gives the more important properties of some common rock types. More data can be found in Lama and Vutukuri (1978) and in Kulhawy (1975).

Laboratory testing methods are generally well established and testing techniques have been recommended by the International Society for Rock Mechanics (ISRM) and the American Society for Testing and Materials (ASTM). Detailed procedures for performing laboratory tests are available as ISRM *Suggested Methods* (1981) or ASTM Standards. A complete list of the test methods investigated by the ISRM is given in Table 5.5.

The strength and deformation properties of intact rock material are affected by many factors some of which are listed in Table 5.6. The most important of these factors are:
1. Anisotropy;
2. Moisture content/pore water pressure;
3. Confining pressure;
4. Time-dependent deformation (creep) and rate of loading;
5. Specimen size and shape.

The effect of anisotropy is important because it is seldom found that rock contains discontinuities of equal size and random orientation. Consequently, it is necessary to test rock samples under different orientations of the discontinuities to the direction of the applied load. In some cases, the highest strength can be as much as five times the lowest strength (Hoek, 1964).

The influence of moisture upon the strength of rock may be severe with a saturated specimen being only one-half as strong as a dry specimen (Colback and Wiid, 1965). The practical significance of the influence of moisture content and pore water pressure is the danger of a normally stable structure to become unstable under wet conditions. On the other hand, wet conditions result in more efficient cutting, drilling and blasting.

The increase of confining pressure results in an increase in the strength of rock. The effect is very important when estimating the strength of rock at great depths which is reflected in a triaxial state of stress (see Figure 8.6).

The strength and deformation characteristics of rock are known to be time-dependent. Short durations of loading, i.e. high loading rates, result in an increase in the strength of rock (John, 1974). On the other hand, a rock specimen subjected to a constant stress will, in addition to corresponding immediate strain, continue to deform (creep) and – depending on the magnitude of the applied load and duration of test – may eventually fail. Above a certain stress level, which is referred to as the long-term strength, rock materials fail after some time under constant load (Bieniawski, 1967).

Table 5.4. Some properties of rock and coal materials*

Rock type	Uniaxial compressive strength, MPa			Uniaxial tensile strength, MPa			Modulus of elasticity, GPa			Poisson's ratio		
	From	To	Mean	From	To	Mean	From	To	Mean	From	To	Mean
Basalt	42	355	150	2	28	13	16	101	53	0.13	0.38	0.22
Dolerite	227	319	280	12	26	20	60	90	70	0.15	0.29	0.20
Gneiss	73	340	159	3	21	14	16	103	58	0.10	0.40	0.22
Granite	30	324	166	3	39	12	10	74	45	0.10	0.39	0.23
Limestone	48	210	102	2	40	12	1	92	48	0.08	0.39	0.25
Norite	290	326	298	15	25	20	90	110	100	0.21	0.26	0.24
Quartzite	200	304	252	17	28	25	70	105	90	0.11	0.25	0.16
Sandstone	40	179	96	3	7	5	10	46	22	0.10	0.40	0.24
Shale	36	172	95	2	5	3	10	44	28	0.10	0.19	0.14
Pittsburgh coal	14.4	29.7	22.2	1.9	3.2	2.5	1.5	3.7	3.2	–	–	0.37
Pocahontas # 3 coal	18.2	19.5	18.9	–	–	–	2.4	2.7	2.6	–	–	–
Herrin # 6 coal	10.0	14.1	11.4	–	–	–	3.1	3.8	3.5	–	–	0.42
Witbank coal	23.5	39.3	31.6	–	–	–	3.9	5.3	4.6	0.33	0.37	0.35

*See also: Kulhawy (1975), Lama and Vutukuri (1978)

Table 5.5. Test categories published by the ISRM as *Suggested Methods* (after Franklin, 1979)

Field index tests for characterization	Field 'design tests'
Discontinuity orientation	Deformability using a plate test
Discontinuity spacing	Deformability plate test down a borehole
Discontinuity persistence	Deformability radial jacking test
Discontinuity roughness	Deformability borehole jack
Discontinuity wall strength	Shear strength-direct shear
Discontinuity aperture	Shear strength-torsional shear
Discontinuity filling	Piezometric head
Discontinuity number of sets	Permeability
Discontinuity block size	
Discontinuity drill core recovery/RQD	Field 'quality control tests'
Geophysical logging of boreholes	
Seismic refraction (2 methods)	Rockbolt anchor strength
Acoustic logging	Rockbolt tension (torque wrench)
Sonic log	Rockbolt tension (load cells)
Temperature log	
Resistivity logs (2 methods)	Field monitoring
Gamma-gamma log	
	Movement – probe inclinometer
	Movements – fixed-in-place inclinometer
Laboratory index tests for characterization	Movements – tiltmeter
	Movements – borehole extensometers
Water content	Movements – convergence meter
Porosity/density (4 methods)	Pressure – hydraulic cells
Void index (quick absorption)	
Swelling pressure	Laboratory 'design tests'
Swelling strain (2 methods)	
Slake-durability	Triaxial strength
Uniaxial compressive strength	Direct tensile strength
Uniaxial deformability (E, v)	Indirect (Brazil) tensile strength
Point load strength index	Direct shear test
Resistance to abrasion (Los Angeles test)	
Hardness (Schmidt rebound)	
Hardness (Shore scleroscope)	
Sound velocity	
Petrographic description	

The effect of specimen size and shape is of great practical importance because it determines to what extent the tests on small size laboratory specimens are applicable to large in-situ structures in rock. Accordingly, this aspect is discussed in detail in Chapter 9 when dealing with the strength of rock pillars.

Unfortunately, laboratory-measured quantities obtained from tests conducted on small rock specimens generally do not yield data that are directly applicable to the in situ rock mass from which the specimens were taken. If laboratory test results could be scaled reliably to field conditions, then small scale, easily controllable tests, would provide a convenient means for estimating rock mass characteristics.

Rock mass characteristics of particular significance in static rock mechanics are as follows:

1. Modulus of deformation or elasticity, essential for the design of tunnels, chambers, mines and dam foundations;

Table 5.6. Factors governing the behavior of rock (after U.S. National Committee on Rock Mechanics, 1981)

Rock characteristics	External parameters
Material: Lithology and stratigraphy (rock type, occurrence, grain size, color, minerals) Anisotropy Porosity Cracks and weaknesses Specimen geometry (shape, size) Physical and mechanical properties (density, strengths, moduli, failure mode) Chemical properties	**Environment:** Pressure Temperature Hydrologic (moisture content, groundwater flow, pore pressure) Chemical
Mass: Structure (stratification, lamination, dip and strike, size, shape) Discontinuities (type, orientation, spatial configuration, condition) Porosity Permeability Physical and mechanical properties (strengths, moduli, friction angle) Creep	**Stress-strain state:** In situ stresses (magnitude, direction, distribution) External loads (type, magnitude, direction, distribution and configuration, nature, rate) Nonmechanical stresses (thermal, electrical, magnetic)

2. Compressive strength, important in the design of mine pillars;
3. Shear strength, important in rock slopes, foundations and dam abutments;
4. Tensile strength, important in mine roofs;
5. Frictional properties (cohesion and friction angle) important in fractured masses, yield zones, residual strength and rockbolt design;
6. Post-failure modulus, important in longwall mining and pillar design;
7. Bearing capacity, important for mine floors and foundations;
8. Thermo-mechanical response, important in nuclear waste disposal.

In situ tests

There are many types of in-situ tests for determining rock mass characteristics.

For deformability data, the following tests are available: plate bearing tests (Misterek et al., 1974, Dodds 1974); flat jack tests (Rocha and daSilva, 1970, Pratt et al., 1974); radial press tests (Misterek, 1970); pressure chamber tests (Schneider, 1967); borehole jacks (Goodman et al., 1972, Hustrulid, 1976, Heuze and Salem, 1977, de la Cruz, 1978), dilatometers (Rocha, 1974, Hustrulid, 1979); tunnel relaxation tests (Deklotz and Boisen, 1970) and 'petite sismique' (Bieniawski, 1980). Furthermore, compressive tests (Bieniawski and van Heerden, 1975) and shear tests (Franklin, 1979) can be used. Bearing capacity is determined by plate bearing tests (Rhodes et al., 1978).

In-situ tests are advantageous because the tests involve large volumes of rock so that the results obtained can be more representative of rock mass conditions than the results of laboratory tests, both from the point of view of the test volume and the environmental conditions (temperature, humidity). For example, Heuze (1980) compares the test volumes for various deformability and strength tests as follows:

NX sample for laboratory tests	$244 \, cm^3$
100 mm cube laboratory specimen	$1000 \, cm^3$
NX borehole jack in situ	$0.14 \, m^3$
300 mm diameter plate-bearing test	$0.95 \, m^3$
0.9 m diameter plate-bearing test	$26 \, m^3$
Pressure tunnel, 1.5 m dia., 6 m long	$82 \, m^3$

As a result of the large volumes involved, in-situ tests on large samples may show less scatter of results than do laboratory tests on small samples (Pratt et al., 1972). Some in-situ tests are relatively easy to perform but their reliability may be in question unless a comparison of data obtained by several different methods is possible.

In cases of very important engineering structures, large scale in-situ tests and block tests may be indispensable. Yet, in-situ tests have their limitations. Considering deformability data, even the most commonly used plate bearing tests (with standardized test procedures) may provide widely differing results (Rocha and daSilva, 1970, Dodds and Shroeder, 1974). The large flat jack test of Rocha (1974) suffers from theoretical uncertainties (Deklotz and Boisen, 1970, Vogler et al., 1977) while the analytical solution for the results of the popular small flat jack test is limited to square shape jacks. Borehole jacks and dilatometers generally produce modulus values two to three times lower than in-situ values determined by the plate bearing tests (Shuri, 1981). Corrections are required involving either the contact angle between the loading platen and the borehole surface (Hustrulid, 1976) or the stiffness ratio of the platen material to that of the rock (Heuze and Salem, 1977). Depending on which correction is chosen, the difference in the results can be significant. Finally, the petite sismique method, although appearing to hold promise, still requires a thorough assessment (Bieniawski, 1979).

Unfortunately, few projects to date have featured a sufficient number of different tests to allow a meaningful comparison of in-situ test data. Table 5.7 compares field and laboratory moduli. It can be seen that very different in situ results may be obtained depending on the test method. Under these circumstances, it is not helpful to discuss the precision of in-situ methods. For example, an examination of Table 5.7 reveals that even in an extensive in-situ test program in fairly uniform and good quality rock mass conditions, deformability data may feature a standard deviation of 25% or as much as 10 GPa for an average in-situ modulus of 40 GPa. Note that the tests involving full-scale prototype behavior (tunnel relaxation) give different results by comparison with other in-situ tests. The choice of the design value for the in-situ modulus of deformation thus becomes a matter of engineering judgment. This means that it is difficult to rely on any one in-situ method alone; two or more methods should be used to crosscheck the results. Clearly then, if in-situ test results are method dependent and lead to large scatters in data, the potential of any relevant laboratory tests assumes particular importance. It should be noted, nevertheless, that some laboratory tests may also be method dependent.

Although detailed information concerning the costs of in-situ tests is scarce, it is known that the overall cost of an in-situ testing program is typically a small percentage of the construction costs (see Figure 4.2).

Table 5.7. Field and laboratory moduli from major projects (after Bieniawski, 1978, and Heuze, 1980)

Project date	Type of rock	Type of field test	No. of tests	E_F (GPa)[a]	E_L (GPa)[a]	E_F/E_L
Oroville Dam (1961)	Amphibolite (massive)	Plate bearing	5	10.4	89.0	0.11
		Tunnel relaxation	22	17.9		0.20
		Flat jacks	30	51.8		0.58
Tumut 2 (1962)	Gneiss/granite	Plate bearing	6	6.9	59.1	0.12
		Tunnel relaxation	3	11.0		0.19
		Flat jacks	6	57.5		0.97
		Pressure chamber	2	17.7		0.30
Poatina (1965)	Mudstone	Flat jacks	Not known	20.6	34.5	0.60
Dworshak Dam (1966)	Granite/gneiss (massive)	Plate bearing	24	23.5	51.7	0.45
		Goodman jack	14	23.6		0.45
Tehachapi Tunnel (1967)	Diorite gneiss (fractured)	Plate bearing	4	4.8	77.9	0.06
		Goodman jack	4	5.8		0.07
Crestmore Mine (1966 to 1974)	Marble (blocky)	Plate bearing	2	15.0	47.5	0.31
		Flat jacks	12	12.4		0.26
		Goodman jack	30	14.0		0.30
Gordon Scheme (1971)	Quartzite	Plate bearing	8	19.0	67.0	0.28
		Dilatometer	2	25.0		0.37
		Tunnel relaxation	10	25.0		0.37
		Flat jacks	16	58.0		0.87
Churchill Falls (1972)	Gneiss (massive)	Plate bearing	10	41.5	55.0	0.75
Waldeck II (1973)	Greywacke	Plate bearing	Not known	5.0	20.0	0.25
		Tunnel relaxation		15.0		0.75
Mica Project (1974)	Quartzite gneiss	Plate bearing	12	27.6	27.0	1.04
		Flat jacks	19	28.8		1.07
		Goodman jack	132	16.6		0.61
LG-2 Project (1976)	Granite (massive)	Plate bearing	Not known	50.0	80.0	0.62
Elandsberg (1977)	Greywacke	Plate bearing	33	39.6	73.4	0.54
		Small flat jacks	37	45.5		0.62
		Large flat jacks	3	42.2		0.57
		Goodman jack	39	28.4		0.39
		Tunnel relaxation	23	42.5		0.58
		Petite sismique	43	26.0		0.35
		RQD prediction	34	35.5		0.48
		RMR prediction	45	41.3		0.56
York Canyon Mine (1977)	Coal	Smaller bearing plate (15 cm × 15 cm)	9	0.31	9.4	0.033
		Larger bearing plate (36 cm × 36 cm)	4	0.16		0.017
	Shaly sandstone	Smaller bearing plate (15 cm × 15 cm)	5	0.65	43.4	0.015
Stripa Mine (1979)	Granite	CSM cell	385	36.8	51.3	0.72
Climax/NTS (1980)	Quartz monzonite	Goodman jack	Not known	25.0	70.0	0.36
		de la Cruz jack	Not known	66.0		0.94
		Tunnel relaxation	Not known	27.0		0.38
		Petite sismique	Not known	50.0		0.71

[a]E_F, field modulus; E_L, laboratory modulus at 50 percent strength.

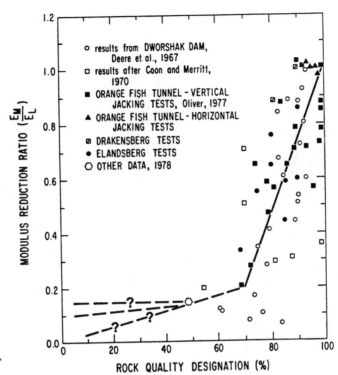

Figure 5.11. Correlation between RQD and modulus ratio E_M/E_L (after Bieniawski, 1978).

Scaling of laboratory test data to in-situ values

There are a number of 'links' or correlations that can be used for extrapolating laboratory-measured quantities to in situ values. For example, use has been made of the correlation between the RQD (rock quality designation) index and the modulus reduction ratio E_M/E_L – the ratio of the rock mass modulus E_M to the laboratory modulus E_L, determined from small rock-material samples. A recent study (Heuze, 1980) of the scale effects on the determination of rock-mass deformability shows that the moduli values measured in the laboratory are, on the average, 2.5 times higher than the values determined in situ. In particular, most of the in situ modulus results seem to be between 0.2 and 0.6 of the laboratory values. It must be noted, however, that these values are dependent on the rock quality, as depicted in Figure 5.11.

Herget and Unrug (1974) and Kendorski (1975) studied the scaling of laboratory test results to field problems involving mining structures such as pillars and drifts. Kendorski (1980) investigated rock-mass strength assessment for tunnel design. Bieniawski (1967) studied the scaling of test data on coal aimed at estimating the in situ strength of coal pillars.

It should be noted that numerical or physical modeling is an important approach for scaling measured quantities to in situ conditions. In fact, with the development of sophisticated computer techniques, numerical modeling is extensively used for this purpose (St. John et al., 1979).

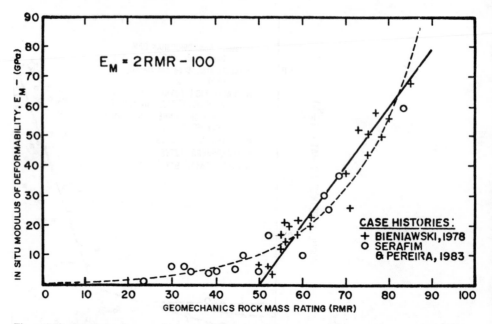

Figure 5.12. Correlation between the in situ modulus of deformation and the Geomechanics Classification rock-mass rating (RMR).

Deformability data

Deere et al. (1967) suggested the use of quality indices to estimate rock-mass deformability – either the RQD index or the velocity index $(V_F/V_L)^2$. Coon and Merritt (1970) showed that the RQD index correlated with the modulus reduction ratio, E_M/E_L, with a correlation coefficient of 0.544, but the velocity index showed a poorer correlation (coefficient 0.368). However, the RQD data for the correlation with the E_M/E_L ratio were mainly from good-quality rock and predominantly from one project, the Dworshak Dam, although a few results were included from three other projects. These results were undated recently by Bieniawski (1978) and are shown in Figure 5.11.

Kulhawy (1978) proposed a modified RQD model, enabling the reduction of rock-material properties caused by the presence of discontinuities, and showed a better correlation of the RQD index with the modulus reduction ratio as a function of discontinuity properties (stiffness). Dershowitz et al. (1979) discussed currently used empirical correlations and analytical models and showed that the RQD index may be sufficient (in the statistical sense) to describe rock-mass deformability, particularly for lower-quality rock masses. In this respect, use was made of the findings by Priest and Hudson (1976), who proposed a relationship between RQD and the spacing as well as the orientation of discontinuities.

For better quality rock masses, Bieniawski (1978) obtained a good correlation (coefficient 0.9612) directly between the in situ modulus (not the modulus ratio) and the rock-mass rating (RMR). This is shown in Figure 5.12. The RMR approach has the advantage that the scatter inherent in laboratory values, which affects the modulus reduction ratio, is avoided because no laboratory data are used in this case.

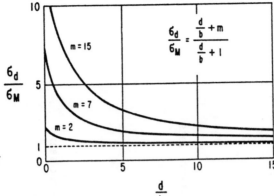

Figure 5.13. Graphical representation of the Protodyakonov formula.

Correlations between RQD and RMR were recently studied by Serafim and Pereira (1983) and provided many results in the range RMR < 50.

Strength data
The subject of strength reduction from the data determined in the laboratory to in situ values has received considerable attention in the past, particularly as related to mine pillars. However, only two approaches seem to be promising, namely those of Protodyakonov (1964) and of Hoek and Brown (1980).

Protodyakonov proposed a method whereby the strength of the rock mass can be estimated from the following equation:

$$\frac{\sigma_d}{\sigma_M} = \frac{d/b + m}{d/b + 1} \tag{5.6}$$

where σ_d is the strength of a cubical specimen with side length d, σ_M is the in-situ strength of the rock mass, b is the distance between discontinuities in the rock mass, and m is the strength reduction factor. The curves representing this relationship are given in Figure 5.13. From experimental data on a number of rock types, it is evident that the value of m depends both on the type of rock material and on the stress state to which the specimen is subjected, namely:

Rock strength	Compression	Tension
> 75 MPa	$2 < m < 5$	$5 < m < 15$
< 75 MPa	$5 < m < 10$	$15 < m < 30$

The strength reduction in weaker (more fissured) rock is more pronounced than in stronger rock containing only minor cracks. The effect is greater in tension, when cracks open and give rise to large strength reduction, than in compression, when cracks close and thus the disturbances are reduced (Muller, 1974).

The concept of the 'critical size' (Bieniawski, 1967) is depicted in Figures 5.14 and 5.15. The phenomenon of strength reduction with increasing specimen size is apparent

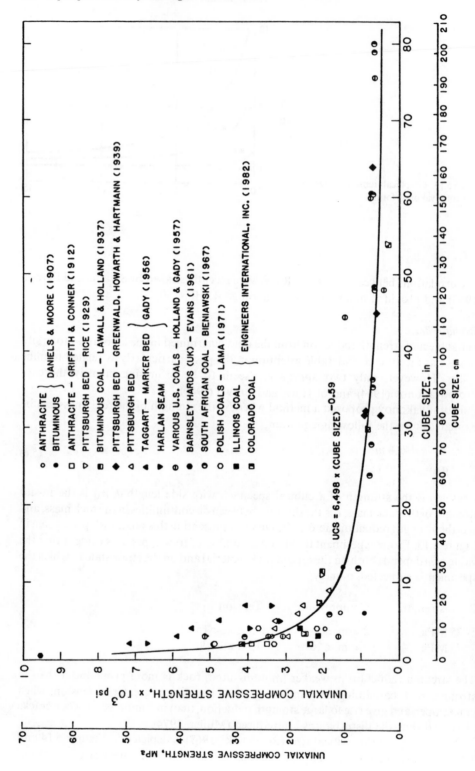

Figure 5.14. Effect of size on compressive strength of coal (after Singh, 1981).

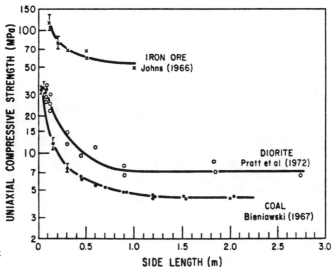

Figure 5.15. Variation of rock strength with specimen size.

and it will be noted that from a certain size onward, the in-situ strength remains constant, irrespective of specimen size. Consequently, attempts to extrapolate the laboratory specimen data to in situ values may not prove reliable because the best fit must be truncated when the constant in situ strength is reached. The significance of the phenomenon of 'critical size' is that the strength values at the critical specimen size are directly applicable to full size rock pillars (see Chapter 9).

Hoek and Brown (1980) proposed an empirical criterion of failure for rock mass strength as follows:

$$\frac{\sigma_1}{\sigma_c} = \frac{\sigma_3}{\sigma_c} + \sqrt{m\frac{\sigma_3}{\sigma_c} + s} \qquad (5.7)$$

where σ_1 is the major principal stress at failure, σ_3 is the applied minor principal stress, σ_c is the uniaxial compressive strength, and m and s are constants that depend on the properties of the rock and the extent to which it has been fractured by being subjected to σ_1 and σ_3. For intact rock, $m = m_i$ is determined from a fit of the above equation to triaxial-test data from laboratory specimens, taking $s = 1$ for rock material. For rock masses, Hoek and Brown (1980) have compiled a list of approximate m and s values, as reproduced in Table 5.8.

For rock masses, Priest and Brown (1983) proposed the following estimates:

$$m = m_i \cdot \exp\left[\frac{RMR - 95}{13.4}\right]$$

$$s = \exp\left[\frac{RMR - 100}{6.3}\right]$$

Table 5.8. Approximate relationship between rock mass quality and constants (after Hoek and Brown, 1980)

Empirical failure criterion $\sigma_1 = \sigma_3 + \sqrt{m\sigma_c\sigma_3 + s\sigma_c^2}$ σ_1 = major principal stress; σ_3 = minor principal stress; σ_c = uniaxial compressive strength of intact rock, and m, s = empirical constants	Carbonate rocks with well developed crystal cleavage Dolomite, limestone and marble	Lithified argillaceous rocks Mudstone, siltstone, shale and slate (normal to cleavage)	Arenaceous rocks with strong crystals and poorly developed crystal cleavage Sandstone and quartzite	Fine grained polyminerallic igneous crystalline rocks Andesite, dolerite, diabase and rhyolite	Coarse grained polymineralic igneous and metamorphic crystalline rocks
Intact rock samples					
Laboratory size specimens free from joints RMR = 100 Q rating 500	$m = 7.0$ $s = 1.0$	$m = 10.0$ $s = 1.0$	$m = 15.0$ $s = 1.0$	$m = 17.0$ $s = 1.0$	$m =$ $s =$
Very good quality rock mass					
Tightly interlocking undisturbed rock with unweathered joints at 1 to 3 m RMR = 85 Q rating 100	$m = 3.5$ $s = 0.1$	$m = 5.0$ $s = 0.1$	$m = 7.5$ $s = 0.1$	$m = 8.5$ $s = 0.1$	$m =$ $s =$
Good quality rock mass					
Fresh to slightly weathered rock, slightly disturbed with joints at 1 to 3 m RMR = 65 Q rating 10	$m = 0.7$ $s = 0.004$	$m = 1.0$ $s = 0.004$	$m = 1.5$ $s = 0.004$	$m = 1.7$ $s = 0.004$	$m =$ $s =$
Fair quality rock mass					
Several sets of moderately weathered joints spaced at 0.3 to 1 m RMR = 44 Q rating 1	$m = 0.14$ $s = 0.0001$	$m = 0.20$ $s = 0.0001$	$m = 0.30$ $s = 0.0001$	$m = 0.34$ $s = 0.0001$	$m =$ $s =$
Poor quality rock mass					
Numerous weathered joints at 30 to 500 mm with some gouge. Clean compacted waste rock RMR = 23 Q rating 0.1	$m = 0.04$ $s = 0.00001$	$m = 0.05$ $s = 0.00001$	$m = 0.08$ $s = 0.00001$	$m = 0.09$ $s = 0.00001$	$m =$ $s =$
Very poor quality rock mass					
Numerous heavily weathered joints spaced < 50 mm with gouge. Waste rock with fines RMR = 3 Q rating 0.01	$m = 0.007$ $s = 0$	$m = 0.010$ $s = 0$	$m = 0.015$ $s = 0$	$m = 0.017$ $s = 0$	$m =$ $s =$

Notation: RMR – rock mass rating from the Geomechanics Classification;
Q – quality of rock mass from the Q-System.

INTEGRAL APPROACH TO SITE CHARACTERIZATION OF ROCK MASSES

Based on the above considerations and practical experience, the following guidelines are recommended for assessing characteristics of rock masses:

Firstly, a detailed engineering geological assessment of the rock mass conditions is required which should be expressed in quantitative terms by an engineering classification of the rock masses encountered.

Secondly, at least two different in-situ tests should be selected and a sufficient number of the tests conducted to determine in-situ rock mass deformability and strength in the representative structural regions of the rock masses. For this purpose, in the case of in-situ deformability, the plate bearing test and a borehole jack test are recommended. An example of a layout of pilot excavations for in situ testing is given in Figure 5.16.

Thirdly, the stress field should be established by means of either an overcoring technique or small flat jacks. This last method can also provide an additional check on rock mass deformability. Stress measurements are necessary also for the interpretation of in-situ deformability results because the applied and existing stress field was found to

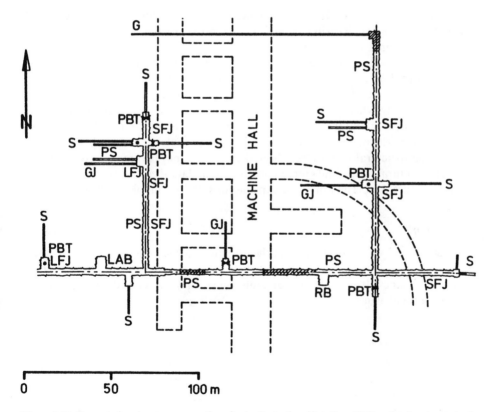

Figure 5.16. Layout of exploratory excavations for in situ testing. Notation: PBT – plate bearing tests; S – stress measurements; SFJ – small flat jacks; LFJ – large flat jacks; GJ – Goodman jack tests; PT – petite sismique; RB – rockbolting tests.

be an important factor affecting plate bearing tests (Dodds, 1974). Most of all, however, in-situ stress measurements are required as the boundary conditions for design analyses. In the case where underground adits are not available for stress measurements by means of overcoring or small flat jacks, the hydrofracturing method may be employed in deep boreholes (Haimson, 1978).

Fourthly, since in-situ tests are performed at a few locations only, seismic velocity geophysical surveys should be conducted to determine the continuity of the rock mass conditions throughout the area of the proposed engineering project. The petite 'sismique' technique can provide a check on the static in-situ modulus of deformation as well as a rough check on the quality of the rock mass by comparing the field seismic velocity with the sonic velocity of intact rock tested in the laboratory.

Fifthly, diamond drilling of good quality core of NX size (54 mm diameter) must be undertaken at all in-situ test sites so that the rock quality designation (RQD) can be established and samples can be selected for laboratory tests to determine the static strengths, moduli and the sonic velocity on intact rock specimens.

SUMMARY OF PARAMETERS FOR INPUT DATA COLLECTION

The parameters needed for site characterization are summarized here for the convenience of the engineering geologists responsible for the collection of geological data for use in engineering design.

The first step is to divide the rock mass into a number of structural regions. These regions are geological zones of rock masses in which certain features are more or less uniform. Although rock masses are discontinuous in nature, they may nevertheless be uniform in regions when, for example, the type of rock or the spacings of discontinuities are the same throughout the region. In most cases, the boundaries of structural regions will coincide with such major geological features as faults and shear zones.

Once the structural regions have been delineated, input parameters are established for each structural region and entered onto an input data sheet, an example of which is given in Figure 5.17. The following explanations and terminology are relevant.

Discontinuities

This term means all discontinuities in the rock mass, which may be technically joints, bedding planes, minor faults, or other surfaces of weakness such as cleavage and schistocity planes. It excludes major faults since they are considered as structural regions of their own.

Intact rock strength

The uniaxial compressive strength of a rock material constitutes the highest strength limit of the rock mass of which it forms a part. It is determined in accordance with the standard laboratory procedures, but for the purpose of rock mass classification, the use of the well-known point load strength index is recommended. The reason is that the index can be determined in the field on rock core retrieved from borings and the core does not require any specimen preparation. Using simple portable equipment, a piece

Site of survey:
Conducted by: REGION
Date:

DRILL CORE QUALITY R.Q.D.*

Excellent quality: 90 - 100%
Good quality: 75 - 90%
Fair quality: 50 - 75%
Poor quality: 25 - 50%
Very poor quality: <25%

*R.Q.D. = Rock Quality Designation

GROUND WATER

INFLOW per 10 m litres/minute
of tunnel length

or

WATER PRESSURE kPa

or

GENERAL CONDITIONS (completely dry, damp, wet, dripping or flowing under low/medium or high pressure:

SPACING OF DISCONTINUITIES

	Set 1	Set 2	Set 3	Set 4
Very wide: Over 2 m				
Wide: 0.6 - 2 m				
Moderate: 200 - 600 mm				
Close: 60 - 200 mm				
Very close: <60 mm				

NOTE: These values are obtained from a joint survey and not from borehole logs.

STRIKE AND DIP ORIENTATIONS

Set 1	Strike:	(from	to	) Dip:	(direction)
	Strike:	(average)		(angle)	
Set 2	Strike:	(from	to	) Dip:	
Set 3	Strike:	(from	to	) Dip:	
Set 4	Strike:	(from	to	) Dip:	

NOTE: Refer all directions to magnetic north.

WALL ROCK OF DISCONTINUITIES

Unweathered
Slightly weathered
Moderately weathered
Highly weathered
Completely weathered
Residual soil

STRENGTH OF INTACT ROCK MATERIAL

Designation	Uniaxial compressive strength, MPa	OR	Point-load strength Index, MPa
Very high:	Over 250		>10
High:	100 - 250		4-10
Medium high:	50 - 100		2-4
Moderate:	25 - 50		1-2
Low:	5 - 25		< 1
Very low:	1 - 5		

CONDITION OF DISCONTINUITIES

	Set 1	Set 2	Set 3	Set 4

PERSISTENCE (CONTINUITY)

Very low: <1 m
Low: 1 - 3 m
Medium: 3 - 10 m
High: 10 - 20 m
Very high: > 20 m

SEPARATION (APERTURE)

Very tight joints: <0.1 mm
Tight joints: 0.1 - 0.5 mm
Moderately open joints: 0.5 - 2.5 mm
Open joints: 2.5 - 10 mm
Very wide aperture > 10 mm

ROUGHNESS (state also if surfaces are stepped, undulating or planar)

Very rough surfaces:
Rough surfaces:
Slightly rough surfaces:
Smooth surfaces:
Slickensided surfaces:

FILLING (GOUGE)

Type:
Thickness:
Uniaxial compressive strength, MPa
Seepage:

MAJOR FAULTS OR FOLDS

Describe major faults and folds specifying their locality, nature and orientations.

GENERAL REMARKS AND ADDITIONAL DATA

NOTE:
(1) For definitions and methods consult ISRM document: *"Quantitative description of discontinuities in rock masses."*
(2) The data on this form constitute the minimum required for engineering design. The geologist should, however, supply any further information which he considers relevant.

Figure 5.17. Input data from: Engineering classification of rock masses.

of drill core is compressed between two points. The core fails as a result of fracture across its diameter. The point-load strength index is calculated as the ratio of the applied load to the square of the core diameter. A close correlation exists (to within approximately 20 percent) between the uniaxial compressive strength and the point-load strength index I_s as depicted in Figure 5.18.

In rock engineering, information on the rock material strength is preferable to that on rock hardness. The reason is that rock hardness, which is defined as the resistance to

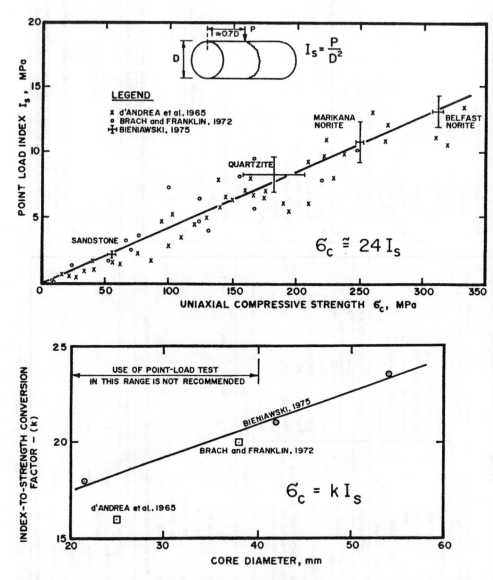

Figure 5.18. Correlations between the point-load strength index and the uniaxial compressive strength.
a) Correlation for NX core (54 mm diameter)
b) Size correction graph for index-to-strength conversion

indentation or scratching, is not a quantitative parameter but is subjective to a geologist's personal opinion. It was employed in the past before the advent of the point-load strength index which can now assess rock strength in the field. For the sake of completeness, the following hardness classification was used in the past:

a) Very soft rock: Material crumbles under firm blow with a sharp end of a geological pick and can be peeled off with a knife.

b) Soft rock: Material can be scraped and peeled with a knife; indentations 1.5 to 3 mm show in the specimen.

c) Medium hard rock: Material cannot be scraped or peeled with a knife; hand-held specimen can be broken with the hammer end of a geological pick with a single firm blow.

d) Hard rock: Hand-held specimen breaks with hammer end of pick under more than one blow.

e) Very hard rock: Specimen requires many blows with geological pick to break through intact material.

It can be seen from the above that for the lower ranges up to medium hard rock, hardness can be assessed from visual inspection and by scratching with a knife and striking with a hammer. However, experience shows that for rock having the uniaxial compressive strength of more than 25 MPa hardness classification ceases to be meaningful due to the difficulty of distinguishing by the 'scratchability test' the various degrees of hardness. In any case, hardness is only indirectly related to rock strength, the relationship being between the uniaxial compressive strength and the product of hardness and density (Deere and Miller, 1966, ISRM, 1981).

Rock quality designation (RQD)

This index is used as a classification parameter, because although it is not sufficient on its own for a full description of a rock mass, the RQD has been found most useful in tunneling applications as a guide for selection of tunnel support. It has been employed extensively in the United States and in Europe, and is a simple, inexpensive, and reproducible way to assess the quality of rock core (Deere, 1964).

This quantitative index is a modified core recovery percentage which incorporates only those pieces of core that are 100 mm or greater in length. Shorter lengths of core are ignored as they are considered to be due to close shearing, jointing, or weathering in the rock mass. It should be noted that the RQD disregards the influence of discontinuity tightness, orientation, continuity, and gouge (infilling) material.

For RQD determination, the International Society for Rock Mechanics (ISRM) recommends double-tube, N-size core barrels (core diameter of 54 mm). The accepted divisions of RQD values are as follows:

RQD, percent	Core quality
90–100	Excellent
75–90	Good
50–75	Fair
25–50	Poor
< 25	Very poor

Spacing and orientation of discontinuities

The spacing of discontinuities is the mean distance between the planes of weakness in the rock mass in the direction perpendicular to the discontinuity planes. The strike of discontinuities is generally recorded with reference to magnetic north. The dip angle is the angle between the horizontal and the joint plane taken in a direction in which the plane dips.

A classification of discontinuity spacings proposed by ISRM (1981) is reproduced in Table 5.9.

Table 5.9. Classification for discontinuity spacing (after ISRM, 1981)

Description	Spacing of discontinuities	Rock mass condition
Very wide	> 2 m	Solid
Wide	0.6–2 m	Massive
Moderate	200–600 mm	Blocky/seamy
Close	60 mm to 200 mm	Fractured
Very close	< 60 mm	Crushed/shattered

Condition of discontinuities

This parameter includes roughness of the discontinuity surfaces, their separation (distance between the surfaces), their length or continuity (persistence), weathering of the wall rock of the planes of weakness, and the infilling (gouge) material.

Roughness or the nature of the asperities in the discontinuity surfaces is an important parameter characterizing the condition of discontinuities. Asperities that occur on joint surfaces interlock, if the surfaces are clean and closed, and inhibit shear movement along the joint surface. Asperities usually have a base length and amplitude measured in millimeters and are readily apparent on a core-sized exposure of a discontinuity. The applicable descriptive terms are defined below (it should be stated if the surfaces are stepped, undulating, or planar):

a) Very rough. Near vertical steps and ridges occur on the discontinuity surface.

b) Rough. Some ridge and side-angle steps are evident; asperities are clearly visible; discontinuity surface feels very abrasive.

c) Slightly rough. Asperities on the discontinuity surfaces are distinguishable and can be felt.

d) Smooth. Surface appears smooth and feels so to the touch.

e) Slickensided. Visual evidence of polishing exists.

Separation or the distance between the discontinuity surfaces controls the extent to which the opposing surfaces can interlock as well as the amount of water that can flow through the discontinuity. In the absence of interlocking, the discontinuity filling (gouge) controls entirely the shear strength of the discontinuity. As the separation decreases, the asperities of the rock wall tend to become more interlocked, and both the filling and the rock material contribute to the discontinuity shear strength. The shear strength along a discontinuity is therefore dependent on the degree of separation, presence, or absence of filling materials, roughness of the surface walls, and the nature of the filling material. The description of the separation of the discontinuity surface is given as follows:

a) Very tight: <0.1 mm;
b) Tight: 0.1–0.5 mm;
c) Moderately open: 0.5–2.5 mm;
d) Open: 2.5–10 mm;
e) Very wide: 10–25 mm.

Note that where the separation is more than 25 mm, the discontinuity should be described as a major discontinuity.

Continuity of discontinuities influences the extent to which the rock material and the discontinuities separately affect the behavior of the rock mass. In the case of underground excavations, a discontinuity is considered fully continuous if its length is greater than the dimension of the excavation. Consequently, for continuity assessment, the length of the discontinuity should be determined.

Weathering of the wall rock, i.e., the rock constituting the discontinuity surfaces, is classified in accordance with the recommendations of the ISRM Committee on Classification of Rocks (1981):

a) Unweathered/fresh. No visible signs are noted of weathering; rock fresh; crystals bright.

b) Slightly weathered rock. Discontinuities are stained or discolored and may contain a thin filling of altered material. Discoloration may extend into the rock from the discontinuity surfaces to a distance of up to 20 percent of the discontinuity spacing.

c) Moderately weathered rock. Slight discoloration extends from discontinuity planes for greater than 20 percent of the discontinuity spacing. Discontinuities may contain filling of altered material. Partial opening of grain boundaries may be observed.

d) Highly weathered rock. Discoloration extends throughout the rock, and the rock material is partly friable. The original texture of the rock has mainly been preserved, but separation of the grains has occurred.

e) Completely weathered rock. The rock is totally discolored and decomposed and in a friable condition. The external appearance is that of soil. Internally, the rock texture is partly preserved, but grains have completely separated.

It should be noted that the boundary between rock and soil is defined in terms of the uniaxial compressive strength and not in terms of weathering. A material with the strength equal to or above 1 MPa (145 psi) is considered as rock.

The infilling (gouge) has a two-fold influence:

a) Depending on the thickness, the filling prevents the interlocking of the fracture asperities.

b) It possesses its own characteristic properties, i.e., shear strength, permeability, and deformational characteristics.

The following aspects should be described: type, thickness, continuity, and consistency.

Groundwater conditions

In the case of tunnels or mine drifts, the rate of inflow of groundwater in liters per minute per 10 meters of the excavation should be determined. Alternatively, general conditions can be described as completely dry, damp, wet, dripping, and flowing. If actual water pressure data are available, these should be stated and expressed in terms of the ratio of the water pressure to the major principal stress. The latter can be either measured or determined from the depth below surface, i.e., the vertical stress increases with depth at 2.5 MPa per 100 meters (1.1 psi per foot) of the depth below surface.

REFERENCES

Standards

American Society for Testing and Materials. Standard Method of Test for Unconfined Compressive Strength of Rock Core Specimens. *Annual Book of ASTM Standards*, Philadelphia, Part 19, Designation D–2938–71a.

International Society for Rock Mechanics. *Rock Characterization, Testing and Monitoring – ISRM Suggested Methods*, E. T. Brown (editor), Pergamon, Oxford, 1981, 211 p.

International Society for Rock Mechanics. Basic Geotechnical Description of Rock Masses. *Int. J. Rock Mech. & Min. Sci.*, Vol. 18, No. 1, 1981, pp. 85–110.

Books

Attewell, P. B. and Farmer, I. W. *Principles of Engineering Geology.* John Wiley & Sons, New York, 1979, pp. 427–631.

Bell, F. G. *Engineering Geology and Geotechniques.* Newness–Butterworths, Boston, 1980, pp. 10–94.

Blyth, F. G. H. and Freitas, de M. H. *A. Geology for Engineers.* Edward Arnold Publishers, London, 1974, pp. 272–340.

Dowding, C. H. (editor). *Site Characterization and Exploration.* American Society of Civil Engineers, New York, 1978, 395 pp.

Goodman, R. E. *Methods of Geological Engineering.* West Publishing Company, San Francisco, 1976, 472 pp.

Griffiths, D. H. and King, R. F. *Applied Geophysics for Geologists and Engineers*, Pergamon, New York, 1981, 230 pp.

Hoek, E. and Brown, E. T. *Underground Excavations in Rock*, Institution of Mining and Metallurgy, London, 1980, pp. 38–86.

Jaeger, C. and Cook, N. G. W. Fundamentals of Rock Mechanics, 3rd Ed. Chapman and Hall, London, 1979, pp. 465–470.

Stagg, K. G. and Zienkiewicz, D. C. (Editors). *Rock Mechanics in Engineering Practice*, John Wiley & Sons, London, 1968, pp. 120, 55–98.

Zaruba, Q. and Mencl, V. *Engineering Geology*, Elsevier Scientific Publishing Co., New York, 1976, pp. 15–34; 103–145.

Articles

AEG Committee on Core Logging. A guide to core logging for rock engineering, *Proc. Symp. Exploration for Rock Engineering*, A. A. Balkema, Capetown, 1976, Vol. 1, pp. 71–86.

Aggson, J. R. Coal mine floor heave in the Beckley coal bed – an analysis. *Bureau of Mines, RI* 8274, 1978, 32 p.

Barr, M. W. and Hocking, G. Borehole structural logging employing a pneumatically inflatable impression packer, *Proc. Symp. Exploration for Rock Engineering*, Johannesburg, 1976, Publ. A. A. Balkema, Capetown, 1976, Vol. 1, pp. 29–34.

Belesky, R. M. An in situ assessment of deformability and strength of coal pillars, M. S. Thesis, The Pennsylvania State University, 1981, 275 pp.

Bieniawski, Z. T. The mechanism of brittle fracture in rock. *Int. J. Rock Mech. Min. Sci.*, Vol. 4, 1967, pp. 395–435.

Bieniawski, Z. T. The point-load test in geotechnical practice. *Engineering Geology*, vol. 9, 1975, pp. 1–11.

Bieniawski, Z. T. Determining rock mass deformability – experience from histories, *Int. J. Rock Mech., Min. Sci.*, vol. 15, 1978, pp. 237–247.

Bieniawski, Z. T. Comparison of deformability measurements by petite sismique, the Goodman jack, and flat jacks, *Proc. 1979 Rapid Excav. and Tunnel. Conf.* (A. C. Maevis and W. A. Hustrulid, eds.), American Institute of Mining, Metallurgical, and Petroleum Engineers, New York, 1979, Vol. 1, pp. 901–916.

Bieniawski, Z. T. The petite sismique technique – a review of current developments, *Proc. 2nd Conf. on Acoustic Emission/Microseismic Activity in Geol. Structures and Materials*, Trans. Tech. Publ., Clausthal, Germany, 1980, pp. 305–318.

Bieniawski, Z. T. and Van Heerden, W. L. The significance of in situ tests on large rock specimens, *Int. J. Rock Mech. Min. Sci. and Geomech. Abstr.*, Vol. 12, 1975, pp. 101–113.

Campbell, J. A. L., Petrovic, L. J., Mallio, D. J. and Schulties, C. W. How to predict coal mine roof conditions before mining. *Mining Engineering*, Vol. 27, No. 10, 1975, pp. 37–40.

Colback, P. S. B. and Wild, B. L. The influence of moisture content on the compressive strength of rock, *Proc. 3rd Canadian Rock Mech. Symp.*, Toronto, 1965, pp. 65–83.

Coon, R. F. and Merritt, A. H. Predicting in situ modulus of deformation using rock quality indexes. *ASTM Special Publication 477*, ASTM, Philadelphia, 1970, pp. 154–173.

Dearman, W. R. and Fookes, P. G. Engineering geological mapping for civil engineering practice. *Quart. J. Engineering Geology*, Vol. 7, 1974, pp. 223–256.

Deere, D. U. Technical description of rock cores for engineering purposes, *Rock Mechanics and Engineering Geology*, Vol. 1, No. 1, 1964, pp. 17–22.

Deere, D. U., Hendrom, A. J., Patton, F. D. and Cording, E. J. Design of surface and near surface construction in rock, *Failure and Breakage of Rock*, (Proc. 8th U.S. Symp. on Rock Mech., American Institute of Mining, Metallurgical, and Petroleum Engineers, New York, 1967, pp. 237–302.

Deere, D. U. and Miller, R. P. Engineering classification and index properties of intact rock, *Air Force Weapons Laboratory, Technical Report No. AFNL-TR-65-116*, New Mexico, 1966.

Deklotz, E. J. and Boisen, R. D. Development of equipment for determining deformation modulus and in situ stress by means of large flat jacks, *Determination of the in situ modulus of deformation of rock* (Special Technical Publ. 477), American Society for Testing and Materials, Philadelphia, PA, 1970, pp. 117–125.

de la Cruz, R. W. Modified borehole jack method for elastic property determination in rocks, *Rock Mech.*, Vol. 10, 1978, pp. 221–239.

Dershowitz, W., Baecher, G. B. and Einstein, H. H. Prediction of rock mass deformability, *Proc. 4th Cong. Int. Soc. for Rock Mech. A. A. Balkema*, Rotterdam, 1979, Vol. 1, pp. 605–611.

Dodds, D. J. Interpretation of plate loading test results, *Field Testing and Instrum. of Rock* (Special Technical Publication 554), American Society for Testing and Materials, Philadelphia, PA, 1974, pp. 20–34.

Dodds, D. J. and Schroeder, W. L. Factors bearing on the interpretation of in situ testing results, *Proc. 1974 Rapid Excav. and Tunneling Conf.* (H. C. Pattison and E. D'Appolonia, eds.), American Institute of Mining, Metallurgical and Petroleum Engrs., New York, 1974, pp. 397–414.

Dunham, K. R., Thurman, A. G. and Ellison, R. D. The use of geological/geotechnical investigation as an aid to mine planning. *Proc. 18th U.S. Symp. Rock Mech.*, Keystone, CSM Press, June 1976, pp. IC4–1–6.

Ealy, D. L., Mazurak, R. E. and Laugrand, E. L. A geological approach for predicting unstable roof and floor conditions in advance of mining. *Mining Congress Journal*, Vol. 65, No. 3, 1979, pp. 17–22.

Farr, J. B. Seismic wave attenuation and rock properties. *Site Characterics and Exploration*, Ed. C. E. Dowding, ASCE, New York, 1978, pp. 302–321.

Fisher, P. and Banks, D. Influence of the regional geologic setting on site geologic features. *Site Characterization and Exploration*, Ed. C. E. Dowding, ASCE, New York, 1978, pp. 163–185.

Franklin, J. A. Use of tests and monitoring in the design and construction of rock structures, *Proc., 4th Cong. Int. Soc. for Rock Mech.*, A. A. Balkema, Rotterdam, Vol. 3, 1979, pp. 163–180.

Geological Society of London, Engineering Group. Working Party Report on the logging of rock cores for engineering purposes. *Quarterly Journal Engng. Geol.*, Vol. 3, 1970, pp. 1–24.

Goodman, R. E., Van, T. K. and Heuze, F. E. Measurement of rock deformability in boreholes, *Basic and Applied Rock Mech.* (Proc., 10th U.S. Symp. on Rock Mech.), American Institute of Mining, Metallurgical, and Petroleum Engrs., New York, 1972, pp. 523–545.

Haimson, B. C. The hydrofracturing stress measuring method and recent field results, *Int. J. Rock Mech. Min. Sci. and Geomech. Abstr.*, Vol. 15, 1978, pp. 167–178.

Haimson, B. C. Near-surface and deep hydrofracturing stress measurements in the Waterloo quartzite, *Proc., 19th U.S. Symp. on Rock Mech.*, University of Nevada, Reno, 1978, pp. 345–361.

Hansen, D. E. and Lachel, D. J. Ore body ground conditions. *Tunneling Technology Newsletter*, U.S. National Committee on Tunneling Technology, Washington, DC, No. 32, December 1980, pp. 1–12.

Hast, N. The measurement of rock pressure in mines. *Sveriges Geol. Undersokn*, Arsbok 52, No. 3, 1958.

Herget, G. and Unrug, K. In situ strength prediction of mine pillars based on laboratory tests. *Advances in Rock Mech.* (Proc., 3rd Cong. of the Int. Soc. for Rock Mech.), National Academy of Sciences, Washington, DC, Vol. IIA, 1974, pp. 150–155.

Heuze, F. E. Scale effects in the determination of rock mass strength. *Rock Mechanics*, Vol. 12, 1980, pp. 167–192.

Heuze, F. E. and Salem, A. Rock mass deformability measured in situ – problems and solutions. *Proc. Int. Conf. on Field Measurements in Rock Mech.*, A. A. Balkema, Rotterdam, 1977, pp. 375–387.

Hoek, E. Fracture of anisotropic rock, *J. Sough African Inst. Min. Metall.*, Vol. 64, No. 10, 1964, pp. 510–518.

Hoek, E. Geotechnical considerations in tunnel design and contract preparation. *Trans. Inst. Min. Metall.*, London, Vol. 91, 1982, pp. A101–119.

Hoek, E. and Brown, E. T. Empirical strength criterion for rock masses. *Journal of Geotechnical Engineering*, ASCE, Vol. 106, No. GT9, 1980, pp. 1013–1035.

Hustrulid, W. A. An analysis of the Goodman jack. *Site Characterization* (Proc., 17th U.S. Symp. on Rock Mech.), Utah Engineering Experiment Station, Salt Lake City, 1976, pp. 4B10–1–8.

Hustrulid, W. A. An analysis of several borehole techniques for determining stress and modulus. *Proc., 4th Congr. Int. Soc. for Rock Mech.*, A. A. Balkema, Rotterdam, 1979, Vol. 2, pp. 249–258.

Hylbert, D. K. The classification evaluation and projection of coal mine roof rocks in advance of mining. *Mining Engineering*, Vol. 30, No. 12, 1978, pp. 1667–1676.

John, M. Time-dependence of fracture processes of rock materials. *Adv. in Rock Mech.* (Proc., 3rd Cong. of Int. Soc. for Rock Mech.), National Academy of Sciences, Washington, DC, Vol. IIA, 1974, pp. 330–335.

Kendorski, F. S. Caving operations drift support design. *Design Methods in Rock Mech.* (Proc., 16th U.S. Symp. nn Rock Mech.), American Society of Civil Engrs., New York, 1975, pp. 277–286.

Kendorski, F. S. Field and laboratory assessment of rock mass strength for tunnel design with allowance for dilation. *Underground Rock Engr.* (Proc., 13th Canadian Rock Mech. Symp.), Canadian Institute of Mining and Metallurgy, Montreal, Quebec, 1980, pp. 162–167.

Kendorski, F. S. and Bischoff, J. A. Engineering inspection and appraisal of rock tunnels. *Proc. Rapid Excav. and Tunneling Conf.*, AIME, New York, 1976, pp. 81–99.

Kulhawy, F. H. Stress deformation properties of rock and rock discontinuities. *Engineering Geology*, Vol. 9, 1975, pp. 327–350.

Kulhawy, F. H. Geomechanical model for rock foundation settlement. *J. Geotech. Engr. Div. ASCE*, Vol. 4 (GT2), 1978, pp. 211–227.

Lama, R. D. and Vutukuri, V. S. *Handbook on Mechanical Properties of Rocks*, Trans. Tech. Publications, Clausthal, 1978, Vol. 2, 481 p.

Lindner, E. N. and Halpern, J. A. In situ stress in North America: a compilation. *Int. J. Rock Mech. Min. Sci. and Geomech. Abstr.*, Vol. 15, 1978, pp. 183–203.

Lytle, R. J. Geophysical characterization using advanced data processing. *Site Characteristics and Exploration*, Ed. C. E. Dowding, ASCE, New York, 1978, pp. 291–301.

Merritt, A. H. and Baecher, G. B. Site characterization in rock engineering. *Proc. 22nd U.S. Symp. on Rock Mechanics*, Massachusetts Institute of Technology, Cambridge, Mass., 1981, pp. 415–428.

Misterek, D. L. Analysis of data from radial jacking tests. *Determination of the in situ modulus of deformation of rock* (Special Technical Publ. 477), American Society for Testing and Materials, Philadelphia, PA, 1970, pp. 27–38.

Misterek, D. L. Slebir, E. J. and Montgomery J. S. Bureau of reclamation procedures for conducting uniaxial jacking tests. *Field Testing and Instrumentation of Rock* (Special Technical Publication 554), American Society for Testing and Materials, Philadelphia, PA, 1974, pp. 35–51.

Muller, L. Rock mass behavior – determination and application in engineering practice. *Adv. in Rock Mech.* (Proc., 3rd Cong. Int. Soc. for Rock Mech.), National Academy of Sciences, Washington, DC, Vol. 1A, 1974, pp. 205–215.

Newman, D. A. Engineering Geological Characterization of Coal Bearing Strata, M. S. Thesis, The Pennsylvania State University, 1981, 158 p.

Olivier, H. J. A new engineering-geological rock durability classification. *Eng. Geol.* Vol. 14, No. 4, 1979, pp. 255–279.

Overby, W. K., Komar, C. A. and Posini, J. Predicting probable roof fall areas in advance of mining by geological analysis. *USBM TPR-70*, USBM, 1973, 15 pp.

Pratt, H. R., Black, A. D. and Brace, W. F. Friction and deformation of jointed quartz diorite. *Advances in Rock Mech.* (Proc., 3rd Congress Int. Soc. for Rock Mech.), National Academy of Sciences, Washington, DC, Vol. IIA, 1974, pp. 306–310.

Pratt, H. R., Black, A. D., Brown, W. S. and Brace, W. F. The effect of specimen size on the mechanical properties of unjointed diorite. *Int. J. Rock Mech. Min. Sci.*, Vol. 9, 1972, pp. 513–529.

Pratt, H. R., Black, A. D., Brown, W. S. and Brace, W. F. A new technique for determining the deformation and frictional characteristics of in situ rock. *Field Testing and instrumentation of Rock* (Special Technical Publication 554), American Society for Testing and Materials, Philadelphia, PA, 1974, pp. 3–19.

Priest, S. D. and Brown, E. T. Probabilistic stability analysis of variable rock slopes. *Trans. Inst. Min. Metall.*, London, Sect. A, Vol. 92, 1983, pp. 1–12.

Priest, S. D. and Hudson, L. Discontinuity spacings in rock. *Int. J. Rock Mech. Min. Sci.*, Vol. 13, 1976, pp. 135–148.

Protodyakonov, M. M. The size effect in investigations of rock and coal. *Proc., Int. Conf. on Stress in the Earth's Crust*, Henry Krumb School of Mines, New York, 1964, unpaginated addendum.

Rhodes, G. W., Stephenson, R. W. and Rockaway, J. D. Plate bearing tests on coal underclay. *Proc., 19th U.S. Symp. on Rock Mech.* (supplement), University of Nevada, Reno, 1978, pp. 16–27.

Rinkenberger, R. K. Implementing remote sensing techniques for evaluating mine ground stability. *MESA IR-1054*, 1977, 36 pp.

Rocha, M. A method of integral sampling of rock masses. *Rock Mechanics*, Vol. 3, No. 1, 1967, pp. 1–12.

Rocha, M. Present possibilities of studying foundations of concrete dams. *Adv. in Rock Mech.*, (Proc., 3rd Cong. Int. Soc. for Rock Mech.), National Academy of Sciences, Washington, DC, Vol. 1A, 1974, pp. 879–896.

Rocha, M. and da Silva, J. N. A method for the determination of deformability in rock masses. *Proc., 2nd Cong. Int. Soc. for Rock Mech.*, Institut za vodoprivredu 'Jaroslav Cerni', Belgrade, Yugoslavia, Vol. 1, 1970, pp. 423–437.

Roussel, J. M. Etude theoretique et experimentale du modul dynamique des massifs rocheux, *Revue Industrie Minerale*, Vol. 150, No. 8, 1968.

Schneider, B. Contribution a l'etude des massifs de fondation de barrages. *Trans. du labor de geol.*, Memoir no. 7, Grenoble, 1967, 263 pp.

Serafim, J. L. and Pereira, J. P. Considerations of the Geomechanics Classification of Bieniawski. *Proc. Int. Symp. on Engng Geol. and Underground Constr.*, LNEC, Lisbon, Portugal, 1983.

Shuri, F. S. Borehole diameter as a factor in borehole jack results. *Proc. 22nd U.S. Symp. on Rock Mech.*, MIT, Cambridge, Mass., 1981, pp. 392–397.

Singh, M. M. Strength of rock. *Physical Properties of Rocks and Minerals*. McGraw-Hill Book Co., New York, 1981, Vol. II-2, pp. 83–121.

St. John, C. M., Christianson, M. and Hardy, M. P. Geotechnical analysis of underground mining methods. *Proc. 20th U.S. Symp. on Rock Mech.*, University of Texas, Austin, 1979, pp. 87–94.

Taranik, J. V. Geological remote sensing and space shuttle. *Mining Congress Journal*, July 1982, pp. 18–44.

Van Heerden, W. L. Practical application of CSIR triaxial strain cell for rock stress measurements. *Proc. Symp. Expl. Rock Engr.*, Johannesburg, 1976, A. A. Balkema, Cape Town, Vol. 1, 1977, pp. 189–194.

Vogler, V.W., Deffur, R. E. and Bieniawski, Z. T. CSIR large flat jack equipment for mass deformability, *Proc., Symp. Exploration for Rock Engineering*, A. A. Balkema, Cape Town, 1977, Vol. 2, pp. 105–111.

U.S. National Committee on Rock Mechanics. *Rock Mechanics Research Requirements for Resource Recovery, Construction, and Earthquake – Hazard Reduction*, National Academy Press, Washington, DC, 1981, 222 p.

An unstable roof in a coal mine indicating the need for improved strata control.

CHAPTER 6

Empirical methods of design

*It is the mark of an educated man to look for precision
in each class of things just so far as the nature of the
subject admits.*

Aristotle

Empirical design methods relate practical experience gained on previous projects to the conditions anticipated at a proposed site.

Rock mass classifications form the backbone of the empirical design approach and are widely employed in rock engineering. In fact, on many projects, the classification approach serves as the only practical basis for the design of complex underground structures. Most of the tunnels constructed at present make use of some classification system. The most used and the best known of these is Terzaghi's rock load classification which was introduced over 35 years ago (Terzaghi, 1946). Since then this classification has been modified (Deere et al., 1970) and new rock classification systems have been proposed. These systems took cognizance of the new advances in rock support technology, namely, rockbolts and shotcrete, as well as addressed different engineering projects: tunnels, chambers, mines, slopes and foundations. Today, there are so many different rock classification systems in existence that it is useful to tabulate the more common ones as presented in Table 6.1.

Rock mass classifications have been successfully applied throughout the world: in the United State (Deere, 1964, Wickham et al., 1972, Bieniawski, 1979), Canada, (Coates, 1964, Franklin, 1975), Western Europe (Lauffer, 1958, Pacher et al., 1974, Barton et al., 1974), South Africa (Bieniawski, 1973, Oliver, 1976, Laubscher, 1975), Australia (Barton, 1977, Baczynski, 1980), New Zealand (Rutledge, 1978), Japan (Ikeda, 1970), USSR (Protodyakonov, 1974), and in some East European countries (Kidybinski, 1979).

CLASSIFICATION SYSTEMS IN ROCK ENGINEERING

Rock mass classification can, if certain conditions are fulfilled, effectively combine the findings from observation, experience, and engineering judgment to provide a quantitative assessment of rock mass conditions and support requirements.

Aims of rock classifications

A rock mass classification has the following aims in an engineering application:
  a) To divide a particular rock mass into groups of similar behavior;

97

Table 6.1. Major rock classifications currently in use

Name of classification	Originator and date	Country of origin	Applications
Rock loads	Terzaghi, 1946	USA	Tunnels with steel supports
Stand-up time	Lauffer, 1958	Austria	Tunneling
Rock quality designation	Deere, 1964	USA	Core logging, tunneling
Intact rock strength	Deere & Miller 1966	USA	Communication
RSR concept	Wickham, et al. 1972	USA	Tunneling
Geomechanics Classification (RMR system)	Bieniawski, 1973	S. Africa & USA	Tunnels, mines, foundations
Q-system	Barton, et al. 1974	Norway	Tunneling, large chambers
Strength/block size	Franklin, 1975	Canada	Tunneling
Basic geotechnical classification	ISRM, 1981	International	General

b) To provide a basis for understanding the characteristics of each group;

c) To yield quantitative data for engineering design; and

d) To provide a common basis for communication.

These aims can be fulfilled by ensuring that a classification system has the following attributes:

a) It is simple, easily remembered, and understandable;

b) Each term is clear and the terminology used is widely accepted by engineers and geologists;

c) The most significant properties of the rock masses are included;

d) It is based on measurable parameters which can be determined by relevant tests quickly and cheaply in the field;

e) It is based on a rating system that can weigh the relative importance of the classification parameters; and

f) It is functional by providing quantitative data for the design of rock support.

Classification parameters

An important issue in rock classifications is the selection of the parameters of greatest significance. There appears to be no single parameter or index which can fully and quantitatively describe a jointed rock mass for engineering purposes. Various parameters have different significance and only if taken together can they describe a rock mass satisfactorily.

The strength of the rock material is included as a classification parameter in the majority of the rock mass classification systems. It is a necessary parameter because the strength of the rock material constitutes the strength limit of the rock mass. The uniaxial compressive strength of rock material can be determined in the field indirectly by means of the point load strength index (Franklin, 1975).

The second parameter most commonly employed is the rock quality designation (RQD). This is a quantitative index based on a modified core recovery procedure which incorporates only sound pieces of core which are 100 mm or greater in length. The RQD is a measure of drill core quality or fracture frequency, and disregards the influence of joint tightness, orientation, continuity and gouge (infilling). Consequently, the RQD does not fully describe a rock mass.

Other classification parameters used in current rock mass classifications are: spacing of discontinuities, condition of discontinuities (roughness, continuity, separation, joint-wall weathering, infilling), orientation of discontinuities, groundwater conditions (inflow, pressure), and stress field.

An excellent discussion of the methods for quantitative description of discontinuities in rock masses can be found in a recent ISRM document (ISRM, 1981).

It is believed that in the case of surface excavations and those near-surface underground rock excavations which are controlled by the structural geological features, the following classification parameters are important: strength of intact rock material, spacing of discontinuities, condition of discontinuities, orientation of discontinuities and groundwater conditions. In the case of deep underground excavations where the behavior of rock masses is stress controlled, knowledge of the virgin stress field or the changes in stress can be of greater significance than the geological parameters. Most civil engineering projects, such as tunnels and subway chambers, will fall into the first category of geologically controlled rock mass structures.

Rock classifications may be conveniently divided into two groups: intact rock classifications and rock mass classifications.

Intact rock classifications

The subject of intact rock strength classification is a fairly controversial topic since a number of classifications for rock material strength have been proposed. For completeness, they are compared in Table 6.2. The engineering classification proposed by Deere and Miller (1966) has been widely recognized as particularly realistic and convenient for use in the field of rock mechanics. Recently, the ISRM Commission on Rock Classification has recommended different ranges of values for intact rock strength (ISRM, 1981). The main reason for the new ISRM ranges was the opinion that the Deere-Miller classification did not include differentiation in the strength in the range below 25 MPa. It should also be noted that this led to a recommendation that the convenient value of 1 MPa (145 lbf/in^2) for the uniaxial compressive strength may be taken as the lowest strength limit for rock materials. Hence, the materials with a strength lower than 1 MPa should be considered as soils and described in accordance with soil mechanics practice.

The major limitation of the intact rock classifications is that they do not provide quantitative data for engineering design purposes. Therefore, their main value lies in enabling better communication while discussing intact rock properties.

Table 6.2 Various strength classifications for intact rock

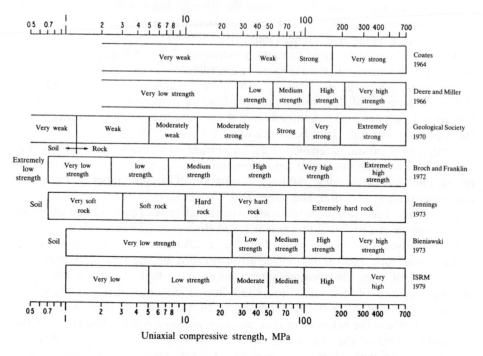

Uniaxial compressive strength, MPa

Rock mass classifications

Of the many rock mass classification systems in existence today, six require special attention because they are most commonly known, namely, those proposed by: Terzaghi (1946), Lauffer (1958), Deere (1964), Wickham, Tiedemann and Skinner (1972), Bieniawski (1973), and Barton, Lien and Lunde (1974).

The rock load-classification of Terzaghi (1946), was the first practical classification system introduced and has been dominant in the United States for over 35 years, proving very successful for tunneling with steel supports. Lauffer's classification (1958) was based on the work of Stini (1950) and was a considerable step forward in the art of tunneling since it introduced the concept of the stand-up time of the active span in a tunnel, which is highly relevant in determining the type and amount of tunnel support. Deere's classification (1964) introduced the rock quality designation (RQD) index, which is a simple and practical method of describing the quality of rock core from boreholes. The concept of rock structure rating (RSR), developed in the United States by Wickham, Tiedemann, and Skinner (1972, 1974), was the first system featuring classification ratings for weighing the relative importance of classification parameters. The Geomechanics Classification (RMR system) proposed by Bieniawski (1973) and the Q-system proposed by Barton, Lien and Lunde (1974) were developed independently and both provide quantitative data for the selection of modern tunnel reinforcement measures such as rockbolts and shotcrete. The Q-system has been developed specifically for tunnels and chambers while the Geomechanics Classification, although also initially developed for tunnels, has been applied to rock slopes and foundations, ground rippability assessment, as well as to mining problems (Laubscher, 1975, Ghose and Raju, 1981, Kendorski et al., 1983).

TERZAGHI'S ROCK LOAD CLASSIFICATION

Terzaghi (1946) formulated the first rational method of evaluating rock loads appropriate to the design of steel sets. This was an important development because support by steel sets has been the most commonly used system for containing rock tunnel excavations during the past 50 years. It must be emphasized, however, that while this classification is appropriate for the purpose for which it was evolved, i.e., for estimating rock loads for steel-arch supported tunnels, it is not so suitable for modern

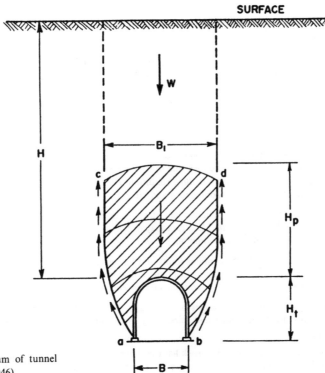

Figure 6.1. Simplified diagram of tunnel rock-load (after Terzaghi, 1946).

During construction of a tunnel, some relaxation of the rock mass will occur above and on the sides of the tunnel. The loosened rock within the area *acdb* will tend to move in towards the tunnel. This movement will be resisted by friction forces along the lateral boundaries *ac* and *bd* and these friction forces transfer the major portion of the overburden weight W onto the material on either side of the tunnel. The roof and sides of the tunnel are required only to support the balance which is equivalent to a height H_p. The width B_i of the zone of rock in which movement occurs will depend upon the characteristics of the rock mass and upon the tunnel dimensions H_t and B.

Table 6.3. Terzaghi's rock load classification of 1946.

Rock load H_p in feet of rock on tunnel roof with width B(ft) and height H_t(ft) at depth of more than $1.5(B + H_t)$.

Rock condition	Rock load H_p in feet	Remarks
1. Hard and intact	Zero	Light lining required only if spalling or popping occurs.
2. Hard stratified or schistose	0 to 0.5B	Light support, mainly for protection against spalls. Load may change erratically from point to point.
3. Massive, moderately jointed	0 to 0.25B	
4. Moderately blocky and seamy	$0.25B$ to $0.35(B + H_t)$	No side pressure.
5. Very blocky and seamy	$(0.35$ to $1.10)(B + H_t)$	Little or no side pressure.
6. Completely crushed	$1.10(B + H_t)$	Considerable side pressure. Softening effects of seepage towards bottom of tunnel require either continuous support for lower ends of ribs or circular ribs.
7. Squeezing rock, moderate depth	$(1.10$ to $2.10)(B + H_t)$	Heavy side pressure, invert struts required. Circular ribs are recommended.
8. Squeezing rock, great depth	$(2.10$ to $4.50) (B + H_t)$	
9. Swelling rock	Up to 250 feet, irrespective of the value of $(B + H_t)$	Circular ribs are required. In extreme cases use yielding support.

Definitions:

Intact rock contains neither joints nor hair cracks. Hence, if it breaks, it breaks across sound rock. On account of the injury to the rock due to blasting, spalls may drop off the roof several hours or days after blasting. This is known as a *spalling* condition. Hard, intact rock may also be encountered in the *popping* condition involving the spontaneous and violent detachment of rock slabs from the sides or roof.

Stratified rock consists of individual strata with little or no resistance against separation along the boundaries between strata. The strata may or may not be weakened by transverse joints. In such rock, the spalling condition is quite common.

Moderately jointed rock contains joints and hair cracks, but the blocks between joints are locally grown together or so intimately interlocked that vertical walls do not require lateral support. In rocks of this type, both spalling and popping conditions may be encountered.

Blocky and *seamy* rock consists of chemically intact or almost intact rock fragments which are entirely separated from each other and imperfectly interlocked. In such rock, vertical walls may require lateral support.

Crushed but chemically intact rock has the character of a crusher run. If most or all of the fragments are as small as fine sand grains and no recementation has taken place, crushed rock below the water table exhibits the properties of a water-bearing sand.

Squeezing rock slowly advances into the tunnel without perceptible volume increase. A prerequisite for squeeze is a high percentage of microscopic and sub-microscopic particles of micaceous minerals or of clay minerals with a low swelling capacity.

Swelling rock advances into the tunnel chiefly on account of expansion. The capacity to swell seems to be limited to those rocks which contain clay minerals such as montmorillonite, with a high swelling capacity.

Table 6.4. Terzaghi's rock load classification as modified by Deere et al., 1970

Fracture spacing (cm)	RQD (%)	Rock condition	Rock load, H_p Initial	Rock load, H_p Final		Remarks
		1. Hard and intact	0	0	Generally no side pressure. Erratic load changes from point to point.	Lining only if spalling or popping
−50	98	2. Hard stratified or schistose	0	0.25B		Spalling common
	95					
	90	3. Massive, moderately jointed	0	0.5B		Side pressure if strata inclined, some spalling
−20		4. Moderately blocky and seamy	0	0.25B to 0.35C		
	75					
−10	50	5. Very blocky, seamy and shattered	0 to 0.6C	0.35C to 1.1C		Little or no side pressure
	25	6. Completely crushed		1.1C		Considerable side pressure. If seepage, continuous support
	10					
−5	2					
−2		7. Gravel and sand	0.54C to 1.2C	0.62C to 1.38C		Dense Side pressure $P_h = 0.3\gamma(0.5H_t + H_p)$
			0.94C to 1.2C	1.08C to 1.38C		Loose
		8. Squeezing, moderate depth		1.1C to 2.1C		Heavy side pressure. Continuous support required
		9. Squeezing, great depth		2.1C to 4.5C		
		10. Swelling		up to 250 ft.		Use circular support. In extreme cases: yielding support

(Left margin lower section labelled: **Weak and coherent**)

Notes:
1. For rock classes 4, 5, 6, 7, when above ground water level, reduce loads by 50%.
2. B is tunnel width, $C = B + H_t$ = width + height of tunnel.
3. γ = density of medium.

tunneling methods using shotcrete and rockbolts. After detailed studies, Cecil (1970) concluded that Terzaghi's classification was too general to permit an objective evaluation of rock quality and that it provided no quantitative information on the properties of rock masses.

The main features of Terzaghi's classification are depicted in Figure 6.1 and are listed in Tables 6.3 and 6.4. The latest revision of Terzaghi's rock-load coefficients was presented by Rose (1982).

LAUFFER-PACHER CLASSIFICATION

The 1958 classification by Lauffer has its foundation in the earlier work on tunnel geology by Stini (1950) who is considered the father of the 'Austrian School' of tunneling and rock mechanics. Stini emphasized the importance of structural defects in rock masses. Lauffer proposed that the stand-up time for any active unsupported rock span is related to the various rock mass classes. An active unsupported span is the width of the tunnel or the distance from the face to the support if this is less than the tunnel width. The stand-up time is the period of time that a tunnel will stand unsupported after excavation. It should be noted that a number of factors may affect the stand-up time, such as orientation of tunnel axis, shape of cross-section, excavation method and support method. Lauffer's original classification is no longer used since it has been modified a number of times by other Austrian engineers, notably by Pacher, von Rabcewicz and Golser (1974). Pacher's contributions were particularly notable and are well summarized by Edeling and Maidl (1980).

The main significance of the Lauffer-Pacher classification is that an increase in tunnel span leads to a major reduction in the stand-up time. This means, for example, that while a pilot tunnel having a small span may be successfully constructed full face in fair rock conditions, a large span opening in this same rock may prove impossible to support in terms of the stand-up time. Only with a system of smaller headings and benches or multiple drifts can a large cross-section tunnel be constructed in such rock conditions.

This classification introduced the stand-up time and the span as relevant parameters in determining the type and amount of tunnel support, and it has influenced the development of more recent rock mass classification systems.

DEERE'S ROCK QUALITY DESIGNATION

Deere proposed in 1964 a quantitative index based on a modified core recovery procedure which incorporates only sound pieces of core that are 100 mm or greater in length. This rock quality designation (RQD) has been widely used and has been found very useful for the selection of tunnel support, see Table 6.5. For RQD determination, the International Society for Rock Mechanics recommends a core size of at least NX diameter (54 mm) drilled with double-tube diamond drilling equipment. The following relationship between the RQD index and the engineering quality of the rock was proposed by Deere (1964):

RQD, percent	Rock quality
< 25	Very poor
25–50	Poor
50–75	Fair
75–90	Good
90–100	Excellent

Cording, Hendron, and Deere (1972) attempted to relate the RQD index to Terzaghi's rock load factor. They found a reasonable correlation for steel-supported tunnels but not for openings supported by rockbolts. This supports the opinion that Terzaghi's rock load concept should be limited to tunnels supported by steel sets (Cording and Deere, 1972).

Merritt (1972) found that the RQD could be of considerable value in estimating support requirements for rock tunnels (see Table 6.5) but pointed out a limitation of the RQD index in areas where the joints contain thin clay fillings or weathered material. The influence of clay seams and fault gouge on tunnel stability was discussed by Brekke and Howard (1972).

Although the RQD is a quick and inexpensive index, it has limitations such as the disregarding of joint orientation, tightness, and gouge (infilling) material. Consequently, while it is a practical parameter for core quality estimation, it is not sufficient on its own to provide an adequate description of a rock mass.

RSR (ROCK STRUCTURE RATING) CONCEPT

The RSR concept, a ground support prediction model, was developed in the United States in 1972 by Wickham, Tiedemann, and Skinner. The concept presents a quantitative method for describing the quality of a rock mass and for selecting the appropriate ground support. It was the first complete rock mass classification system proposed since that introduced by Terzaghi in 1946.

The RSR concept was a step forward in a number of respects: firstly, it was a quantitative classification, unlike Terzaghi's qualitative one; secondly, it was a rock mass classification incorporating many parameters unlike the RQD index that is limited to core quality; thirdly, it was a complete classification having an input and an output, unlike a Lauffer-type classification that relies on practical experience to decide on a rock mass class, which then gives an output in terms of the stand-up time and span.

The main contribution of the RSR concept was that it introduced a rating system for rock masses. This was the sum of the weighted values of the individual parameters considered in this classification system. In other words, the relative importance of the various classification parameters could be assessed. This rating system was determined on the basis of case histories as well as reviews of various books and technical papers dealing with different aspects of ground support it tunneling.

The RSR concept considered two general categories of factors influencing rock mass behavior in tunneling: geological parameters and construction parameters. The

Table 6.5. Support recommendations for tunnels in rock (6 m to 12 m diameter) based on RDQ (after Deere et al., 1970)

Rock quality	Tunneling method	Alternative support systems		
		Steel sets[2]	Rockbolts[3]	Shotcrete
Excellent[1] RQD > 90	Boring machine	None to occ. light set. Rock load (0.0–0.2)B	None to occasional	None to occ. local application
	Conventional	None to occ. light set. Rock load (0.0–0.3)B	None to occasional	None to occ. local application 2 in. to 3 in.
Good[1] 75 < RQD < 90	Boring machine	Occ. light sets to pattern on 5-ft to 6-ft ctr. Rock load (0.0 to 0.4)B	Occasional to pattern on 5-ft to 6-ft centers	None to occ. local application 2 in. to 3 in.
	Conventional	Light sets, 5-ft to 6-ft ctr. Rock load (0.3 to 0.6)B	Pattern 5-ft to 6-ft centers	Occ. local application 2 in. to 3 in.
Fair 50 < RQD < 75	Boring machine	Light to medium sets, 5-ft to 6-ft ctr. Rock load (0.4–1.0)B	Pattern, 4-ft to 6-ft ctr.	2 in. to 4 in. crown
	Conventional	Light to medium sets, 4-ft to 5-ft ctr. Rock load (0.6–1.3)B	Pattern 3-ft to 5-ft ctr.	4 in. or more crown and sides
Poor[2] 25 < RQD < 50	Boring machine	Medium circular sets on 3-ft to 4-ft ctr. Rock load (1.0–1.6)B	Pattern, 3-ft to 5-ft ctr.	4 in. to 6 in. on crown and sides. Combine with bolts
	Conventional	Medium to heavy sets on 2-ft to 4-ft ctr. Rock load (1.3–2.0)B	Pattern, 2-ft to 4-ft ctr.	6 in. or more on crown and sides. Combine with bolts
Very poor[3] RQD < 25 (Excluding squeezing or swelling ground)	Boring machine	Medium to heavy circular sets on 2-ft ctr. Rock load (1.6 to 2.2)B	Pattern, 2-ft to 4-ft ctr.	6 in. or more on whole section. Combine with medium sets
	Conventional	Heavy circular sets on 2-ft ctr. Rock load (1.6 to 2.2)B	Pattern, 3-ft center	6 in. or more on whole section. Combine with medium to

Very poor[3] (Squeezing or swelling)			
Boring machine	Very heavy circular sets on 2-ft ctr. Rock load up to 250-ft.	Pattern, 2-ft to 3-ft ctr.	6 in. or more on whole section. Combine with heavy sets
Conventional	Very heavy circular sets on 2-ft ctr. Rock load up to 250-ft.	Pattern, 2-ft to 3-ft ctr.	6 in. or more on whole section. Combine with heavy sets

Notes:

1. In good and excellent rock, the support requirement will be, in general, minimal but will be dependent upon joint geometry, tunnel diameter, and relative orientations of joints and tunnel.
2. Lagging requirements will usually be zero in excellent rock and will range from up to 25% in good rock to 100% in very poor rock.
3. Mesh requirements usually will be zero in excellent rock and will range from occasional mesh (or straps) in good rock to 100% mesh in very poor rock.
4. B = tunnel width.

geologic parameters were: a) rock type, b) joint pattern (average spacing of joints), c) joint orientations (dip and strike), d) type of discontinuities, e) major faults, shears, and folds, f) rock material properties, and g) weathering or alteration. Some of these factors were treated separately; others were considered collectively. The authors pointed out that in some instances it would be possible to define accurately the above factors, but in others, only general approximations could be made. The construction parameters were: a) size of tunnel, b) direction of drive, and c) method of excavation.

All the above factors were grouped by Wickham, Tiedemann, and Skinner (1972) into three basic parameters, A, B, and C (Tables 6.6, 6.7, and 6.8, respectively), which in themselves were evaluations as to the relative effect of various geological factors on the support requirements. These three parameters were as follows:

a) Parameter A: General appraisal of a rock structure is on the basis of:

1. Rock type origin (igneous, metamorphic, sedimentary).

2. Rock hardness (hard, medium, soft, decomposed).

3. Geologic structure (massive, slightly faulted/folded, moderately faulted/folded, intensely faulted/folded).

b) Parameter B: Effect of discontinuity pattern with respect to the direction of tunnel drive is on the basis of:

1. Joint spacing.

2. Joint orientation (strike and dip).

3. Direction of tunnel drive.

c) Parameter C: Effect of groundwater inflow is based on:

1. Overall rock mass quality due to parameters A and B combined.

2. Joint condition (good, fair, poor).

3. Amount of water inflow (in gallons per minute per 1000 feet of the tunnel).

The RSR value of any tunnel section is obtained by summarizing the weighted numerical values determined for each parameter. This reflects the quality of the rock mass with respect to its need for support. Since a lesser amount of support was expected for machine-bored tunnels than when excavated by drill and blast methods, it was suggested that RSR values be adjusted for machine-bored tunnels in the manner given in Figure 6.2.

Table 6.6. Rock structure rating – Parameter A: general area geology (after Wickham et al., 1974)

	Basic rock type				Geological structure			
	Hard	Med.	Soft	Decomp.	Massive	Slightly faulted or folded	Moderately faulted or folded	Intensely faulted or folded
Igneous	1	2	3	4				
Metamorphic	1	2	3	4				
Sedimentary	2	3	4	4				
Type 1					30	22	15	9
Type 2					27	20	13	8
Type 3					24	18	12	7
Type 4					19	15	10	6

Table 6.7. Rock structure rating – Parameter *B*: joint pattern, direction of drive (after Wickham et al., 1974)

Average joint spacing	Strike ⊥ to axis					Strike ‖ to axis		
	Direction of drive					Direction of drive		
	Both With dip			Against dip		Both		
	Dip of prominent joints*					Dip of prominent joints*		
	Flat	Dipping	Vertical	Dipping	Vertical	Flat	Dipping	Vertical
1. Very closely jointed								
< 2 in.	9	11	13	10	12	9	9	7
2. Closely jointed 2–6 in.	13	16	19	15	17	14	14	11
3. Moderately jointed								
6–12 in.	23	24	28	19	22	23	23	19
4. Moderate to blocky								
1–2 ft.	30	32	36	25	28	30	28	24
5. Blocky to massive								
2–4 ft.	36	38	40	33	35	36	34	28
6. Massive > 4 ft.	40	43	45	37	40	40	38	34

Table 6.8. Rock structure rating – Parameter *C*: ground water, joint condition (after Wickham et al., 1974)

Anticipated water inflow (gpm/1000 ft)	Sum of parameters *A* + *B*					
	13–44			45–75		
	Joint condition**					
	Good	Fair	Poor	Good	Fair	Poor
None	22	18	12	25	22	18
Slight < 200 gpm	19	15	9	23	19	14
Moderate 200–1000 gpm	15	11	7	21	16	12
Heavy > 1000 gpm	10	8	6	18	14	10

*Dip: flat: 0–20 deg; dipping: 20–50 deg; and vertical: 50–90 deg.
**Joint condition: Good = tight or cemented; Fair = slightly weathered or altered; Poor = severely weathered, altered, or open.

It should be noted that Tables 6.6, 6.7, and 6.8 are reproduced not from the original 1972 reference but from a report published two years later. The RSR ratings were changed in 1974 and the latter report represents the latest information available.

A total of 53 projects were evaluated, but since each tunnel was divided into typical geological sections, a total of 190 tunnel sections were analyzed. The RSR values were determined for each section, and actual support installations were obtained from as-built drawings.

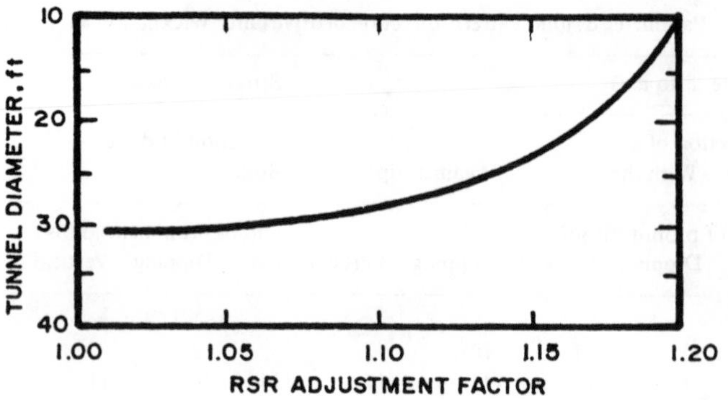

Figure 6.2. RSR concept: adjustment for machine boring (after Wickham et al., 1972).

The support was distributed as follows:

Sections with steel ribs	147	(89.6%)
Sections with rockbolts	14	(8.6%)
Sections with shotcrete	3	(1.8%)
Total supported	164	(100.0%)
Total unsupported	26	
Total	190 sections	

The RSR prediction model was developed primarily with respect to steel rib support. Insufficient data were available to correlate rock structures and rockbolt or shotcrete support. However, an appraisal of rockbolt requirements was made by considering rock loads with respect to the tensile strength of the bolt. The authors pointed out (Wickham et al., 1972) that this was a very general approach: it assumed that anchorage was adequate and that all bolts acted in tension only; it did not allow either for interaction between adjacent blocks or for an assumption of a compression arch formed by the bolts. In addition, the rock loads were developed for steel supported tunnels. Nevertheless, the following relation was given for 25 mm diameter rockbolts with a working load of 24,000 lb:

$$\text{Spacing (ft)} = \frac{24}{W} \tag{6.1}$$

where W is the rock load in 1000 lb/ft^2.

No correlation could be found between geologic prediction and shotcrete requirements, so that the following empirical relationship was suggested:

$$t = 1 + \frac{W}{1.25} \quad \text{or} \quad t = \frac{D}{150}(65 - \text{RSR}) \tag{6.2}$$

where

t = shotcrete thickness, inches;
W = rock load, lb/ft^2;
D = tunnel diameter, ft.

Support requirement charts have been prepared that provide a means of determining typical ground support systems based on RSR prediction as to the quality of the rock mass through which the tunnel is to be driven. Charts for 3 m, 6 m, 7 m, and 10 m diameter tunnels are available, an example being given in Figure 6.3. The three steel rib curves reflect typical sizes used for the particular tunnel size. The curves for rockbolts and shotcrete are dashed to emphasize that they are based on assumptions and were not derived from case histories. The charts are applicable to either circular or horseshoe-shaped tunnels of comparable widths.

The RSR concept is a very useful method for selecting steel rib support for rock tunnels. As with any empirical approach, one should not apply the concept beyond the range of the sufficient and reliable data used for developing it. For this reason, the RSR concept is not recommended for selection of rockbolt and shotcrete support. It should be noted that, although definitions of the classification parameters were not explicitly stated by the proposers, most of the input data needed would be normally included in a standard joint survey; however, the lack of definitions (e.g., 'slightly faulted' or 'folded' rock) may lead to some confusion.

A practical example using the RSR concept follows:

Consider a 6 m diameter tunnel to be driven in a slightly faulted strata featuring medium hard granite. The joint spacing is 2 ft and the joints are open. The estimated water inflow is 250 gal/min per 1000 ft of the tunnel length. The tunnel will be driven against a dip of 45 degrees and perpendicular to the jointing.

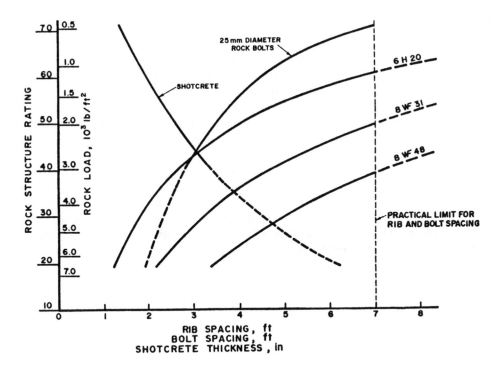

Figure 6.3. RSR concept: support chart for a 6 m-diameter tunnel (after Wickham et al., 1972).

Solution: From Table 6.6: For igneous rock of medium hardness (basic rock type 2) in slightly faulted rock, parameter $A = 20$. From Table 6.7: For moderate to blocky jointing, with strike perpendicular to the tunnel axis and with a drive against the dip of 45 deg, parameter $B = 25$. From Table 6.8: For $A + B = 45$, poor joint condition and moderate water flow, parameter $C = 12$.

Thus: RSR $= A + B + C = 57$. From Figure 6.3, the support requirements for a 6 m-dia. tunnel with RSR $= 57$ (estimated rock load 1.5 kips/sq ft) will be 6H20 steel ribs at 6-ft spacing.

GEOMECHANICS CLASSIFICATION (RMR SYSTEM)

The Geomechanics Classification or the rock mass rating (RMR) system was developed by Bieniawski in 1973. This engineering classification of rock masses, utilizes the following six parameters, all of which are measurable in the field and can also be obtained from borehole data:

a) Uniaxial compressive strength of intact rock material;
b) Rock quality designation (RQD);
c) Spacing of discontinuities;
d) Condition of discontinuities;
e) Groundwater conditions;
f) Orientation of discontinuities.

To apply the geomechanics classification, the rock mass along the tunnel route is divided into a number of structural regions, i.e., zones in which certain geological features are more or less uniform within each region. The above six classification parameters are determined for each structural region from measurements in the field and entered into the standard input data sheet as shown in Chapter 5 (Fig. 5.17).

The Geomechanics Classification is presented in Table 6.9. In Section A of Table 6.9, the first five parameters are grouped into five ranges of values. Since the various parameters are not equally important for the overall classification of a rock mass, importance ratings are allocated to the different value ranges of the parameters, a higher rating indicating better rock mass conditions. These ratings were determined from 49 case histories (Bieniawski, 1976).

Once the classification parameters are determined, the importance ratings are assigned to each parameter according to Table 6.9, Section A. In this respect, the typical rather than the worst conditions are evaluated. Furthermore, it should be noted that the importance ratings, which are given for discontinuity spacings, apply to rock masses having three sets of discontinuities. Thus, when only two sets of discontinuities are present, a conservative assessment is obtained.

After the importance ratings of the classification parameters are established, the ratings for the five parameters listed in Section A of Table 6.9 are summed to yield the basic rock mass rating for the structural region under consideration.

At this stage, the influence of the strike and dip of discontinuities is included by adjusting the basic rock mass rating according to Section B of Table 6.9. This step is treated separately because the influence of discontinuity orientation depends upon engineering application, e.g., tunnel (mine), slope, or foundation. It will be noted that the 'value' of the parameter 'discontinuity orientation' is not given in quantitative terms

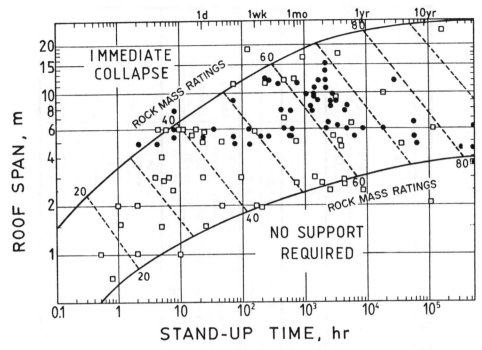

Figure 6.4. Geomechanics Classification of rock masses: output for mining and tunneling; ● = case histories of roof falls in mining; □ = tunneling roof falls; contour lines = limits of applicability.

but by qualitative descriptions such as 'favorable'. To facilitate a decision whether strike and dip orientations are favorable or not, reference should be made to Table 6.10, which is based on studies by Wickham, Tiedemann, and Skinner (1972). In the case of civil engineering projects, an adjustment for discontinuity orientations will suffice. For mining applications, other adjustments may be called for such as the stress at depth or a change in stress (Kendorski et al., 1983).

After the adjustment for discontinuity orientations, the rock mass is classified according to Section C of Table 6.9, which groups the final (adjusted) rock mass ratings (RMR) into five rock mass classes. Note that the rock mass classes are in groups of twenty ratings each.

Next, Section D of Table 6.9 gives the practical meaning of each rock mass class by relating it to specific engineering problems. In the case of tunnels and chambers, the output from the Geomechanics Classification is the stand-up time and the maximum stable rock span for a given rock mass rating, as depicted in Figure 6.4.

Support load can be determined from the Geomechanics Classification as (Unal, 1983):

$$P = \frac{100 - RMR}{100} \gamma B = \gamma h_t \qquad (6.3)$$

where P is the support load,

Table 6.9. Geomechanics Classification of rock masses

A. Classification parameters and their ratings

	PARAMETER		RANGES OF VALUES						
1	Strength of intact rock material	Point-load strength index	> 10 MPa	4 - 10 MPa	2 - 4 MPa	1 - 2 MPa	For this low range – uniaxial compressive test is preferred		
		Uniaxial compressive strength	>250 MPa	100 - 250 MPa	50 - 100 MPa	25 - 50 MPa	5-25 MPa	1-5 MPa	<1 MPa
		Rating	15	12	7	4	2	1	0
2	Drill core quality RQD		90% - 100%	75% - 90%	50% - 75%	25% - 50%	< 25%		
	Rating		20	17	13	8	3		
3	Spacing of discontinuities		>2 m	0,6 - 2 m	200 - 600 mm	60 - 200 mm	<60 mm		
	Rating		20	15	10	8	5		
4	Condition of discontinuities		Very rough surfaces. Not continuous No seperation Unweathered wall rock.	Slightly rough surfaces. Separation < 1 mm Slightly weathered walls	Slightly rough surfaces. Separation < 1 mm Highly weathered walls	Slickensided surfaces OR Gouge < 5 mm thick OR Separation 1-5 mm Continuous	Soft gouge > 5 mm thick OR Separation > 5 mm. Continous		
	Rating		30	25	20	10	0		
5	Ground water	Inflow per 10 m tunnel length	None OR	<10 litres/min OR	10-25 litres/min OR	25 - 125 litres/min OR	> 125 OR		
		Ratio joint water pressure / major principal stress	0 OR	0,0-0,1 OR	0,1-0,2 OR	0,2-0,5 OR	> 0,5 OR		
		General conditions	Completely dry	Damp	Wet	Dripping	Flowing		
	Rating		15	10	7	4	0		

B. Rating adjustment for discontinuity orientations

Strike and dip orientations of joints		Very favourable	Favourable	Fair	Unfavourable	Very unfavourable
Ratings	Tunnels	0	-2	-5	-10	-12
	Foundations	0	-2	-7	-15	-25
	Slopes	0	-5	-25	-50	-60

C. Rock mass classes determined from total ratings

Rating	100←81	80←61	60←41	40←21	<20
Class No.	I	II	III	IV	V
Description	Very good rock	Good rock	Fair rock	Poor rock	Very poor rock

D. Meaning of rock mass classes

Class No	I	II	III	IV	V
Average stand-up time	10 years for 15 m span	6 months for 8 m span	1 week for 5 m span	10 hours for 2,5 m span	30 minutes for 1 m span
Cohesion of the rock mass	> 400 kPa	300 - 400 kPa	200 - 300 kPa	100 - 200 kPa	< 100 kPa
Friction angle of the rock mass	< 45°	35° - 45°	25° - 35°	15° - 25°	< 15°

Table 6.10. Effect of discontinuity strike and dip orientations in tunneling

Strike perpendicular to tunnel axis			
Drive with dip		Drive against dip	
Dip 45°–90°	Dip 20°–45°	Dip 45°–90°	Dip 20°–45°
Very favorable	Favorable	Fair	Unfavorable

Strike parallel to tunnel axis		Irrespective of strike
Dip 20°–45°	Dip 45°–90°	Dip 0°–20°
Fair	Very unfavorable	Fair

$$h_t = \left[\frac{100 - RMR}{100} \right] B \quad \text{is the rock-load height in meters} \qquad (6.4)$$

where

B is the tunnel width in meters;
RMR is the rock mass rating from the Geomechanics Classification;
γ is the density of the rock, kg/m^3.

The variation of the rock-loads from equation (6.3) for various rock classes as a function of roof span is presented in Figure 6.5.

The Geomechanics Classification provides guidelines for the selection of roof support to ensure long-term stability of various rock mass classes, as given in Table 6.11. These guidelines depend on such factors as the depth below surface (in situ stress), tunnel size and shape, and the method of excavation.

It should be noted that the support measures given in Table 6.11 represent the permanent and not the primary support. Hence, additional concrete lining is not required for structural purposes. However, to ensure full structural stability it is recommended that tunnel monitoring during construction be undertaken to provide a check on stabilization of rock movements.

The Geomechanics Classification has been used extensively in mining, particularly in the United States. Initially, Laubscher and Taylor (1976) applied the Geomechanics Classification in asbestos mines in Africa specifically to assess cavability of ore, while Ferguson (1979) extended this classification to mining tunnels and haulages. Since mining is a dynamic process, additional adjustments to the classification parameters were introduced, such as in-situ stresses, as shown in Table 6.12. Most recently, the Geomechanics Classification was applied to coal mining in the United States (Bieniawski et al., 1980, Newman, 1981, Unal, 1983) and in India (Ghose and Raju, 1981) as well as to hard rock mining in the USA (Cummings et al., 1982, Kendorski et al., 1983). Further details of mining applications are given in Chapter 10 both for hard-rock mining and coal mining.

The Geomechanics Classification is also applicable to rock foundations (Bieniawski and Orr, 1976) and slopes (Steffen, 1976). This is a useful feature that can assist with the

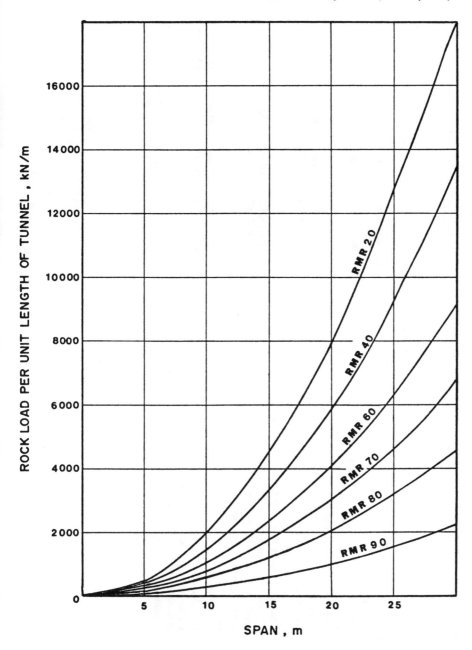

Figure 6.5. Variation of rock-load as a function of roof span in different rock classes in the Geomechanics Classification (after Unal, 1983).

Table 6.11. Geomechanics Classification guide for excavation and support in rock tunnels
Shape: horseshoe; **Width**: 10 m; **Vertical stress**: below 25 MPa; Construction: drilling and blasting

Rock mass class	Excavation	Support		
		Rockbolts (20 mm dia, fully bonded)	Shotcrete	Steel sets
1. Very good rock RMR: 81–100	Full face: 3 m advance	Generally no support required except for occasional spot bolting		
2. Good rock RMR: 61–80	Full face: 1.0–1.5 m advance; Complete support 20 m from face	Locally bolts in crown 3 m long, spaced 2.5 m with occasional wire mesh	50 mm in crown where required	None
3. Fair rock RMR: 41–60	Top heading and bench: 1.5–3 m advance in top heading; Commence support after each blast; Complete support 10 m from face	Systematic bolts 4 m long, spaced 1.5 m–2 m in crown and walls with wire mesh in crown	50–100 mm in crown and 30 mm in sides	None
4. Poor rock RMR: 21–40	Top heading and bench: 1.0–1.5 m advance in top heading; Install support concurrently with excavation–10 m from face	Systematic bolts 4–5 m long, spaced 1–1.5 m in crown and walls with wire mesh	100–150 mm in crown and 100 mm in sides	Light ribs spaced 1.5 m where required
5. Very poor rock RMR: < 20	Multiple drifts: 0.5–1.5 m advance in top heading; Install support concurrently with excavation; shotcrete as soon as possible after blasting	Systematic bolts 5–6 m long, spaced 1–1.5 m in crown and walls with wire mesh. Bolt invert	150–200 mm in crown 150 mm in sides and 50 mm on face	Medium to heavy ribs spaced 0.75 m with steel lagging and forepoling if required. Close invert

Table 6.12. Adjustments to the Geomechanics Classification for mining applications

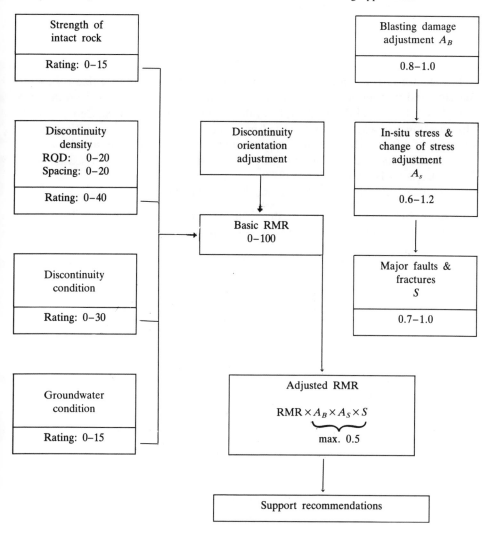

design of slopes near the tunnel portals as well as allow estimates of the deformability of foundations for such structures as bridges and dams.

In the case of rock foundations, the rock mass rating RMR from the Geomechanics Classification has been related (Bieniawski, 1978) to the in situ modulus of deformation in the manner shown in Chapter 5, Figure 5.12.

The following correlation was obtained:

$$E_M = 2 \times \text{RMR} - 100 \tag{6.5a}$$

where E_M is the in-situ modulus of deformation in GPa and RMR > 50.

Most recently, Serafim and Pereira (1983) provided many results in the range RMR < 50 and proposed a new correlation:

$$E_M = 10^{\frac{RMR-10}{40}} \tag{6.5b}$$

In the case of rock slopes, the output is given in Section D of Table 6.9 as the cohesion and friction of the rock mass. These output values were based on the data compiled by Hoek and Bray (1977). The validity of the output from the Geomechanics Classification to rock slopes was tested by Steffen (1976) who analyzed 35 slopes of which 20 had failed. He used the Geomechanics Classification to obtain the average values of cohesion and friction and then calculated the safety factor based on slope design charts by Hoek and Bray (1977).

A practical example using the Geomechanics Classification follows:

Consider a slightly weathered quartzite in which a 6 m span tunnel is to be driven. The following classification parameters were determined:

Item	Value	Rating
1. Strength of rock material	152 MPa	12
2. RQD	80–90%	17
3. Spacing of discontinuities	0.3–1 m	12
4. Condition of discontinuities:		20
continuous joints		
slightly rough surfaces		
separation 1 mm		
highly weathered rock wall		
no gouge		
5. Groundwater	Moderate inflow (wet rock)	7
	Basic rock mass value	68
6. Orientation of joints	Fair	− 5
	Final RMR	63
	Rock mass class: II – good rock	

Output: From Figure 6.4, for RMR = 63 and unsupported span = 6 m the stand-up time will be about 6 months. From Table 6.11, recommended tunnel support is rockbolts in crown 3 m long, spaced at 2.5 m with shotcrete 50 mm thick and wire mesh. From Figure 5.12, the modulus of deformation is estimated as 26 GPa.

It is important that the chart in Figure 6.4 is correctly applied for the selection of the output data. For this purpose, the actual RMR values are used which are represented by the series of near parallel lines in Figure 6.4.

The intercept of an RMR line with the desired tunnel span determines the stand-up time. Alternatively, the intercept of an RMR line with the top boundary line determines the maximum span possible in a given rock mass; any larger span would result in immediate roof collapse. An intercept of the RMR line with the lower boundary line determines the maximum span that can stand unsupported indefinitely.

Q-SYSTEM

The Q-system of rock mass classification was developed in Norway in 1974 by Barton, Lien and Lunde, all of the Norwegian Geotechnical Institute. Its development represented a major contribution to the subject of rock mass classification for a number of reasons: the system was proposed on the basis of an analysis of some 200 tunnel case histories from Scandinavia, it is a quantitative classification system, and it is an engineering system enabling the design of tunnel supports.

The Q-system is based on a numerical assessment of the rock mass quality using six different parameters: a) RQD, b) number of joint sets, c) roughness of the most unfavorable joint or discontinuity, d) degree of alteration or filling along the weakest joint, e) water inflow, and f) stress condition.

The above six parameters are grouped into three quotients to give the overall rock mass quality Q as follows:

$$Q = \frac{RQD}{J_n} \times \frac{J_r}{J_a} \times \frac{J_w}{SRF} \tag{6.6}$$

where

RQD = rock quality designation;
J_n = joint set number;
J_r = joint roughness number;
J_a = joint alteration number;
J_w = joint water reduction number;
SRF = stress reduction factor.

In Table 6.13, the numerical values of each of the above parameters are interpreted as follows: The first two parameters represent the overall structure of the rock mass, and their quotient is a relative measure of the block size. The quotient of the third and the fourth parameters is said to be an indicator of the interblock shear strength (of the joints). The fifth parameter is a measure of water pressure, while the sixth parameter is a measure of: a) loosening load in the case of shear zones and clay bearing rock, b) rock stress in competent rock, and c) squeezing and swelling loads in plastic incompetent rock. This sixth parameter is regarded as the 'total stress' parameter. The quotient of the fifth and the sixth parameters describes the 'active stress'.

Barton et al. (1974) consider the parameters, J_n, J_r, and J_a, as playing a more important role than joint orientation, and if joint orientation had been included, the classification would have been less general. However, orientation is implicit in parameters J_r and J_a, because they apply to the most unfavorable joints.

The Q value is related to tunnel support requirements by defining the equivalent dimensions of the excavation. This equivalent dimension, which is a function of both the size and the purpose of the excavation, is obtained by dividing the span, diameter, or the wall height of the excavation by a quantity called the excavation support ratio (ESR).

Thus,

$$\text{Equivalent dimension} = \frac{\text{Excavation span, diameter, or height (meters)}}{\text{ESR}}$$

Table 6.13. Classification ratings for Q-system (after Barton, 1976)

1.   Descriptions and ratings for the parameter RQD

Rock quality designation	(RQD, %)
A. Very poor	0–25
B. Poor	25–50
C. Fair	50–75
D. Good	75–90
E. Excellent	90–100

Note:
(i) Where RQD is reported or measured as ≤ 10, (including 0) a nominal value of 10 is used to evaluate Q.
(ii) RQD intervals of 5, i.e. 100, 95, 90, etc. are sufficiently accurate.

2.   Descriptions and ratings for the parameter J_n

Joint set number	(J_n)
A. Massive, no or few joints	0.5–1.0
B. One joint set	2
C. One joint set plus random	3
D. Two joint sets	4
E. Two joint sets plus random	6
F. Three joint sets	9
G. Three joint sets plus random	12
H. Four or more joint sets, random, heavily jointed, "sugar-cube" etc.	15
J. Crushed rock, earthlike	20

Note:
(i) For intersections use $(3.0 \times J_n)$.
(ii) For portals use $(2.0 \times J_n)$

3.   Descriptions and ratings for the parameter J_r

Joint roughness number a) Rock wall contact and b) Rock wall contact before 10 cm shear	(J_r)
A. Discontinuous joints	4
B. Rough or irregular, undulating	3
C. Smooth, undulating	2
D. Slickensided, undulating	1.5
E. Rough or irregular, planar	1.5
F. Smooth, planar	1.0
G. Slickensided, planar	0.5

Note:
(i) Descriptions refer to small scale features and intermediate scale features, in that order.
c) No rock wall contact when sheared

H. Zone containing clay minerals thick enough to prevent rock wall contact	1.0
J. Sandy, gravelly or crushed zone thick enough to prevent rock wall contact	1.0

Note:
(ii) Add 1.0 if the mean spacing of the relevant joint set is greater than 3 m.
(iii) $J_r = 0.5$ can be used for planar slickensided joints having lineations, provided the lineations are orientated for minimum strength.

Table 6.13 (continued)

4. Descriptions and ratings for the parameter J_a

		(J_a)	(ϕ_r)
	Joint alteration number		(approx.)
	a) Rock wall contact		
A.	Tightly healed, hard, non-softening, impermeable filling i.e. quartz or epidote	0.75	(–)
B.	Unaltered joint walls, surface staining only	1.0	(25–35°)
C.	Slightly altered joint walls. Non-softening mineral coatings, sandy particles, clay-free disintegrated rock tec.	2.0	(25–30°)
D.	Silty-, or sandy-clay coatings, small clay fraction (non-soft.)	3.0	(20–25°)
E.	Softening or low friction clay mineral coatings, i.e. kaolinite or mica. Also chlorite, talc, gypsum, graphite etc., and small quantities of swelling clays.	4.0	(8–16°)
	b) Rock wall contact before 10 cm shear		
F.	Sandy particles, clay-free disintegrated rock etc.	4.0	(25–30°)
G.	Strongly over-consolidated non-softening clay mineral fillings (continuous, but < 5 mm thickness)	6.0	(16–24°)
H.	Medium or low over-consolidation, softening, clay mineral fillings (continuous but < 5 mm thickness)	8.0	(12–16°)
J.	Swelling-clay fillings, i.e. montmorillonite (continuous, but < 5 mm thickness). Value of J_a depends on percent of swelling clay-size particles, and access to water etc.	8–12	(6–12°)
	c) No rock wall contact when sheared		
K.	Zones or bands of disintegrated or crushed rock and clay (see G, H, J for description of clay condition)	6, 8, or 8–12	(6–24°)
L.	Zones or bands of silty- or sandy-clay, small clay fraction (non-softening)	5.0	(–)
M.	Thick, continuous zones or bands of clay (see G, H, J for description of clay condition)	10, 13 or 13–20	(6–24°)

5. Descriptions and ratings for the parameter J_w

		(J_w)	Approx. water pres. (kg/cm^2)
	Joint water reduction factor		
A.	Dry excavations or minor inflow, i.e. < 5 l/min. locally	1.0	< 1
B.	Medium inflow or pressure, occasional outwash of joint fillings	0.66	1–2.5
C.	Large inflow or high pressure in competent rock with unfilled joints	0.5	2.5–10
D.	Large inflow or high pressure, considerable outwash of joint fillings	0.3	2.5–10
E.	Exceptionally high inflow or water pressure at blasting, decaying with time	0.2–0.1	> 10
F.	Exceptionally high inflow or water pressure continuing without noticeable decay	0.1–0.05	> 10

Note:
(i) Factors C to F are crude estimates. Increase J_w if drainage measures are installed.
(ii) Special problems caused by ice formation are not considered.

6. Description and ratings for parameter SRF

		(SRF)
	Stress reduction factor	
	a) Weakness zones intersecting excavation, which may cause loosening of rock mass when tunnel is excavated.	
A.	Multiple occurrences of weakness zones containing clay or chemically disintegrated rock, very loose surrounding rock (any depth)	10

Table 6.13 (continued)

B.	Single weakness zones containing clay or chemically disintegrated rock (depth of excavation ≤ 50 m)	5
C.	Single weakness zones containing clay or chemically disintegrated rock (depth of excavation > 50 m)	2.5
D.	Multiple shear zones in competent rock (clay-free), loose surrounding rock (any depth)	7.5
E.	Single shear zones in competent rock (clay-free) (depth of excavation ≤ 50 m)	5.0
F.	Single shear zones in competent rock (clay-free) (depth of excavation > 50 m)	2.5
G.	Loose open joints, heavily jointed or 'sugar cube' etc. (any depth)	5.0

Note:
(i) Reduce these values of SRF by 25–50% if the relevant shear zones only influence but do not intersect the excavation.

b) Competent rock, rock stress problems

		σ_c/σ_1	σ_t/σ_1	(SRF)
H.	Low stress, near surface	> 200	> 13	2.5
J.	Medium stress	200–10	13–0.66	1.0
K.	High stress, very tight structure (usually favorable to stability, may be unfavorable for wall stability)	10–5	0.66–.33	0.5–2
L.	Mild rockburst (massive rock)	5–2.5	0.33–.16	5–10
M.	Heavy rockburst (massive rock)	< 2.5	< 0.16	10–20

Note:
(ii) For strongly anisotropic virgin stress field (if measured): when $5 \le \sigma_1/\sigma_3 \le 10$, reduce σ_c and σ_t to 0.8 σ_c and 0.8 σ_t. When $\sigma_1/\sigma_3 > 10$, reduce σ_c and σ_t to 0.6 σ_c and 0.6 σ_t, where: σ_c = unconfined compression strength, and σ_t = tensile strength (point load) and σ_1 and σ_3 are the major and minor principal stresses.
(iii) Few case records available where depth of crown below surface is less than span width. Suggest SRF increase from 2.5 to 5 for such cases (see H).

		(SRF)
	c) Squeezing rock: plastic flow of incompetent rock under the influence of high rock pressure	
N.	Mild squeezing rock pressure	5–10
O.	Heavy squeezing rock pressure	10–20
	d) Swelling rock: chemical swelling activity depending on presence of water	
P.	Mild swelling rock pressure	5–10
R.	Heavy swelling rock pressure	10–15

Additional notes on the use of Table 6.13

When making estimates of the rock mass quality (Q) the following guidelines should be followed, in addition to the notes listed above:

1. When borecore is unavailable, RQD can be estimated from the number of joints per unit volume, in which the number of joints per meter for each joint set are added. A simple relation can be used to convert this number to RQD for the case of clay-free rock masses:

$$RQD = 115 - 3.3 J_v (\text{approx.})$$

where

J_v = total number of joints per m³;
(RQD = 100 for J_v < 4.5)

2. The parameter J_n representing the number of joint sets will often be affected by foliation, schistocity, slately cleavage or bedding etc. If strongly developed these parallel 'joints' should obviously be counted as a complete joint set. However, if there are few 'joints' visible, or only occasional breaks in borecore due to these features, then it will be more appropriate to count them as 'random joints' when evaluating J_n.

3. The parameters J_r and J_a (representing shear strength) should be relevant to the weakest significant joint set or clay filled discontinuity in the given zone. However, if the joint set or discontinuity with the minimum value of (J_r/J_a) is favorably oriented for stability, then a second, less favorably oriented joint set or discontinuity may sometimes be of more significance, and its higher value of J_r/J_a should be used when evaluating Q. The value of (J_r/J_a) should in fact relate to the surface most likely to allow failure to initiate.

The ESR is related to the use for which the excavation is intended and the degree of safety demanded, as shown below.

	Excavation category	ESR	No. of cases
A.	Temporary mine openings	3–5	2
B.	Vertical shafts:		
	Circular section	2.5	–
	rectangular/square section	2.0	–
C.	Permanent mine openings, water tunnels for hydropower (excluding high-pressure penstocks), pilot tunnels, drifts, and headings for large excavations	1.6	83
D.	Storage rooms, water treatment plants, minor highway and railroad tunnels, surge chambers, access tunnels.	1.3	25
E.	Power stations, major highway or railroad tunnels, civil defense chambers, portals, inter-sections	1.0	73
F.	Underground nuclear power stations, railroad stations, factories	0.8	2

The relationship between the index Q and the equivalent dimension of an excavation determines the appropriate support measures. Barton et al. (1974) provide 38 support categories which give estimates of permanent support. For temporary support determination, either Q is increased to 5Q or ESR is increased to 1.5 ESR. For selection of the support measures using the Q-system, the reader should consult the original paper by Barton et al. (1974) or the book by Hoek and Brown (1980).

The maximum unsupported span can be obtained as follows:

$$\text{Maximum span (unsupported)} = 2(\text{ESR})Q^{0.4} \tag{6.7}$$

The relationship between the Q value and the permanent support pressure P_{roof} is calculated from the following equation:

$$P_{roof} = \frac{2.0}{J_r} Q^{-1/3} \tag{6.8}$$

If the number of joint sets is less than three, the equation is expressed as:

$$P_{roof} = \tfrac{2}{3} J_n^{1/2} J_r^{-1} Q^{-1/3} \tag{6.9}$$

---

4. When a rock mass contains clay, the factor SRF appropriate to loosening loads should be evaluated. In such cases the strength of the intact rock is of little interest. However, when jointing is minimal and clay is completely absent the strength of the intact rock may become the weakest link, and the stability will then depend on the ratio rock-stress/rock-strength.

5. The compressive and tensile strengths (σ_c and σ_t) of the intact rock should be evaluated in the saturated condition if this is appropriate to present or future in situ conditions. A very conservative estimate of strength should be made for those rocks that deteriorate when exposed to moist or saturated conditions.

A practical example using the Q-system follows:

Consider a water tunnel of 9-m span in a phyllite rock mass. The following is known:

Joint set 1: smooth, planar $j_r = 1.0$
   chlorite coatings $J_a = 4.0$
   15 joints per meter
Joint set 2: smooth, undulating $J_r = 2$
   slightly altered walls $J_a = 2$
   5 joints per meter
Thus, $J_v = 15 + 5 = 20$ and RQD $= 115 - 3.3\ J_v = 50\%$
   $J_n = 4$

Minor water inflows: $J_w = 1.0$
Uniaxial compressive strength of phyllite: $\sigma_c = 40\ \text{MPa}$
Major principal stress: $\sigma_1 = 3\ \text{MPa}$
Minor principal stress: $\sigma_3 = 1\ \text{MPa}$
Hence $\sigma_1/\sigma_3 = 3$ and $\sigma_c/\sigma_1 = 13.3$ (medium stress), SRF $= 1.0$

$$Q = \tfrac{50}{4} \times \tfrac{1}{4} \times \tfrac{1}{1} = 3.1\ \text{(poor rock)}$$

Support estimate: $B = 9m$, ESR $= 1.6$
B/ESR $= 5.6$

For $Q = 3.1$: support category $= 21$
Permanent support: untensioned rockbolts spaced 1 m, bolt length 2.9 m, and
   shotcrete 2–3 cm thick
Temporary support: none

GUIDE TO CLASSIFICATION PROCEDURES

Apart from the Terzaghi classification, three other rock mass classification systems are most commonly used: the RSR concept, the Geomechanics Classification, and the Q-system. Since the Terzaghi classification is well described elsewhere (Terzaghi, 1946, Department of the Army, 1978), step-by-step design procedures are summarized for the other three classification systems.

Guide to the RSR concept

The RSR concept, a ground support prediction model developed in the United States by Wickham, Tiedemann, and Skinner (1972) is particularly suitable for the selection of steel support for rock tunnels. It requires the determination of three parameters A, B, and C listed in Tables 6.6, 6.7, and 6.8.

   Step 1: Divide the proposed tunnel route into geological regions such that each region would be geologically similar and would require one type of support; i.e., it will not be economical to change tunnel support until rock mass conditions change distinctly, that is, a new structural region can be distinguished.
   Step 2: Complete classification input data worksheet, as given in Figure 5.17, for each structural region.

Step 3: From Tables 6.6 to 6.8, determine the individual classification parameters *A*, *B*, and *C* and their sum, which gives the RSR = *A* + *B* + *C*.

Step 4: Adjust the RSR value in accordance with Figure 6.2 if the tunnel is to be excavated by a tunnel boring machine.

Step 5: Select a support requirement chart appropriate for the tunnel size, e.g., the chart for 6 m-dia. tunnel in Figure 6.3. These charts are applicable to both circular and horseshoe-shaped tunnels. From the selected chart, determine the rib type and spacing corresponding to the RSR value. Ignore curves for rock bolt and shotcrete support since they are not based on sufficient case history data.

Guide to the Geomechanics Classification (RMR system)

The Geomechanics Classification, which was developed by Bieniawski (1973), enables determination of the RMR, tunnel span, stand-up time, support requirements, in situ rock mass modulus, and the cohesion and friction of a rock mass.

Step 1: Divide the proposed tunnel route into structural regions, such that each region would be geologically similar and would require one type of support.

Step 2: Complete classification input data worksheet, as given in Figure 5.17, for each structural region.

Step 3: From Table 6.9, determine the ratings of the six individual classification parameters and the overall RMR value.

Step 4: From Figure 6.4, determine the maximum unsupported rock span possible for a given RMR. If this span is smaller than the span of the proposed tunnel, the heading and bench or multidrift construction should be adopted.

Step 5: From Figure 6.4, determine the stand-up time for the selected tunnel span. If the tunnel falls below the lower limit line, no support will be required. If the stand-up time is not sufficient for the life of the tunnel, the appropriate support measures must be selected.

Step 6: From Table 6.11, select the appropriate tunnel support measures and note that these represent the permanent support.

Step 7: For comparison purposes, determine the support pressure from equation (6.3).

Step 8: If foundation design is contemplated for nearby structures select, from Figure 5.12 or equation (6.5), the in-situ modulus of deformation of the rock mass.

Step 9: If the rock slopes near the tunnel portals are to be designed, select from Section D of Table 6.9 the cohesion and friction data.

Step 10: Consider a monitoring program during the tunnel construction for sections requiring special attention.

Guide to the Q-system

The rock mass quality Q-system, which was developed in Norway by Barton, Lien and Lunde (1974), enables the design of rock support in tunnels and large underground chambers.

Step 1: Divide the proposed tunnel route into structural regions, such that each region would be geologically similar and would require one type of support.

Step 2: Complete classification input data worksheet, as given in Figure 5.17, for each structural region.

Step 3: Determine the ratings of the six classification parameters from Table 6.13 and calculate the Q value from equation (6.6).

Step 4: Select the excavation support ratio (ESR)

Step 5: Determine the support measures for the Q value and the tunnel span/ESR ratio from a paper by Barton et al. (1974).

Step 6: Estimate the possible maximum unsupported span from equation (6.7).

Step 7: For comparison purposes, determine the support pressure from equation (6.8) or (6.9).

A correlation has been provided between the RMR and the Q-value (Bieniawski, 1976). A total of 117 case histories were analyzed involving 68 Scandinavian cases, 28 South African cases, and 21 other documented case histories from the United States, Canada, Australia, and Europe. The results are plotted in Figure 6.6 from which it will be seen that the following relationship is applicable:

$$RMR = 9 \ln Q + 44 \tag{6.10}$$

Rutledge (1978) determined in New Zealand the following correlations between the three classification systems:

$$RMR = 13.5 \log Q + 43 \quad \text{(standard deviation} = 9.4) \tag{6.11}$$

$$RSR = 0.77 \, RMR + 12.4 \quad \text{(standard deviation} = 8.9) \tag{6.12}$$

$$RSR = 13.3 \log Q + 46.5 \quad \text{(standard deviation} = 7.0) \tag{6.13}$$

A comparison of the stand-up time and the maximum unsupported span, as shown in Figure 6.7 reveals that the Geomechanics Classification is more conservative than the Q-system, which is a reflection of the different tunneling practice in Scandinavia based on generally excellent rock and long experience in tunneling.

A comparison of the support recommendations by six different classification systems is given in Table 6.14. This study was made (Bieniawski, 1976) during the construction of a railroad tunnel described by Bieniawski and Maschek, 1975. The tunnel, 5.5 m wide and 3.8 km long, was characterized by highly variable rock conditions – from very poor to very good. In addition, a one-year tunnel-monitoring program featuring 16 measuring stations facilitated a comparison between the classification ratings of rock conditions with the amount of rock movement, the rate of face advance, and the support used. This project thus afforded an ideal opportunity for comparing the various classification systems.

More recently, Moreno Tallon (1982) made a detailed comparison of the rock mass classification schemes in a tunnel in Spain.

Although the above comparisons are interesting and useful, it is believed that one should not necessarily rely on any one classification system but should conduct a sensitivity analysis and cross-check the findings from one classification with another. This would enable a better 'feel' for the rock mass.

RECENT DEVELOPMENTS

Looking back over the past ten years, three positive aspects are evident:

1. No matter what classification system is used, the very process of rock

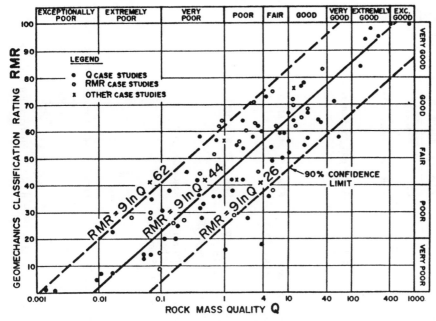

Figure 6.6. Correlation between Geomechanics Classification and Q-system.

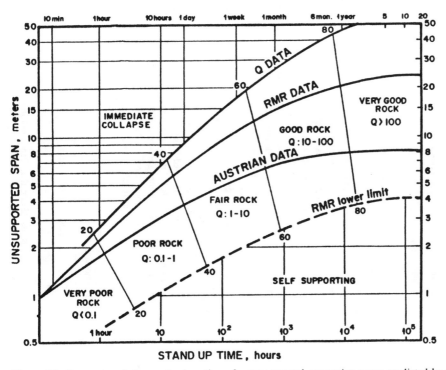

Figure 6.7. Comparison between stand-up times for unsupported excavation spans predicted by the Q-system, RMR and Austrian rock mass classification systems. Ratings are for the Geomechanics Classification (RMR).

Table 6.14. Comparison of rock mass classifications applied at a railroad tunnel (width 5.5 m)

Locality	Geomechanics Classification (Bieniawski, 1973) Class	Support	Q-system (Barton, 1974) Class	Support	RSR classification (Wickham, 1974) Class	Support
H 6	I Very good rock RMR = 83	Occasional spot bolting	Good rock Q = 33.0	Spot bolting only	RSR = 68	Bolts at 2 m
H 4	II Good rock RMR = 67	Locally, grouted bolts (20 mm dia.) spaced 2–2.5 m, (length 2.5 m plus mesh; shotcrete 50 mm thick if req.	Good rock Q = 12.5	Systematic grouted bolts (20 mm dia.) spaced 1 m–2 m; length 2.8 m	RSR = 60	Medium ribs at 2 m
H 2	III Fair rock RMR = 52	Systematic grouted bolts (spaced 1.5–2 m, length 3 m plus mesh and 100 mm thick shotcrete	Fair rock Q = 8.5	Systematic grouted bolts spaced 1.5 m, length 2.8 m; and mesh	RSR = 57	Ribs 6H20 at 1.7 m
H 3	IV Poor rock RMR = 29	Systematic grouted bolts spaced 1–1.5 m, length 3 m, mesh plus 100–150 mm shotcrete (ribs at 1.5 m)	Poor rock Q = 1.5	Shotcrete only: 75–100 mm thick or bolts at 1 m, 20–30 mm shotcrete and mesh	RSR = 52	Ribs 6H20 at 1.2 m
H 5	V Very poor rock RMR = 15	Systematic grouted bolts spaced 0.7–1 m, length 3.5 m, 150–200 mm shotcrete and mesh plus medium steel ribs at 0.7 m. Closed invert	Extremely poor rock Q = 0.09	Shotcrete only: 75–100 mm thick or tensioned bolts at 1 m plus 50–75 mm shotcrete and mesh	RSR = 25	N/A

Locality	RQD classification (Deere, 1970) Class	Support	Austrian classification (Pacher, 1974) Class	Support	French classification (Louis, 1974) Class	Support
H 6	Excellent RQD > 90	Occasional bolts only	I Stable	Bolts 26 mm dia, 1.5 m long spaced 1.5 m in roof plus wire mesh	A	50-mm shotcrete or 3 m long bolts at 3.1 m
H 4	Good RQD: 75–90	Bolts 25 mm dia, 2 m–3 m long spaced 1.5–1.8 m and some mesh or 50–75 shotcrete or light ribs	II Over-breaking	Bolts 2–3 m long spaced 2–2.5 m, shotcrete 50–100 mm with mesh	B	100 mm shotcrete with mesh and 3 m bolts at 2.8 m

H 2	Fair to good RQD: 50–90	III Fractured to very fractured	Bolts 2 m–3 m long at 0.9–1 m plus mesh or 50–100 mm shotcrete or light/medium ribs at 1.5 m	C	Perfo-bolts 26 mm dia., 3–4 m long spaced 2 m plus 150 mm shotcrete plus wire mesh and steel arches TH16 spaced 1.5 m	150 mm shotcrete with mesh and 3 m bolts at 2.5 m
H 3	Poor RQD: 25–50	IV Stressed rock	Bolts 2 m–3 m long at 0.6–1.2 m with mesh or 150 mm shotcrete with bolts at 1.5 m or medium to heavy ribs	D	Perfo-bolts 4 m long, spaced 1 m by 2 m plus 200 mm shotcrete plus mesh plus steel arches TH21 spaced 1 m. Concrete lining 300 mm	210 mm shotcrete with mesh and 3 m bolts at 2 m and steel ribs
H 5	Very poor RQD < 25	V Very stressed rock	150 mm shotcrete all around plus medium to heavy circular ribs at 0.6 m centers with lagging	E	Perfo-bolts 4 m long spaced 1 m plus 250 mm shotcrete plus mesh and steel arches TH29 spaced 0.75 m. Closed invert. Concrete lining 500 mm	240 mm shotcrete with mesh and 3 m bolts at 1.7 m; steel ribs at 1.2 m. Closed invert

classification enables the designer to gain a better understanding of the influence of the various geologic parameters in the overall rock mass behavior and, hence, gain a better appreciation of all the factors involved in the engineering problem. This leads to better engineering judgment. Consequently, it does not really matter that there is no general agreement on a single rock classification system; it is better to try two or more systems and, through a parametric study, obtain a better 'feel' for the rock mass.

2. Once a few rock classification systems have been applied to a given project, it may be found that a simplified classification, particularly suited for that project, will evolve. Examples of this approach are the Dinorwic Scheme in Wales and the Washington Metro in the United States.

3. Quite apart from the engineering benefits such as design data, rock classifications have been particularly successful in ensuring better communication on the project. This leads to a high morale as well as economical and technical benefits.

Use of borehole data

A trend has emerged to select engineering geological parameters on the basis of borehole data alone which should be sufficient for rock mass classification purposes without the need for tests in adits or pilot tunnels. As a result of the availability of more advanced coring techniques such as directional drilling and oriented core sampling as well as both borehole and core logging procedures, rock mass classifications can be conducted on the basis of input data from boreholes alone (Cameron-Clarke and Budavari, 1981).

Assessing the strength of rock masses

As discussed in Chapter 5, Hoek and Brown (1980) recently proposed a method for the prediction of rock mass strength involving rock mass classifications (see Table 5.8). To enable application of the Hoek-Brown criterion to coal mining, Bieniawski and Bauer (1981) prepared a list of appropriate m and s values for coal.

Application in mining

Recently, major advances were made in the use of rock mass classifications in coal mining (Unal, 1983, Ghose and Raju, 1981, Bieniawski et al., 1980) and in hard rock (metal) mining (Cummings et al., 1982, Kendorski et al., 1983). Detailed examples of these developments are given in Chapter 10. In longwall mining, the rock mass classification approach has been utilized for assessment of roof spans and rock cavability (Unrug and Szwilski, 1980, Kidybinski, 1979).

REFERENCES

Baczynski, N. Rock Mass Characterization and Its Application to Assessment of Unsupported Underground Openings. Ph.D. Thesis, University of Melbourne, 1980, 233 p.

Barton, C. M. A geotechnical analysis of rock structure and fabric in the C.S.A. Mine, *Geomechanics Paper No. 24*, CSIRO, Australia, 1977, pp. 1–30.

Barton, N. Recent Experience with the Q-system for Tunnel Support. *Proceedings, Symposium Exploration for Rock Engineering*, ed. Z. T. Bieniawski, A. A. Balkema, Rotterdam, 1976, Vol. 1, pp. 107–114.

Barton, N., Lien, R. and Lunde, J. Engineering Classification of Rock Masses for the Design of Tunnel Support. *Rock Mechanics*, Vol. 6, No. 4, 1974, pp. 183–236.

Bieniawski, Z. T. Engineering Classification of Jointed Rock Masses. *Transactions, South African Institution of Civil Engineers*, Vol. 15, No. 12, 1973, pp. 335–344.

Bieniawski, Z. T. Geomechanics Classification of rock masses and its application in tunneling. *Proceedings, Third International Congress Rock Mechanics*, International Society for Rock Mechanics Denver, Colo., 1974, Vol. IIA, pp. 27–32.

Bieniawski, Z. T. The Point-Load Test in Geotechnical Practice. *Engineering Geology*, Vol. 9, 1975, pp. 1–11.

Bieniawski, Z. T. Rock mass classifications in rock engineering, *Proceedings Symposium on Exploration for Rock Engineering*, ed. Z. T. Bieniawski, A. A. Balkema Rotterdam, 1976, pp. 97–106.

Bieniawski, Z. T. Determining rock mass deformability: experience from case histories. *Int. J. Rock Mech. Min. Sci.*, Vol. 15, 1978, pp. 237–248.

Bieniawski, Z. T. Tunnel Design by Rock Mass Classifications. U.S. Army Corps of Engineers, *Waterways Experiment Station, Technical Report*, GL-79-19, September 1979, 133 p.

Bieniawski, Z. T. The Geomechanics Classification in rock engineering applications. *Proc. 4th Int. Congress Rock Mechanics*, ISRM, Montreux, A. A. Balkema, Rotterdam, 1979, Vol. 2, pp. 51–58.

Bieniawski, Z. T. and Bauer, J. Discussion on the empirical strength criterion of Hoek and Brown. J. Geotechn. Div., ASCE, Vol. 108, GT4, 1982, pp. 670–672.

Bieniawski, Z. T. and Maschek, R. K. A. Monitoring the Behavior of Rock Tunnels during Construction. *Transactions of the South African Institution of Civil Engineers*, Vol. 17, No. 10, 1975, pp. 255–264.

Bieniawski, Z. T. and Orr, C. M. Rapid site appraisal for dam foundations by the Geomechanics Classification. *Proc. 12th Int. Congr. on Large Dams*, ICOLD, Mexico City, 1976, pp. 483–501.

Bieniawski, Z. T., Rafia, F. and Newman, D. A. Ground control investigations for assessment of roof conditions in coal mines. *Proc. 21st U.S. Symposium on Rock Mechanics*, Rolla, Mo., AIME, 1980, p. 691–700.

Brekke, T. L. and Howard, T. Stability Problems Caused by Seams and Faults. *Proceedings, Rapid Excavation and Tunneling Conference*, American Institution of Mining Engineers, New York, 1972 pp. 25–41.

Cameron-Clarke, I. S. and Budavari, S. Correlation of rock mass classification parameters obtained from borecore and in situ observations. *Engineering Geology*, Vol. 17, 1981, pp. 19–53.

Cecil, O. S. Correlation of Rockbolts-Shotcrete Support and rock Quality Parameters in Scandinavian Tunnels. Ph. D. Thesis, University of Illinois, Urbana, 1970, 414 p.

Coates, D. F. Classification of Rock for Rock Mechanics, *International Journal of Rock Mechanics and Mining Science*, Vol. 1, 1964, pp. 421–429.

Cording, E. J. and Deere, D. U. Rock Tunnel Supports and Field Measurements. *Proceedings, Rapid Excavation and Tunneling Conference*, American Institution of Mining Engineers, New York, 1972, pp. 601–622.

Cording, E. J., Hendron, A. J. and Deere, D. U. Rock Engineering for Underground Caverns. *Proceedings, Symposium on Underground Rock Chambers*, American Society of Civil Engineers, Pheonix, Arizona, 1972, pp. 567–600.

Cummings, R. A., Kendorski, F. S. and Bieniawski, Z. T. *Caving Mine Rock Mass Classification and Support Estimation*, U.S. Bureau of Mines Contract No. J0100103, Engineers International, 1982, 195 p.

Deere, D. U. Technical Description of Rock Cores for Engineering Purposes, *Rock Mechanics and Engineering Geology*, Vol. 1, No. 1, 1964, pp. 17–22.

Deere, D. U. Geological Considerations. *Rock Mechanics in Engineering Practice*, eds. R. G. Stagg and O. C. Zienkiewicz, John Wiley & Sons, London, 1968, pp. 1–20.

Deere, D. U. and Miller, R. P. Engineering classification and index properties for intact rock. *Techn. Report No. AFNL-TR-65-116*, Air Force Weapons Laboratory, New Mexico, 1966.

Deere, D. U., Peck, R. B., Parker, H., Monsees, J. E. and Schmidt, B. Design of tunnel support systems. *Highway Research Record*, No. 339, 1970, pp. 26–33.

Department of the Army, Corps of Engineers. *Engineering and Design, Tunnels, and Shafts in Rock*. Engineer Manual EM 1110-2-2901, Washington, DC, January 15, 1978. See also ETL-1110-2-283, May 31, 1983.

Edeling, H. and Maidl, B. Tunnelling Support Methods and their possible Application to Machine Excavation in Coal Mining. *Proc. Eurotunnel '80*, Inst. Min. Metall., London, 1980, pp. 120–129.

Einstein, H. H., Steiner, W. and Baecher, G. B. Assessment of Empirical Design Methods for Tunnels in Rocks. *Proc. 4th Rapid Excavation Tunneling Conf.*, AIME, New York, 1979, Vol. 1, pp. 683–706.

Ferguson, G. A. Optimization of block caving with a complex environment. *Mining Magazine*, Vol. 140, 1979, pp. 126–139.

Franklin, J. A. Safety and Economy of Tunneling. *Proceedings, Tenth Canadian Rock Mechanics Symposium*, Kingstone, 1975, pp. 27–53.

Franklin, J. A. An observational approach to the selection and control of rock tunnel lining. *Shotcrete for Ground Support*, Amer. Concrete Inst. Publ. SP-54, 1977, pp. 556–596.

Ghose, A. K. and Raju, M. N. Characterization of rock mass vis-a-vis application of rock bolting – modeling of India coal measures. *Proc., 22nd U.S. Symp. on Rock Mech.*, MIT, Cambridge, Mass., 1981, pp. 422–427.

Hoek, E. and Bray, J. W. *Rock Slope Engineering*, Revised Second Edition, Institution of Mining and Metallurgy, London, 1977, pp. 113–115 and 150–192.

Hoek, E. and Brown, E. T. *Underground Excavations in Rock*, Institution of Mining and Metallurgy, London, 1980, 527 p.

Hoek, E. and Brown, E. T. Empirical strength criterion for rock masses, *Journal of Geotechnical Engineering*, ASCE, Vol. 106, No. GT9, September 1980, pp. 1013–1035.

Hoek, E. and Londe, P. The Design of Rock Slopes and Foundations. *Proceedings, Third International Congress Rock Mechanics*, International Society for Rock Mechanics, Denver, Colo., 1974, Vol. 1A, pp. 613–752.

Ikeda, K. A. Classification of rock conditions for tunneling. *Proceedings, First International Congress Engineering Geology*, International Association of Engineering Geologist, Paris, 1970, pp. 1258–1265.

International Society for Rock Mechanics. *Rock Characterization, Testing and Monitoring* (ISRM Suggested Methods), Pergamon, New York, 1981, 211 p.

International Society for Rock Mechanics. Basic technical descripion of rock masses. *Int. J. Rock Mech. Min. Sci.*, Vol. 18, 1981, pp. 85–110.

Kendorski, F. S., Cummings, R. A., Bieniawski, Z. T. and Skinner, E. H. Rock mass classification for block caving mine drift support. *Proc., 15th Int. Congr. Rock Mech.*, ISRM, Melbourne, 1983, pp. B101–113.

Kidybinski, A. Experience with rock penetrometers used for mine rock stability predictions. *Proc., 4th Int. Cong. on Rock Mech.*, ISRM, Montreux, A. A. Balkema, Rotterdam, 1979, Vol. 2, pp. 293–301.

Kirsten, H. A. D. A classification system for excavation in natural materials. *S. Afr. Civil Engr.*, July 1982, pp. 293–308.

Lane, K. S. Field Test Sections Save Cost in Tunnel Support. *Underground Construction Research Council, American Society of Civil Engineers*, New York, 1975.

Lang, T. A., Kendorski, F. S. and Chawla, K. S. Effect of Rapid Water Pressure Fluctuations on Unlined Water Tunnel Stability. *Proceedings, Rapid Excavation and Tunneling Conference*, American Institution of Mining Engineers, New York, 1976, pp. 417–429.

Laubscher, D. H. Class distinction in rock masses. *Coal, Gold and Base Minerals of S. Africa*, Vol. 23, No. 6, 1975, pp. 37–50.

Laubscher, D. H. and Taylor, H. W. The Importance of Geomechanics Classification of Jointed Rock Masses in Mining Operations. *Exploration for Rock Engineering*, ed. Z. T. Bieniawski, A. A. Balkema, Rotterdam, 1976, Vol. 1, pp. 119–128.

Lauffer, H. Gebirgsklassifizierung fur den Stollenbau. *Geologie und Bauwesen*, Vol. 24, No. 1, 1958, pp. 46–51.

Louis, C. Reconnaissance des Massifs Rocheux par Sondages et Classifications Geotechniques des Roches. *Annales Sols et Foundations*, No. 108, 1974, pp. 97–122.

Merritt, A. H. Geologic Prediction for Underground Excavations. *Proceedings, Rapid Excavation and Tunneling Conference*, American Institution of Mining Engineers, New York, 1972, pp. 115–132.

Moreno-Tallon, E. Comparison and application of geomechanics classification schemes in tunnel construction. *Proc. Tunneling '82 Conference*, Institution of Mining and Metallurgy, London, 1982, pp. 241–146.

Newman, D. A. Engineering Geological Characterization of Coal Measure Rocks, M. S. Thesis, The Pennsylvania State University, 1981.

Olivier, H. J. Importance of rock durability in the engineering classification of Karoo rock masses for tunneling. *Exploration for Rock Engineering*, ed. Z. T. Bieniawski, A. A. Balkema, Rotterdam, 1977, Vol. 1, pp. 137–144.

Olivier, H. J. A new engineering-geological rock durability classification. *Engineering Geology*, Vol. 14, 1979, pp. 255–279.

Pacher, F., Rabcewicz, L. and Golser, J. Zum der seitigen Stand der Gebirgsklassifizierung in Stollen-und Tunnelbau. *Proceedings, XXII Geomechanics Colloquium*, Salzburg, 1974, pp. 51–58.

Protodyakonov, M. M. Klassifikacija Gorotworu (originally in Russian), translated into French, *Tunnels at Ouvrages Souterrains*, Vol. 1, No. 1, 1974, pp. 31–34.

Rose, D. Revising Terzaghi's tunnel rock load coefficients. *Proc. 23rd U.S. Symposium on Rock Mechanics*, AIME, New York, 1982, pp. 953–960.

Rutledge, J. C. and Preston, R. L. Experience with Engineering Classifications of Rock for the Prediction of Tunnel Support, *Proceedings, International Tunneling Symposium*, Tokyo, 1978, pp. A-3-1:7.

Schneider, B. Ground Classification for Tunnel Excavation. *Tunnels and Tunneling*, July 1980, pp. 59–62.

Selmer-Olsen, R. and Broch, E. General Design Procedure for Underground Openings in Norway. *Proceedings, First International Conference on Storage in Excavated Rock Caverns*, ITA, Stockholm, 1977, pp. 219–226.

Serafim, J. L. and Pereira, J. P. Considerations of the Geomechanics Classification of Bieniawski. *Proc. Int. Symp. on Engng Geol. and Underground Constr.*, LNEC, Lisbon, Portugal, 1983.

Steffen, O. K. H. Research and development needs in data collection for rock engineering. *Exploration for Rock Engineering*, ed. Z. T. Bieniawski, A. A. Balkema, Rotterdam, 1976, Vol. 2, pp. 93–104.

Stini, I. *Tunnelbaugeologie*. Springer-Verlag, Vienna, 1950, 336 p.

Terzaghi, K. Rock Defects and Loads on Tunnel Support. *Rock Tunneling with Steel Supports*, eds. R. V. Proctor and T. White, Commercial Shearing Co., Youngstown, Ohio, 1946, pp. 15–99.

Unal, E. Design Guidelines and Roof Control Standards for Coal Mine Roofs. Ph.D. Thesis, The Pennsylvania State University, 1983.

Unrug, K. and Szwilski, A. Z. Influence of strata control parameters on longwall mining desing. *Proc. 21st U.S. Symposium on Rock Mechanics*, Univ. of Missouri, Rolla, Mo., 1980, pp. 720–728.

Wickham, G. E., Tiedemann, H. R. and Skinner, E. H. Support Determination Based on Geologic Predictions. *Proceedings, Rapid Excavation and Tunneling Conference*, AIME, New York, 1972, pp. 43–64.

Wickham, G. E., Tiedemann, H. R. and Skinner, E. H. Ground Support Prediction Model – RSR Concept. *Proceedings, Rapid Excavation and Tunneling Conference*, AIME, New York, 1974, pp. 691–707.

A Mined Rock Cavern for oil storage (Courtesy of Ing. S. Johansson, Neste Oy).

CHAPTER 7

Observational methods of design

Experimental science does not receive truth from superior sciences; she is the mistress and other sciences are the servants.

Roger Bacon

Designing underground mining and tunneling excavations by observational methods involves interpretations of monitoring data during construction. Essentially, therefore, an observational method of design is a 'design as you go' method but in some cases a whole philosophy has been attached to an observational method making it distinct from other approaches.

An example is the 'New Austrian Tunneling Method' (NATM) (Rabcewicz, 1964) which has received considerable attention in the field of tunneling and has some very promising results to its credit. Most recently, the NATM has been applied to a coal mining project in Germany (Albers et al., 1982, Spaun and Jagsch, 1983). The convergence-confinement method has also emerged within the last three years. Both these methods rely on a number of principles for monotoring the behavior of underground excavations during construction. Whether or not any observational method is distinct in its own right, it is important to understand the broad concepts involved in monitoring rock structures during construction. Accordingly one should consider observational methods of design under three topics: rock monitoring techniques, the New Austrian Tunneling Method, and the convergence-confinement method.

ROCK MONITORING TECHNIQUES

Monitoring the behavior of underground excavations during construction is recognized today as an important, and often essential, aid in the design and construction of excavations. Systematic in situ monitoring of the performance of both the rock mass and the support was found to be one of the most promising developments in underground construction in recent years.

Dunnicliff and Schmidt (1974), analyzing the value of in situ monitoring of tunnels, make the following observation:

> To be effective and useful, monitoring of tunnel construction must be carefully planned throughout all the steps. A vital and frequently overlooked step is a clear definition of the specific purposes of the instrumentation. Most tunnel construction monitoring has in the past been of benefit to research and the advancement of

137

tunnelling practice, wittingly or not. The development of monitoring instrumentation for the benefit of the project, from which the construction data are recovered, has very significant potential for risk and cost reduction in tunnelling.

In mining, Obert and Duvall (1967) and many others have conducted over the years, extensive mine monitoring programs leading to much improved ground control procedures in coal mining and hard rock mining. In situ monitoring is very important in both mining and tunneling, mainly because of the complex nature of rock masses. Practical experience and engineering judgment still constitute the main foundation on which the design and construction of underground excavations is based. By checking the initial design with observations and measurements during construction adequate safeguards can be provided for any assumptions made during the planning stage.

Let us then discuss the practical potential of monitoring techniques as well as the problems associated with monitoring, bearing in mind the two trends identified by Cording (1974):

> There is a trend towards increased use of instrumentation in tunnels. There will also be a trend towards an increase in the number of instrumentation programs which provide little useful information on the performance of tunnels. The second trend should not materialize if the instrumentation program is related to significant engineering design and construction problems and is organized and carried out in close coordination with the design and construction staff.

Purpose and advantages of monitoring

The main purpose of in-situ monitoring measurements is to determine stability conditions in an underground excavation by providing quantitative data on the behavior of the rock mass and the support. After all, design of underground excavations is basically the design of underground support systems (Hoek and Brown, 1980). The benefits of tunnel monitoring were realized a long time ago by Ladislaus von Rabcewicz (1964) when he introduced, in Austria, a design approach based on in situ measurements which he called 'empirical dimensioning' otherwise known as the New Austrian Tunneling Method.

Of the various monitoring techniques available, displacement measurements in underground excavations have proven to be the most useful. There are two main reasons. Firstly, displacement is a quantity which can be measured directly and monitored continuously (and relatively easily). Stress, on the other hand, must be determined indirectly from other measurements and is difficult to monitor continuously.

Secondly, displacement measurements provide information on overall movement of the rock mass within the measured distance and thus do not display a large variability such as is apparent when a quantity is measued at one point (e.g. strain or pressure). The need for displacement measurements can best be demonstrated by considering the interaction between support and rock.

Mechanism of rock-support interaction

The behavior of an opening and the performance of the support system depend upon the load-deformation characteristics of the rock and of the support as well as of the

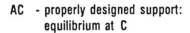

AC - properly designed support: equilibrium at C

OD - radial deformation for stable unlined tunnel

AeE - support yields before stabilizing opening

AF - support too flexible

GH - support too delayed

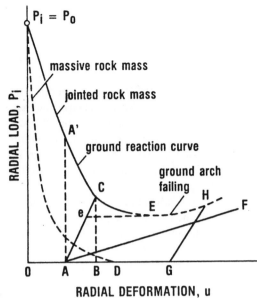

Figure 7.1. The concept of ground reaction curve for rock tunnels (after Deere et al., 1970)

manner and timing of support installation. The interaction between support and rock mass is qualitatively illustrated by a ground reaction curve given in Figure 7.1. This concept was developed in detail by Deere et al. (1970) but was discussed by R. Fenner in Austria as early as 1938. Most recently, the concept was studied by Brown et al. (1983).

When a tunnel is excavated, the rock moves inwards. The ground reaction curve displays the load that must be applied to the roof or the walls of the tunnel to prevent further movement. The movement which occurs before support can be installed is denoted by the line OA. If the support were perfectly incompressible, the load of the support would be represented by the line AA'. Support, however, deforms and, with the walls of the tunnel also deforming, an equilibrium is attained at point C at a radial displacement of the walls equal to OB and a support deformation equal to AB, at which stage the support load is BC.

However, the equilibrium at point C is only reached if the support is properly designed and placed timely. Line AeE in Figure 7.1 depicts support which yields before stabilizing the opening, line AF represents support which is too flexible, while line GH is support too delayed in installation, hence ineffective. Accordingly, it is important to note that the practical engineer tries to install support as soon as possible so that the early rock deformation loads the support at the same time that the rock mass is generating interior arching movement and shear stress in an attempt to be self supporting. Furthermore, the less competent the rock the earlier the support should be installed. Clearly, then, active rock reinforcement will be more effective and will require less capacity than passive support but installation must take place as soon as possible after each face advance. Active rock reinforcement will require less support because the ability of the rock to support itself is being utilized while with passive support the full weight of the rock is being supported.

Although the concept of the ground reaction curve has been studied extensively by Deere et al. (1970), Rabcewicz (1964) and by Pacher (1977), unfortunately the ground reaction curve cannot as yet be theoretically defined for rock masses. Furthermore, even if a theory could be used to predict the curve, Deere believes that the large local variations in construction procedures would inhibit the usefulness of the curve for the practical design of supports, not to mention that the load-deformation characteristics of some supports are also not clearly understood. The only possibility of obtaining quantitative data on the required support resistance and ground reaction behavior lies in measurements in situ. From measurements of the radial displacement of tunnel surface and of the displacement inside the rock mass as a function of time during tunneling, the stabilization process as well as the loading of the support can be established.

Recently, the subject of tunnel support design has been studied in detail by Daemen (1977) using the concept of the ground reaction curve. With reference to Figure 7.2, consider a tunnel being driven by the full face drill and blast method with steel set supports being installed after each mucking cycle. The horizontal and vertical in situ stresses are assumed to be equal and to have a magnitude p_0 (Hoek and Brown, 1980).

In Step 1, the tunnel face has not yet reached section $X-X'$ which defined the tunnel

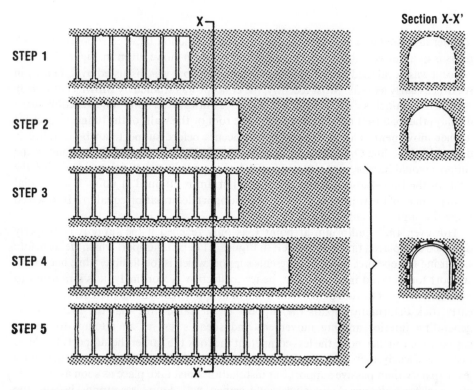

Figure 7.2. Hypothetical example of a tunnel being advanced by full face drill and blast method with blocked steel sets being installed after each mucking cycle (after Daemen, 1977). The load-deformation curves for the rock mass and the support system are given in Figure 7.1.

section under consideration. The rock mass inside the proposed tunnel profile, shown dotted in the step 1 cross-section drawing, is in equilibrium with the rock mass surrounding the tunnel. The internal support pressure p_i acting across the proposed excavation profile is equal to the in situ stress p_0 (Figure 7.1).

In Step 2, the tunnel face has been advanced beyond section $X-X'$ and the support pressure p_i, previously provided by the rock inside the tunnel, has dropped to zero. However, the tunnel will not collapse because the radial deformation u is limited by the proximity of the tunnel face which provides a significant amount of restraint. If this restraint provided by the face were not available, an internal support pressure p_i, given by $A-A'$ in the graph in Figure 7.1, would be required to limit the radial deformation to the same value. The support pressure which would be required to limit the deformation of the roof is higher than that required to limit the sidewall deformation because the weight of the zone of loosened rock above the tunnel roof must be added to the support pressure required to limit the stress-induced displacement of the roof.

In Step 3, the tunnel has been mucked out and steel sets have been installed close to the face. At this stage, the supports carry no load, as shown by point A on the graph in Figure 7.1, because no further deformation of the tunnel has taken place. Assuming that the rock mass does not exhibit time-dependent deformation characteristics, the radial deformation of the tunnel is still that defined by OA.

In Step 4, the tunnel face has been advanced about 1.5 tunnel diameters beyond section $X-X'$ and the restraint provided by the proximity of the face is now considerably reduced. This causes further radial deformation of the tunnel sidewalls and roof as indicated by the curve $A'CE$ in Figure 7.1. This inward radial deformation or convergence of the tunnel induces load in the support system which acts like a stiff spring. The support pressure p_i available from the blocked steel sets increases with radial deformation of the tunnel as indicated by the line AC in Figure 7.1.

In step 5, the tunnel face has advanced so far beyond section $X-X'$ that it no longer provides any restraint for the rock mass at section $X-X'$. If no support has been installed, the radial deformations in the tunnel would increase as indicated by the dashed curve marked EH in Figure 7.1. In the case of the sidewalls, the pressure required to limit further deformation drops to zero at point D and, in this case, the sidewalls would be stable since there is no remaining driving force to induce further deformation. On the other hand, the support required to limit deformation of the roof drops to a minimum and then begins to increase again. This is because the downward displacement of the zone of loosened rock in the roof causes additional rock to become loose and the weight of this additional loose rock is added to the required support pressure. In the example illustrated, the roof would collapse if no support had been installed in the tunnel.

As illustrated in Figure 7.1, the support reaction curve intersects the load-deformation curve for the tunnel at point C. At this point, the support pressure required to limit further deformation of the roof is exactly balanced by the support pressure available from the steel sets. The tunnel and the support system are in stable equilibrium.

Although the concept of the ground reaction curve adds greatly to the understanding of tunnel support mechanics, the ground reaction curve is difficult to determine for a given rock mass. The best possibility of obtaining quantitative data on the required support resistance and ground reaction behavior lies in measurements in situ. Using convergence and extensometer measurements, as a function of time during tunneling, the stabilization process as well as the loading of the support can be established.

Instrumentation for tunnel monitoring

Many instruments are available throughout the world and some manufacturers specialize in this field. The easiest way to find out about instrumentation is to consult the list of exhibitors at major rock mechanics conferences. As always, 'comparison shopping' before equipment selection is highly advisable. Experience by users, a list of whom should be provided by the manufacturers, should also be a factor in the selection.

Borehole extensometers measuring the displacements inside the rock mass provide information on the behavior and extent of the zone of loosened and fractured rock around the tunnel. These instruments incorporate grouted anchors at various positions in a borehole, each anchor being connected by rods or wires to the instrument head where relative movements between the anchors and the head are measured with a depth micrometer (dial gauge). Remote monitoring is also possible. Measurements of radial displacement of tunnel surfaces, that is measurements of tunnel convergence between points on the opposite sides of the tunnel, are made using such devices as tape or rod extensometers. Borehole and surface displacement data are complementary and related. Experience shows that for the evaluation of rock tunnel stability, displacement measurements should be made to a precision of ± 0.05 mm (ISRM, 1981).

At the present time, many instruments are available. However, only a few may be recommended as being sufficiently reliable, accurate and economical. The common features are robust construction, simplicity of design and installation as well as uncomplicated calibration and readout procedures. Instruments based on purely mechanical principles are generally superior to their much more sophisticated electronic counterparts. Elements such as dust, moisture, shocks, etc. which inevitably accompany all excavations affect the functioning of electronic components, considerably reducing their reliability and accuracy.

Convergence devices

Convergence measuring devices have been designed to measure the change in distance between two measuring points, such as, bolts grouted in short boreholes drilled in opposite excavation walls or the roof. A measuring distance may be inclined at any angle, ranging from vertical to horizontal. The maximum length is generally limited to 25 meters.

A reading is taken by connecting the readout unit and the tape to the bolts. The tape is uncoiled to the required length and connected to a readout unit. It is prevented from further uncoiling by a pin which is engaged in one of the spaced punched holes of the tape. The correct tension is applied to the tape by an incorporated spring mechanism. By lifting and shifting the readout unit very slightly up and down and sideways the needle of the dial gauge will move between an upper and lower point. The lower point indicates the condition of least slackness of the tape and is to be taken as the reading. For periodic checks, a standard calibration frame is supplied with the instrument.

Borehole extensometers

Extensometers in boreholes may be used to measure the total displacement of the rock wall, due to excavation operations with reference to a fixed point within a rock mass (unaffected by excavation), or the relative displacements of selected points within the rock mass along the length of a borehole.

A typical instrument consists of three main sections, namely, the headpiece, the movement transmission element and the anchor cone with anchor point. The headpiece is the only part visible when the instrument is installed and it represents the point of reference; it is held in position either mechanically or by grout. The readout unit incorporates a dial gauge which is removed after a reading has been taken. Such borehole extensometers can be read and are repeatable to 0.02 mm (ISRM, 1981).

Monitoring stations

A monitoring program at a tunnel usually includes two kinds of measuring stations, namely convergence measuring stations and borehole extensometer stations. Where borehole extensometers and convergence measuring stations are installed such a station is termed a full station. When no borehole extensometers are installed, this station is referred to as a convergence station.

As shown in Figure 7.3(a), a full station comprises a number of borehole extensometers and convergence points. It is very important that each measuring station is described in detail from the point of view of geological conditions, i.e. engineering geological mapping and drill core logging must be carefully performed. In addition, groundwater conditions must be fully investigated. Rock samples should be taken for laboratory tests and thin sections for petrographic analyses should be selected.

Microseismic monitoring

The phenomenon of microseismic activity is associated with the fact that when a structure is loaded, acoustic signals are generated within the structure, often at stresses well below the failure point. These signals are indicative of the stability of the structure and with suitable instrumentation they may be detected at considerable distance from their source. Basic and applied research associated with microseismic activity has been underway for some 40 years, although the major developments have occurred during the last 15 years (Hardy, 1982). In geologic materials, the origin of the observed microseismic activity appears to be related to the processes of deformation and failure which are accompanied by a sudden release of strain energy. As geologic materials are basically polycrystalline in nature, such activity may originate at the microlevel as a result of dislocations by grain boundary movement or initiation and propagation of fractures through and between mineral grains, and at the megalevel by fracturing and failure of large areas of material or relative motion between structural units. It is assumed that the sudden release of stored elastic strain energy accompanying these processes generates an elastic stress wave which travels from the point of origin within the material to a boundary where it is observed as a microseismic event.

Historically, microseismic studies associated with geologic materials were initiated to study the stability of underground mining operations. During the late 1930s and the early 1940s, Obert and Duvall (1967) at the U.S. Bureau of Mines showed in the laboratory as well as in the field that the microseismic rate increased greatly as the specimen or structure became more highly loaded. Conversely, as equilibrium was

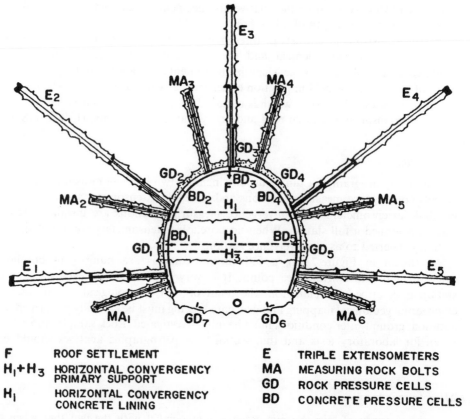

F	**ROOF SETTLEMENT**	**E**	**TRIPLE EXTENSOMETERS**
$H_1 + H_3$	**HORIZONTAL CONVERGENCY PRIMARY SUPPORT**	**MA**	**MEASURING ROCK BOLTS**
		GD	**ROCK PRESSURE CELLS**
H_1	**HORIZONTAL CONVERGENCY CONCRETE LINING**	**BD**	**CONCRETE PRESSURE CELLS**

Figure 7.3 a) Monitoring stations in mining and tunneling: Arlberg Highway Tunnel in Austria (after John, 1980).

reached after a major structural failure, the rate decreased. In other words, the microseismic rate appeared to be a factor indicative of the degree of instability of the structure.

As a tool in the rock mechanics field, the microseismic technique truly 'came of age' in the early 1970s and has been developing rapidly since then. This is due to a number of factors including the extensive foundation of field and laboratory research undertaken in the previous 30 years; coincident rapid development in the electronic field of the necessary detection, signal processing and data analysis equipment; and increased financial support for large field studies by government and private industry.

A detailed review of the current status of the microseismic technique in the field of rock mechanics was provided by Hardy (1982).

Interpretation of monitoring data

The graphs shown in Figures 7.4 and 7.5 give the typical results of the monitoring measurements obtained on an actual engineering project. For an interpretation of these

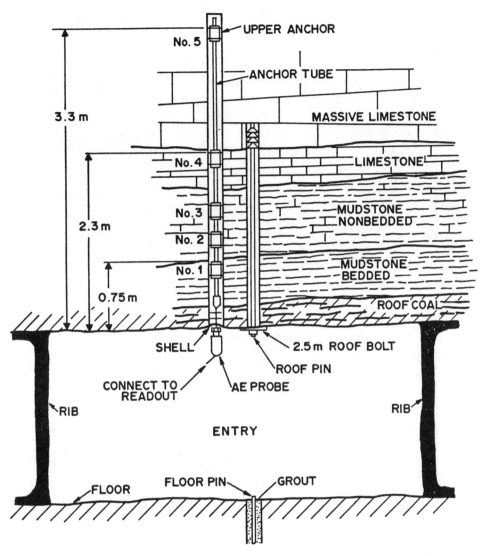

Figure 7.3 b) Monitoring stations in mining and tunneling: Coal mine entry in USA (after Chekan and Babich, 1982).

results, it is appropriate to consider the data obtained by Rabcewicz and Golser (1974) and regarded as classical in the field of in situ monitoring. With reference to Figure 7.5, they provided the following account of the general behavior of a rock mass surrounding a tunnel.

First, the zone of bolted rock arch near the surface monitored by the short extensometer SE begins to expand, causing a movement ΔR towards the tunnel. The zone $B–C$ (controlled by long extensometer LE) moves somewhat later, causing a radial movement $\Delta R(A–C)$. Initially the SE and LE curves almost coincide but, with

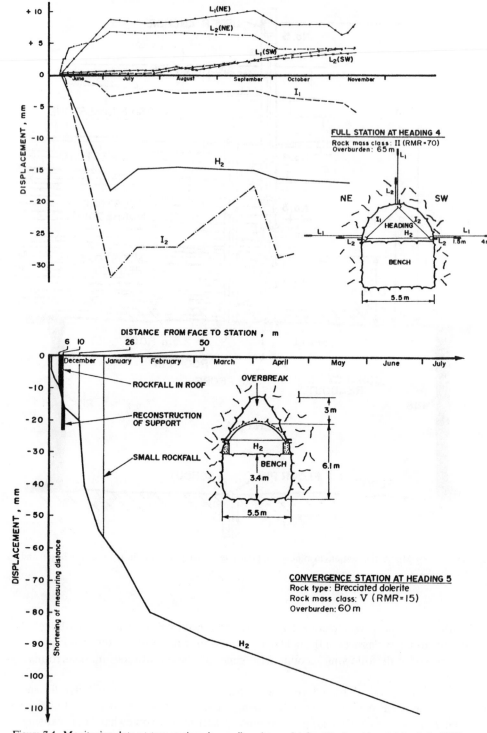

Figure 7.4. Monitoring data at two stations in a railroad tunnel (after Bieniawski and Maschek, 1975).

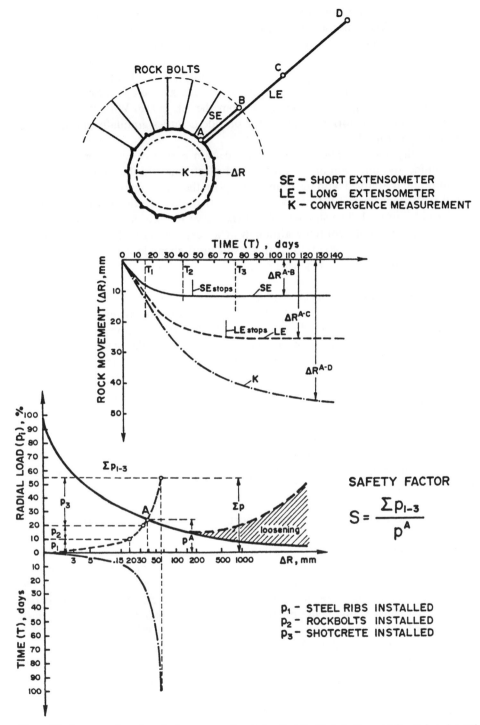

Figure 7.5. Interpretation of results from measuring station 2 at the Tarbela Tunnel (after Rabcewicz and Golser, 1974).

time, the LE curve moves further away from the SE curve. Under the influence of systematic rockbolting the *AB* zone of rock stabilizes at time T_2.

At the same time the movement towards the tunnel proceeds as shown by the LE and K curves. The rock arch created by bolting moves inwards as a whole thus being tangentially shortened. The same sequence of deformation subsequently occurs in the zone *BC* and eventually no more elongation can be measured by the long extensometer LE. The curve K moves further away from the LE curve. With the continuously decreasing rate of deformation, the zone outside *C* settles gradually and the K curve becomes horizontal.

Generally, the movement stops after a certain period of time, depending on the magnitude and direction of the stresses and effectiveness of the support. If a state of equilibrium is attained with the primary support, the final concrete lining will carry no load at all. Rabcewicz (1964) believes, however, that it is exceptional for the movements to be fully stopped. The stabilization of the curve K takes a very long time, hence, movements generally continue although at a very low rate. The inner lining thus becomes loaded with its load slowly increasing until, after a long period, a statement of permanent equilibrium is reached.

Criteria for evaluation of monitoring data
A number of criteria can be used which have been found appropriate for evaluating displacements in underground excavations. Cording (1974) emphasizes that, in most cases, a single criterion is not adequate for evaluating the stability of a tunnel. Furthermore, displacements which indicate local instability such as loosening of a thin rock slab, must be distinguished from those which indicate a more widespread and deep-seated condition affecting the stability of the entire tunnel.

The following criteria may be used to determine whether displacements are indicative of either stable or potentially unstable behavior:
    1. Magnitude of displacement with respect to
    a) displacement as predicted from elastic theory;
    b) measured displacement in well-supported sections of the tunnel, in comparable rock conditions.
    2. Rate of displacement.
    3. Displacement capacity of the support system and of the rock mass.

1. *Magnitude of displacement.* Unstable rock conditions may exist if observed displacements are large with respect to the displacements predicted from the elastic theory by, for example, a finite element elastic solution. The problem is, however, the in situ modulus which is needed for these calculations and is seldom available. Experience shows that calculations made on the basis of an estimated rather than an in-situ determined value of the modulus of elasticity are not reliable.

Where an in situ modulus was available from plate bearing tests, Cording (1974) found on the basis of observed displacements in 13 large underground chambers that movement and loosening along joints were indicated when the observed displacements were more than three times the elastic displacements. In many cases where the displacements exceeded the computed elastic displacements by a factor of five to ten, the excavation and support procedures had to be modified to prevent further large movements. Most of the large displacement observed were of the order of 12 to 75 mm.

In general, displacements measured at several locations in a tunnel are the best criterion for establishing the stability of a tunnel for its given size, geology and support system. When considering the magnitude of displacements, both the depth at which the rock mass is loosening and its area of extent must be known to determine the severity of the problem and the remedial measures to be taken. This is why multiposition extensometers are so useful.

2. *Rate of displacement.* The best way of evaluating rates of displacement is to compare them with the rates previously observed in portions of the same tunnel which were well supported. Experience shows that rates of displacement of the order of 0.001 mm per day indicate stable conditions, rates of 0.05 mm per day are quite high and dangerous for wide chambers while rates of over 1.0 mm per day are excessive and call for additional support measures.

3. *Support capacity.* Observed displacements should not exceed the displacements which will cause failure of the support system. Shotcrete has been observed to crack in tunnels when the differential movements between rock blocks exceed 1.2 and 2.5 mm while 7 meter long rockbolts (tensioned but not grouted) broke when displacements approached 50 mm (Cording, 1974). On the other hand, some studies indicate (Pells, 1974) that fully bonded rockbolts can maintain high loads with joint openings up to 150 mm.

Displacements should also not exceed the capacity of the rock mass to maintain its strength and coherence since rock strength along joints decreases with displacements as the irregularities on joint surfaces are sheared or overriden. In the Washington Metro (Cording, 1974), the range of displacements to cause failure was estimated to be approximately 20 to 50 mm.

Practical aspects of monitoring

Accurate and reliable readout procedures for the various instruments as well as the correct recording of data are of utmost importance. Meaningful results can be achieved only if the personnel in charge are well trained, the instruments properly installed and the different readout units in good working condition.

These requirements are obvious but practical experience often shows a different picture which leads to numerous difficulties and poor quality measurements. Results which are unreliable and doubtful should not form the basis for important design and construction decisions. Timely consideration of the following items is usually fruitful.

1. *Frequency of readings.* Generally, if the measurements indicate a constant increase in deformation, measurements should be taken daily. The results should be plotted as soon as possible and brought to the attention of those in charge of construction. Weekly measurements are sufficient if the results show a distinct tendency to stabilization once the tunnel face has passed the measuring station by a distance of at least two tunnel diameters.

All instruments should be kept operational and accessible for reading as long as possible. In those cases where, for various reasons, an instrument has to be abandoned the very last reading should be taken just before abandonment.

2. *Additional site information.* Apart from the instrument readout data, other additional information to be recorded includes the date and time of the readings as well as the face position and excavation and support-activities. The entries on the data sheet should thus include face chainage, shape of excavation, rock conditions, support used, water inflow, etc.

3. *Training of site personnel.* Training and instruction of site personnel who will be fully responsible for the installation and monitoring of instruments is particularly important. The minimum requirements for site personnel are:

1. Good general knowledge of the tasks in which they are involved and realization of the importance of measurements.

2. Knowledge of the general features of the tunnel being built.

3. Knowledge of site administration.

A trainee should be introduced to the following items:

a) A thorough understanding of rock mechanics measurements. Emphasis should be placed on the practical use of the various measurements.

b) The functions of the instruments to be installed. Practical trial handling of the instruments on dry ground could make later underground operations easier.

c) A trial installation involving: selection of boreholes (location, situation, length, diameter, condition); assembly of instruments or tools; provision for auxiliaries (water, cement, grout, wire, tapes, paint, etc.); actual installation and calibration of instruments and taking of readings.

d) Entering of monitoring results on a data record sheet. After the installation, all necessary information and data concerning a measurement must be properly documented. It is better to enter superfluous information in data sheets than too little. Photographs are very useful in documentation of data.

e) Frequency of data recording. The site training should emphasize how and when the most valuable monitoring results can be obtained.

Dunnicliff and Schmidt (1974) list the following tasks as essential in systematic tunnel monitoring, from conception to full instrumentation:

1. Definition of benefits and purposes;
2. Planning of program in accordance with rock conditions;
3. Selection of monitoring parameters;
4. Selection of instruments;
5. Writing specifications for procurement and installation;
6. Procurement and installation;
7. Reading, maintenance and protection of instruments;
8. Data processing and presentation;
9. Interpretation;
10. Implementation.

It must be emphasized that the focus around which the whole monitoring program evolves is the definition of the specific purpose and benefit desired from the program. The first five tasks are the responsibility of the design engineer who is usually assisted by a specialist rock mechanics engineer. It is essential, however, that the design engineer is also involved in data interpretation (task 9).

Responsibilities of the tunnel contractor include procurement and installation of all instruments, storage, protection and maintenance of instruments and implementation of any remedial measures dictated by the interpretation of monitored data. The contractor should also be assisted by a professional rock mechanics specialist.

Responsibilities of the resident engineer include supervision of instrument installation, reading of instruments and participation with the design engineer in data processing, interpretation, and implementation.

The owners also have certain responsibilities. Although most of the monitoring data may be useful only to the particular project, it may serve to improve the design and construction of the owner's future projects. Thus, the owners should have a very substantial interest in the acquisition of complete and reliable data and should, therefore, provide funds for meeting high standards of monitoring.

Deere and Cording (1974) believe that to be successful in monitoring, a program should satisfy the following:

1. Critical design and construction problems should be recognized prior to construction.

2. Instrumentation programs should be designed to monitor these critical conditions.

3. Specific individuals should be assigned to supervise installation, take readings and summarize observations.

4. Observations of geological conditions must be closely tied to the monitoring program.

5. Details of construction must be correlated with the instrument observations.

6. Close liaison with design and construction personnel must be maintained throughout the construction period. The mechanism for making changes must be available.

7. The simplest, most reliable instruments should be used.

In summary, displacement measurements have proven to be the most suitable for monitoring the behavior of rock tunnels during construction. To ensure that in-situ monitoring programs are successful, it is essential that:

1. The owner and constructor, as well as the designer, are fully acquainted with the purpose and benefits of the measurements. This results in better cooperation between the parties concerned and leads to savings in time and money.

2. Monitoring programs must be carefully planned and executed. Instruments must be installed and readings taken by the site staff permanently assigned to these tasks on a full time basis. Generally, at least two persons are required. Instruments must be installed with care and at the correct time (within 3 m of the face) and the readings must be taken regularly throughout the entire excavation period.

3. The contact between the owner and the contractor should specify in a precise manner the type and object of all instruments to be installed. The contractor should be compensated for the time, allocated staff, and any special work necessary for the monitoring program.

A number of comprehensive publications are available on the subject of monitoring of underground rock excavations, notably, those by Franklin (1977), Londe (1977), Kovari and Amstad (1979), Bieniawski and Maschek (1975), and Lane (1975). Although the use of monitoring has received particular attention in civil engineering, systematic monitoring of mining structures has also been reported. The activities in this area are well summarized by Peng (1978).

THE NEW AUSTRIAN TUNNELING METHOD

The New Austrian Tunneling Method (NATM) is an approach or philosophy integrating the principles of the behavior of rock masses and monitoring the behavior of underground excavations during construction. The word 'method' in the English translation is unfortunate as it led to some misunderstanding. The fact is that the NATM is not a set of specific excavation and support techniques. Many people believe that if shotcrete and rockbolts are used as support, then they are employing the New Austrian Tunneling Method. This is far from the truth. The NATM involves a combination of many established ways of excavation and tunneling but the difference is the continual monitoring of the rock movement and the revision of support to obtain the most stable and economical lining. However, a number of other aspects are also pertinent in making the NATM more of a concept or a philosophy than a method.

The New Austrian Tunneling Method was developed between 1957 and 1965 in Austria. It was given its name in Salzburg in 1962 to distinguish it from the traditional old Austrian tunneling method, described by Szechy (1973). The main contributors to the development of the NATM were Ladislaus von Rabcewicz, Leopold Müller and Franz Pacher.

Essentially the NATM is a scientific empirical approach. It has evolved from practical experience and von Rabcewicz called it 'empirical dimensioning' (Rabcewicz, 1964). However, it has a theoretical basis involving the relationship between the stresses and deformations around tunnels (better known as the ground-reaction curve concept). Its early theoretical foundations were given by two Austrians, Fenner and Kastner. The method makes use of sophisticated in situ instrumentation and monitoring, and interprets these measurements in a scientific manner.

As stated earlier this method is often misunderstood and recently a number of publications have appeared in the international press trying to clarify these misconceptions, notably, those by Leopold Müller (1978), Golser (1979), Muir Wood (1979) and Brown (1981). The author decided to study the NATM in detail and spent three months in Germany and Austria investigating the approach and discussing it in person with Professors von Rabcewicz and Müller, as well as with Drs. Pacher, Spaun, and Golser.

Professor Müller considers the NATM as a concept which observes certain principles. Although he has listed no less than 22 principles (Müller, 1978), there are seven most important features on which the NATM is based. These are:

1. *Mobilization of the strength of the rock mass.* The method relies on the inherent strength of the surrounding rock mass being conserved as the main component of tunnel support. Primary support is directed to enable the rock to support itself. It follows that the support must have suitable load-deformation characteristics and be placed at the correct time.

2. *Shotcrete protection.* In order to preserve the load carrying capacity of the rock mass, loosening and excessive rock deformations must be minimized. This is achieved by applying a thin layer of shotcrete, sometimes together with a suitable system of rockbolting, immediately after face advance. It is essential that the support system used remains in full contact with the rock and deforms with it. While the NATM involves shotcrete, it does not mean that the use of shotcrete alone constitutes the NATM.

3. *Measurements.* The NATM requires the installation of sophisticated instrumentation at the time the initial shotcrete lining is placed, to monitor the deformations of the excavation and the build-up of load in the support. This provides information on tunnel stability and enables optimization of the formation of a load bearing ring of rock strata. The timing of the placement of the support is of vital importance. John (1980) provided a fine example of the use of instrumentation during the construction of the Arlberg Tunnel.

4. *Flexible support.* The NATM is characterized by versatility and adaptability leading to flexible rather than rigid tunnel support. Thus, active rather than passive support is advocated and strengthening is not by a thicker concrete lining but by a flexible combination of rockbolts, wire mesh and steel ribs. The primary support will partly or fully represent the total support required and the dimensioning of the secondary support will depend on the results of the measurements.

5. *Closing of invert.* Since a tunnel is a thick-walled tube, the closing of the invert to form a load-bearing ring of the rock mass is essential. This is crucial in soft-ground tunneling where the invert should be closed quickly and no section of the excavated tunnel surface should be left unsupported even temporarily. However, for tunnels in rock, support should not be installed too early as the load-bearing capability of the rock mass would not be fully mobilized. For rock tunnels the rock mass must be permitted to deform sufficiently before the support takes full effect.

6. *Contractural arrangements.* The above main principles of the NATM, will only be successful if special contractual arrangements are made. Since the NATM concept is based on monitoring measurements, changes in support and construction methods should be possible. This, however, is only possible if the contractual system is such that changes during construction are permissible.

7. *Rock mass classification determines support measures.* Payment for support is based on a rock mass classification after each drill and blast round. In some countries this is not acceptable contractually, and this is why the method has received limited attention in the United States. Figure 7.6 is an example of the main ground classes for rock tunnels and the corresponding support, serving as the guidelines for tunnel reinforcement as well as for payment purposes.

The NATM calls for all parties involved in the design and construction of a tunneling project to accept and understand this approach and to cooperate in decision making and the resolution of problems. The owner, the design-engineer and the contractor need to work as one team. The project should be staffed with well-trained field engineers (competent to interpret the observations and act upon them) and with designers (or consultants) who visit the site frequently and are on call for difficult construction decisions. In Austria, only highly qualified contractors are employed who can demonstrate their expertise in the use of shotcrete.

The European literature is full of descriptions involving successful applications of the New Austrian Tunneling Method, particularly in Austria, Germany, France and Switzerland. However, its applications have also spread to other countries such as Japan, Australia, Brazil, and to a limited extent, to North America.

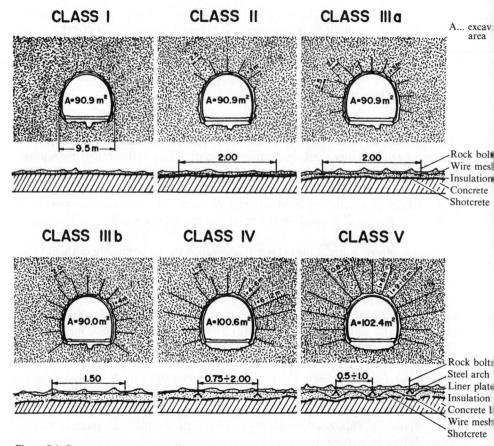

Figure 7.6. Support measures according to rock mass classification in the Arlberg Tunnel (Courtesy of Dr.-ing. M. John, 1980).

Finally, it should be noted that although the NATM is basically a 'build as you go' approach based on rock monitoring, quite apart from theoretical considerations involving the Fenner-Pacher curve as it is called in Austria, attempts have been made to analyze the concept by means of the finite element technique, notably by Wanninger (1979) and by Swoboda (1979).

A further attempt in placing the observational design on some theoretical footing, has led to the convergence-confinement method.

THE CONVERGENCE-CONFINEMENT METHOD

The convergence-confinement method is an attempt to evaluate tunnel stability conditions by means of a mathematical model. The aim is to calculate the support pressure. This is achieved by considering a ground reaction curve (see Figure 7.1) and, more specifically, the intersection of two characteristic curves representing radial stresses as a function of tunnel radial deformation: one for the lining and the other for the ground. The convergence-confinement method takes into account the statically indeterminate nature of the problem posed by tunnel support. It is basically similar to the elastic-plastic methods used in solid mechanics.

The method was proposed in May 1977 in France during a meeting devoted to tunnel calculations by the AFTES (L'Association Francaise des Travaux en Souterrain – French Association for Underground Works). The meeting chose the name convergence-confinement method as appropriate because it portrayed the physical behavior of the ground-lining complex that constitutes a tunnel. The ground tends to deform – this is the convergence – while the lining opposes this convergence with pressure – this is the confinement (of the ground). It is important to realize that in some countries in Europe, e.g. in Germany, the law calls for static calculations for all engineering structures including tunnels. It was observed that while calculations for bridges were well standardized, and the calculation procedures and limiting conditions well known, and hence it was possible to test bridge designs, there was nothing comparable for tunnels where nearly everything was left to engineering judgment. Unable to rely on any standard codes, the tunnel engineer naturally tends to study supports through observations and measurements rather than by theoretical specu-lation. However, the principle of the convergence-confinement method, in which the behavior of the rock mass and the behavior of the lining are depicted in the form of characteristic curves, allows the designers to examine the procedures by which the actual behavior of rock strata during excavation can be studied. The method also considers the sequence of excavation and introduces, to some extent, the time factor. Thus, the convergence-confinement method is responsive to the needs of tunnel design engineers in Europe and contributes to a better understanding of the problems of tunnel construction and hence to better design of tunneling projects.

In its simplest form, the convergence-confinement method consists of calculating the ground characteristic curve and the support curve in Figure 7.1, and determining their intersection. The former curve describes the relationship between the increase in radial convergence and the decrease of the radial pressure; the support characteristic curve expresses the more or less rapid increase of the support reaction with an increase in radial convergence. The method requires more clarification but for its present status the reader is referred to papers by Gesta et al. (1980), Kerisel (1980) and Duddeck (1980). No further discussion will be given here because the convergence-confinement method is not as yet suitable for direct design procedures, except in special cases and only then for comparative purposes.

An excellent treatment of the support pressure-tunnel convergence relationships is given in a most recent paper by Brown, Bray, Ladanyi and Hoek (1983).

REFERENCES

Albiers, H. J., Gallhoff, U. and Jagsch, D. The effects of workings on the New Austrian Tunneling Method. *Gluckauf Translation*, Vol. 118, No. 16, 1982, pp. 327–331.

American Society for Testing and Materials. *Performance Monitoring for Geotechnical Construction*, ASTM Special Technical Publication 584, Philadelphia, 1974, 194 pp.

Bieniawski, Z. T. and Maschek, R. E. Monitoring the behavior of rock tunnels during construction, *The Civil Engineer in South Africa*, Vol. 17, 1975, pp. 255–264.

Braun, W. N. Application of the NATM in Deep Tunnels and Difficult Rock Formations, *Tunnels and Tunneling*, March, 1980, pp. 17–20.

Brown, E. T. Putting the NATM into Perspective, *Tunnels and Tunneling*, November, 1981, pp. 13–17.

Brown, E. T., Bray, J. W., Ladanyi, B. and Hoek, E. Ground response curves for rock tunnels. *Journal of Geotechnical Engineering*, ASCE, Vol. 109, No. 1, 1983, pp. 15–31.

Chadha, S. M. A Designers Viewpoint of Medium-Support Interaction, *Monograph on Rock Mechanics Applications in Mining*, Society of Mining Engineers, AIME, New York, 1977, pp. 223–227.

Chekan, G. J. and Babich, D. R. Investigation of longwall gateroad roof support characteristics at Powhatan No. 4 Mine. *Bureau of Mines Report of Investigations*, RI 8286, 1982, 18 p.

Cording, E. J. Measurement of displacements in tunnels. *Proc. 2nd Int. Congress on Engng. Geol.*, IAEG, Sao Paulo, 1974, pp. VIII–PC–3–1–15.

Cording, E. J., Hendron, A. J., Hansmire, W. H., Mahar, J. W., MacPherson, H. A., Jones, R. A. and O'Rourke, T. D. *Methods for Geotechnical Observations and Instrumentation in Tunneling*, University of Illinois, Urbana, NSF Research Report GI–33644X, December, 1975, 292 p.

Daemen, J. J. Problems in tunnel support mechanics. *Underground Space*, Vol. 1, 1977, pp. 163–172.

Dahl, H. D. and Schonfeldt, von H. A. Rock Mechanics Elements of Coal Mine Design, *Monograph on Rock Mechanics Applications in Mining*, Society of Mining Engineers, AIME, New York, 1977, pp. 31–39.

Deere, D. U. Current Tunnel Design, Construction and Research in the U.S. *Proceedings International Tunnel Symposium on Tunneling under Difficult Conditions*, ITA Japan Association, Tokyo, 1978, pp. AA–8–1 to A–8–6.

Deere, D. U. and Cording, E. J. Rock Tunnel supports and field measurements. *Proc. Rapid Excavation and Tunneling Conf.*, AIME, New York, 1972, pp. 601–622.

Deere, D. U., Peck, R. B., Monsees, J. E. and Schmidt, B. Design of Tunnel Linings and Support Systems. *Highway Research Record*, Washington, DC, No. 339, 1970, pp. 26–33.

Duddeck, H. On the basic requirements for applying the convergence-confinement method. *Underground Space*, Vol. 4, No. 4, 1980, pp. 241–247.

Dunnicliff, C. J. and Schmidt, B. An engineering approach to monitoring the performance of soft ground tunnels under construction. *Proc. Rapid Excavation and tunneling Conference*, AIME, New York, 1974, pp. 377–396.

Duvall, W. I. General Principles of Underground Opening Design in Competent Rock, *Monograph on Rock Mechanics Applications in Mining*, Society of Mining Engineers, AIME, New York, 1977, pp. 101–111.

Franklin, J. A. Some Practical Considerations in the Planning of Field Instrumentation, *Field Measurements in Rock Mechanics*, (K. Kovari Editor), A. A. Balkema, Rotterdam, Vol. 1, 1977, pp. 3–14.

Franklin, J. A. The Monitoring of Structures in Rock, *International Journal of Rock Mechanics and Mining Sciences*, Vol. 14, 1977 pp. 163–192.

Gesta, P., Kerisel, J., Londe, P. Louis, C. and Panet, M. General Report: Tunnel stability by the convergence-Confinement Method. *Underground Space*, Vol. 4, No. 4, February 1980, pp. 225–232.

Golser, J. Another View of the NATM. *Tunnels and Tunneling*, March 1979, p. 41.

Hardy, H. R. Applications of acoustic emission techniques to rock and rock structures: A state-of-the-art review. *Acoustic Emissions in Geotechnical Engineering Practice*, STP750, ASTM, Philadelphia, 1982, pp. 4–92.

Hoek E. and Brown, E. T. *Underground Excavations in Rock*, Institutions of Mining and Metallurgy, London, 1980, pp. 382–396.

Hudson, J. A. Instrumentation and Monitoring, *Tunnels and Tunneling*, September, 1975, pp. 64–70.

International Society for Rock Mechanics. *Rock Characterization, Testing and Monitoring*, Pergamon, Oxford, 1981, pp. 169–211.

John, M. Investigation and Design for the Arlberg Expressway Tunnel, *Tunnels and Tunneling*, April, 1980, pp. 46–51, May, 1980, pp. 54–57, June, 1980, pp. 45–50.

Kerisel, J. Commentary on the General Report on the Convergence-Confinement Method. *Underground Space*, Vol. 4, No. 4, 1980, pp. 233–240.

Kovari, K. (Editor). *Field Measurements in Rock Mechanics*, A. A. Balkema, Rotterdam, 1977, Vol. 1 and 2, 1026 p.

Kovari, K. and Amstad, S. Field Instrumentation in Tunneling as a Practical Design Aid, *Proceedings Fourth International Congress on Rock Mechanics*, ISRM, Montreux, A. A. Balkema, Rotterdam, 1979, Vol. 2, pp. 311–318.

Kulhawy, F. H. and O'Rourke, T. D. Rock mass response and machine performance in a full-face TBM tunnel in Rochester, N. Y., *Proc. Rapid Excavation and Tunneling Conf.*, AIME, New York, 1981, Vol. 1, pp. 605–626.

Lane, K. S. *Field Test Sections Save Cost in Tunnel Support*, American Society of Civil Engineers, October, 1975, 59 p.

Londe, Pierre. Field Measurements in Tunnels, *Field Measurements in Rock Mechanics*, (K. Kovari, Editor), A. A. Balkema, Rotterdam, Vol. 2, 1977, 619–638.

McDonough, J. T. Site Evaluation for Cavability and Underground Support Design at the Climax Mine, *Monograph on Rock Mechanics Applications in Mining*, Society of Mining Engineers, AIME, New York, 1977, pp. 112–126.

Muir Wood, A. M. A Letter on the NATM, *Tunnels and Tunneling*, February, 1979, p. 105.

Muir Wood, A. M. Ground behavior and support for mining and tunneling. *Tunnels and Tunneling*, Vol. 11, No. 4, 1979, pp. 43–48.

Müller, Leopold. Removing Misconceptions on the New Austrian Tunneling Method, *Tunnels and Tunneling*, October 1978, pp. 29–32.

Müller, Leopold. The Reasons for Unsuccessful Applications of the New Austrian Tunneling Method, *Proceedings International Tunnel Symposium on Tunneling under Difficult Conditions*, ITA Japan Association, Tokyo, 1978, pp. A–9–1:6.

Nussbaum, H. Recent Developments of New Austrian Tunneling Method. *Journal of Construction Division*, ASCE, Vol. 99, No. 001, July 1973, pp. 115–132.

Obert, L. and Duvall, W. I. *Rock Mechanics and the Design of Structures in Rock*, John Wiley & Sons, New York, 1967, pp. 545–543.

Pacher, F. Underground openings and tunnels-review and comments. *Design Methods in Rock Mechanics*, Proc. 16th U.S. Symp. on Rock Mech., ASCE, New York, 1977, pp. 223–234.

Pells, P. J. N. The behavior of fully bonded rockbolts. *Proc. 3rd Int. Congress on Rock Mech.*, ISRM, Denver, 1974, Vol. IIB, pp. 1212–1217.

Peng, S. S. *Coal Mine Ground Control*, John Wiley & Sons, New York, 1978, pp. 365–399.

Rabcewicz, L. The New Austrian Tunnelling Method, *Water Power*, November, 1964, pp. 453–457, December, 1964, pp. 511–515, January, 1965, pp. 19–24.

Rabcewicz, L. and Golser, J. Principles of Dimensioning the Supporting System for the New Austrian Tunneling Method, *Water Power*, March, 1973, pp. 88–93.

Rabcewicz, L. and Golser, J. Application of the NATM to the Underground Works at Tarbela, *Water Power*, September, 1974, pp. 314–335.

Rabcewicz, L. and Pacher, F. Die Elements der Neuen Osterreichischen Tunnelbauweise. Osterreichische Ingenieur Zeitschrift, Vol. 18, No. 9, 1975.

Spaun, G. and Jagsch, D. Tunneling with the New Austrian Tunneling Method in a 1100 m deep German coal mine. *Proc. 5th Int. Cong. Rock Mech.*, ISRM, Melbourne, A. A. Balkema, Rotterdam, 1983.

Swoboda, G. Finite Element Analysis of the New Austrian Tunnelling Method, *Proceedings Third International Conference on Numerical Method in Geomechanics*, A. A. Balkema, Rotterdam, 1979, pp. 581–586.

Szechy, K. *The Art of Tunnelling*. Akademiai Kiado, Budapest, 1973, 1096 p.

Wanninger, R. New Austrian Tunnelling Method and Finite Elements, *Proceedings Third International Conference on Numerical Methods in Geomechanics*, A. A. Balkema, Rotterdam, 1979, pp. 587–597.

U.S. Bureau of Mines. *Rock Mechanics Instrumentation for Mine Design*. Information Circular 8525, Department of the Interior, Washington, DC, 1973, 76 p.

A full-scale model mine tunnel for roof support research at the Spokane Mining Research Center. (Courtesy of the U.S. Bureau of Mines).

CHAPTER 8

Analytical methods of design

*Nature is indifferent towards the difficulties it causes
to a mathematician.*

Fourier

Analytical methods involve the formulation and application of certain conceptual models for design purposes. The aim is to reproduce the behavior and response of the prototype rock structure.

In rock mechanics design, analytical modeling can involve the following approaches: conceptual modeling as a framework for investigations, physical scaled models, mathematical modeling (closed form solutions) and numerical modeling (finite element techniques, etc.). Although mathematical and numerical methods are sometimes described as 'analytical or theoretical studies' it is more appropriate to define mathematical approaches as those involving closed-form solutions while numerical methods would include such techniques as finite element, finite difference, boundary element, etc. Since derivation of the necessary closed form solutions is difficult or even impossible in rock mechanics, numerical techniques assume particular importance.

In spite of their great potential, analytical methods in rock engineering are mainly used for comparative design and parametric studies and must be supplemented by other design approaches for solution of practical engineering problems.

The question may be asked why is it really so difficult to design an opening in rock, considering that the shapes of such openings may be very simple while complex mechanical engineering designs abound throughout the world in such sophisticated areas as aircraft design, spacecraft design, or civil engineering concrete structures. There are a number of answers to this question (Brady and St. John, 1982). One important consideration is that the structure, composed of the support and the surrounding rock, is statically indeterminate because the load acting on the support is determined by the deformation of both the support and the structure. The support will not be stressed unless the rock mass undergoes some deformation after the installation of the support.

This principle can be demonstrated by a simple mechanical model, depicted in Figure 8.1. The analogy of this model with the underground situation becomes clear if the upper beam is identified with the surrounding rock, the lower beam with the support, and the blocks with the contact between the rock and the support.

The lower beam in Figure 8.1 will be loaded only if the external load induces some deflection in the upper beam and if the connecting blocks transmit some force to the

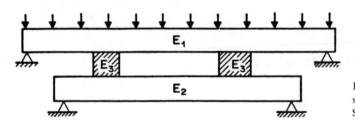

Figure 8.1. A model of rock-support interaction (after Salamon, 1974).

supporting lower beam. The load on the lower beam will increase if any combination of these steps is made:
1. Increasing external load;
2. Making top beam more flexible;
3. Making blocks stiffer;
4. Making lower beam stiffer.

The greatest difficulty in determining support loads accurately arises from the problem of specifying the constitutive law of the rock mass, that is, the prediction of rock displacement. Since this displacement is affected by many factors (field stresses, properties of the rock, changes in moisture, weathering, etc.) there are great practical difficulties in devising a model which describes this component satisfactorily. This is the reason why formulae have been proposed giving the support load independently of the support, e.g. Terzaghi (1946).

NUMERICAL MODELING

Two approaches to numerical modeling of rock masses can be identified, both recognizing geologic structures as being discontinuous due to joints, faults and bedding planes. A continuum approach treats the rock mass as a continuum intersected by a number of discontinuities, while a discontinuum approach views the rock mass as an assemblage of independent blocks or particles (Goodman and St. John, 1977).

Continuum models are of two types: differential and integral. Differential models characterize the entire region of interest and include the finite difference and the finite element methods. The finite element method is uniquely capable of handling complex geometries and inhomogeneities (Zienkiewicz, 1977). Complex systems involving fluid flow and heat transfer can also be handled (Ertekin, 1979). Integral or boundary element models feature discretization only along interior or exterior boundaries (Brebbia and Walker, 1978). The interfaces between different material types and discontinuities are treated as internal boundaries which must be similarly discretized. Boundary-element procedures are most appropriate for modeling linear-elastic systems, although certain forms of nonlinearity may be treated. The boundary-element procedures provide an economical means of two- and three-dimensional analysis of rock masses. They are particularly suitable for use when conditions at the boundary are of most concern (St. John et al., 1979).

Discontinuum models feature numerical procedures involving the equations of motion of particles or blocks rather than the continuum (Cundall, 1976). Discontinuum models should be used whenever independent rock block movements must be specifically recognized. This is the case of failure within a low stress field which allows large movements and rotations on the rock blocks defined by pre-existing geological discontinuities or by stress or blasting induced rock fracture. Examples of this include rock slope failure, roof collapse behind a long wall face or flow of ore in a stope.

When assessing the potential or limitations of numerical techniques in mining and tunneling, three areas of modeling activities should be considered:

1. Model development;
2. Model application;
3. Model validation.

In essence, for mining and tunneling purposes, a wide range of two and three dimensional modeling capabilities is available with computer codes developed for many material behaviors. This includes the following constitutive behaviors: linear-elastic, non-linear elastic, linear viscoelastic, elasto-plastic, elasto-viscoplastic, anisotropic, dilatant, thermal-dependent, and stochastic.

However, much more model application and verification is required before any of those material models can be applied for practical design purposes in mining and tunneling (Brady and St. John, 1982). The reason for this situation is that numerical techniques have outstripped the ability of engineering geology to provide the necessary input parameters. It is, therefore, essential that full consideration be given to the availability of realistic input data before applying sophisticated analytical methods.

Availability of computer codes

A large number of computer codes applicable to problems in geotechnical engineering involving mining and tunneling are available. In fact, 15 codes considered to be representative of the state of the art for mechanical and thermomechanical modeling have been compiled by the U.S. National Committee for Rock Mechanics (1981).

It is evident that a wide range of capabilities exists for the use of analytical modeling techniques. What is required is not only further model development and application but mainly model validation. The validity of numerical methods must be established before they can become accepted as design tools. This is crucial because it has been reported (McClain, 1983) that in the case of a detailed study involving a group of experts having broad experience in computer simulation of the structural behavior of excavations, the current models provide a reasonably reliable qualitative overall picture of the excavation behavior but the quantitative evaluation of the excavation stability is still very limited. In fact, it was found that for an identical problem being solved by a number of computer simulations featuring different codes, widely varying results were obtained.

Applications of numerical modeling

The finite element method is currently by far the most popular and useful technique for application as an analytical design tool. This method is particularly useful in assessing the merits of various design schemes on a comparative basis. In this respect it represents a powerful technique where the effects of various parameters on the overall design may be studied and design variations may be compared with one another. Analytical methods, however, are not as yet suitable as absolute design tools because of deficiencies in provision of the input data.

Practical applications of the numerical methods are particularly directed to modeling the effects of different geological features and to determining the potential fracture zones around excavations at depth (Hoek and Brown, 1980). By using a suitable rock fracture criterion, it is possible to identify weakness zones around excavations and so lead to proper selection of rock support. In addition, the effect of intersections can be assessed by means of three dimensional finite-element analyses.

Intersections are frequently encountered in underground excavations, especially in mining when the room-and-pillar method is used. In this case, entries and crosscuts are developed in different directions. Stability problems are more pronounced in the case of intersections for the following reasons:

1. At intersections the roof span to be supported is larger than the maximum span of any of the openings and a larger span corresponds to a shorter stand-up time;

2. At intersections, three-dimensional situations are created and high stress concentrations develop around the corners;

3. At an intersection, a favourable orientation of discontinuities for one opening means a less favorable one for the other opening;

4. The support provided by the sidewalls of an opening is not available at an intersection.

For these reasons, the design of support at intersections introduces a special problem for the rock engineer. In a recent study, Gercek (1982) investigated the stresses and deformation occurring around a four-way underground intersection located at the center of a room-and-pillar coal panel, employing a three dimensional finite-element program. The conditions of the symmetry of the problem are shown in Figure 8.2. The analysis included the following parameters:

   width-to-height ratio of pillars: $w/h = 2.0, 5.0, 8.0$ and 12.0

   ratio of horizontal stresses to vertical stresses: $\sigma_h/\sigma_v = k = 0.5$, 1.0, and 2.0.
The results of the analyses have yielded the following conclusions:

1. Vertical deformations occurring in the roof (i.e., convergence) and in the floor (i.e., floor heave) decrease as w/h increases from 2.0 to 12.0; however, the magnitude of horizontal stresses does not have a significant effect on the vertical deformations, which are a maximum at the center of intersection and a minimum at the pillar center.

2. Horizontal pillar deformations decrease as w/h increases; however, a higher horizontal in situ stress gives larger horizontal pillar deformations, which are a maximum at the corner and at the mid-height of the pillar.

3. Vertical component of the pillar stresses is always a maximum at the pillar corner and a minimum at the pillar center. Vertical stress concentration factors occurring in the outer regions of the mid-horizontal plane of the pillar are higher than the values given by the tributary area theory for pillar loading.

Based on two-dimensional boundary element studies, Hoek and Brown (1980) have compiled graphs showing the values of the maximum boundary stresses in the roof and sidewalls of excavations for different stress ratios. This information is reproduced in Figure 8.3.

Another important application of analytical modeling is the determination of zones of overstressed rock for rectangular or square tunnels such as are found in deep level mining. Analytical studies show that while tensile failure will first occur in the roof and floor of the rectangular tunnel, these tensile cracks are not expected to have a significant effect upon the stability of the tunnels, because crack propagation will be arrested (Hoek, 1967, 1980).

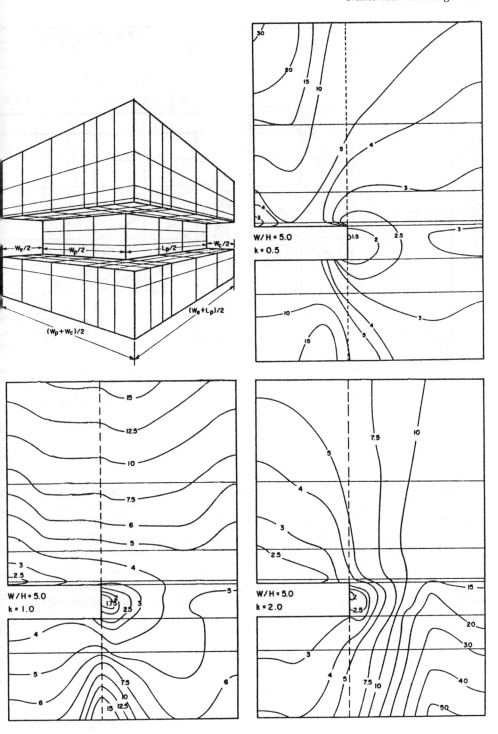

Figure 8.2. Three-dimensional finite element model and contours of safety factors around tunnel intersections (after Gercek, 1982).

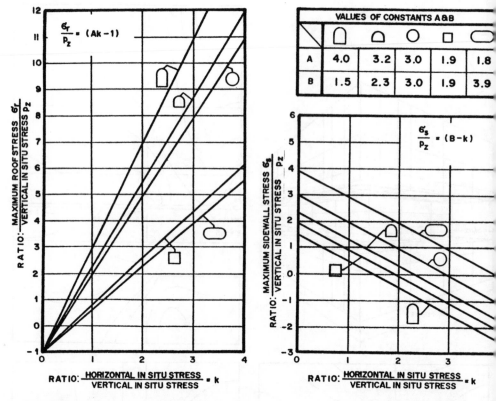

Figure 8.3. Maximum roof and sidewall stresses induced in the rock surrounding excavations of various shapes for different ratios of horizontal to vertical stress (after Hoek, 1981).

Shear failure is initiated in the sharp corners of the rectangular tunnels at relatively low applied stress levels, but, because of the rapid decrease in both major and minor principal stress values with distance from these sharp corners, the zone of overstressed rock is very limited in extent. Because of the very high stress gradient and the confining influence of the surrounding rock, these shear failure zones do not usually give rise to major instability problems in excavations. On the other hand, subsequent failure of the sidewalls will take place. The severity of the sidewall damage appears to be approximately proportional to the volume of overstressed rock adjacent to the sidewall of the excavation (Hoek and Brown, 1980).

PHYSICAL MODELING

Physical models can provide useful information particularly when examining the modes of failure. The use of physical models as tools in rock mechanics has become increasingly popular, especially in Europe. Major activities took place during the 1950s and 1960s. In 1979, an international colloquium on physical geomechanics models was held in Italy indicating a renewed interest in the use of physical modeling.

Beginning in the late 1950s, particularly impressive model studies were carried out in Essen, Germany, by Everling and Jacobi (Everling, 1964). These large, expensive models attempted to simulate the effects of various parameters on the stability of gate entries in longwall coal mining operations in the Ruhr. Nearly every conceivable aspect of the actual situation was modeled.

Hobbs (1968) working with the National Coal Board in Great Britain also carried out an extensive series of experiments dealing with coal mine entries beginning in the mid-1960's. His research was continued by Lawrence (1973) and later, Brook (1977) addressed similar problems but using a new apparatus and a different scaling procedure. Stimpson (1970) provided an excellent treatment of the subject of modeling materials. Included in his paper are extensive charts and tables in addition to a very comprehensive bibliography. Barron and LaRocque (1962), working in Canada in the early 1960's, developed and tested a large scale model of a tunnel in an iron mine. In South Africa, Hoek (1963), Bieniawski and Van Tonder (1969), and Krauland (1970) conducted model studies aimed at simulating fracture around coal and hard rock tunnels. An electrical resistance analog was developed by the Chamber of Mines of South Africa for the determination of stresses and displacements in the strata surrounding tabular mining excavations (Salamon and Oravecz, 1970, Cook and Schumann, 1965).

In the United States, the major thrusts were directed to the development and use of the 'base friction' modeling technique (Goodman, 1969, 1981) and recently, to the design and construction of a full scale model mine tunnel for roof support research by the U.S. Bureau of Mines, Spokane Research Center. The system is designed to simulate a 4.6 meters (15 feet) wide mine entry and consists of two concrete pillars supporting six concrete slabs, 0.3 meters (1 foot) thick each. Loads equivalent to 30 meters of depth can be applied to the model roof (Smelser et al., 1982).

A classic series of physical model tests of roof bolting in bedded rock was performed by Louis Panek (1962) of the U.S. Bureau of Mines during the early 1960's. Panek investigated the reinforcement mechanism of friction and suspension with tension roof bolts. He then combined dimensional analysis with the results of the model tests and derived quantitative formulae for the design of rock bolting patterns.

In a recent study, Mark (1982) showed that the base friction technique can be used successfully to model highly discontinuous coal mine roof conditions. It was also found that it is possible to achieve reproducible experimental results from base friction models if careful model planning and experimental procedures are followed. The base friction technique can be used to model roof strata conditions that have not been modeled by any other technique.

In Mark's study, a mine roof containing numerous cracks oriented at 30° from the horizontal was successfully modeled. In addition, the thickness of the roof layers, the presence of weak layers in the roof sequence and the presence of joints were all shown to have an effect on the stability of the model mine openings. The support mechanism of resin bolts was also observed in base friction models. This enabled studies of the general kinetics of roof behavior which is useful in understanding the support mechanisms (see Figures 8.4 and 8.5). Moreover, the stress distribution was measured within the base friction models by small stress sensors having a capacity of 6.8 kPa (1 psi).

The base friction technique has considerable value as an educational tool. Base friction models can be used as aids for providing the students of rock mechanics with

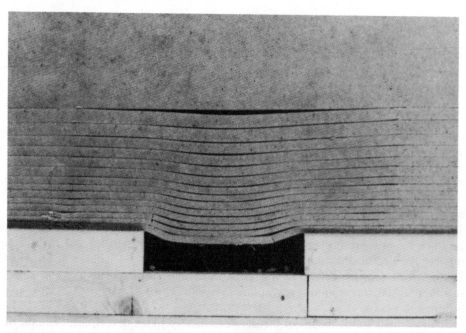

Initiation of failure in an unsupported coal-mine roof in bedded strata. Note cracks developing at the top of several layers over the left rib, and a tension crack near the right rib in the lowest layer.

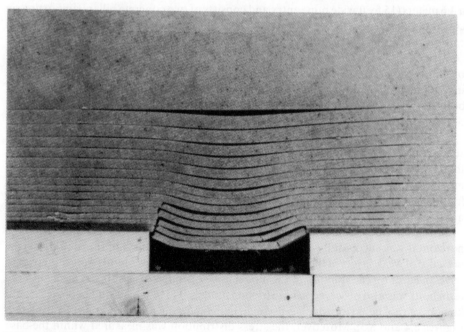

Failure of a uniformly-bedded mine roof. The cracks have coalesced at the left rib and the roof is cantilevered at the right rib.

Figure 8.4. Base friction modeling experiments – unsupported roof (after Mark, 1982).

Failure of a roof span in bedded strata supported by equally spaced resin-bolts.

'Progressive' failure of a coal-mine roof after the failure of the bolted strata.

Figure 8.5. Base friction modeling experiments – supported roof (Mark, 1982).

easily understood demonstrations of ground control problems. This has also been demonstrated by Egger (1979).

Much information can be gained about the behavior of rock structures by constructing and testing physical models that represent several aspects of the mechanical behavior of the prototype. Model studies suffer, however, from a number of disadvantages and they are seldom used to provide actual design data. Their main value lies in providing complementary results to computation and for checking the final design. A very important aspect of physical models is that they are demonstrative and thus can improve communication between the various persons involved in the design of rock excavations.

FAILURE CRITERIA

A criterion of failure is an algebraic expression of the mechanical condition under which a material fails by fracturing or deforming beyond some specified limit. This specification can be in terms of load, deformation, stress, strain, or other parameters.

The search for failure criteria for rock has been conducted for a considerable number of years as is demonstrated in Table 8.1. Although much progress has been made, the practical design engineer is still searching for a failure criterion that fully meets his needs. This is best illustrated by the fact that over 200 years after Coulomb presented his well-known criterion (1773), it was stated: 'In short, a large amount of research has yet to be done on rock failure criteria, possibly even more than has been published to

Table 8.1. Major criteria of failure for rock materials

Name of criterion	Proposer	Date	Reference
Coulomb–Navier	Coulomb	1773	Jaeger and Cook, 1979
Maximum shear stress	Tresca	1864	Nadai, 1950
Maximum principal stress	Rankine	1869	Nadai, 1950
Maximum elastic strain	St. Venant	1870	Nadai, 1950
Constant elastic energy of deformation	Beltrami	1885	Nadai, 1950
Shear failure	Mohr	1900	Jaeger and Cook, 1979
Constant octahedral shearing stress	Huber	1904	Jaeger and Cook, 1979
	Hencky	1920	
Second invariant of stress deviation	von Mises	1913	Jaeger and Cook, 1979
Griffith-original	Griffith	1921	Griffith, 1921, 1924
Statistical failure theory	Weibull	1939	Weibull, 1952
Fracture toughness	Irwin	1960	Irwin, 1960
Griffith-modified	McClintock-Walsh	1962	McClintock and Walsh, 1962
			Hoek and Bieniawski, 1965
Griffith-extended	Murrell	1963	Murrell, 1963
Empirical rock mass strength	Hoek–Brown	1980	Hoek and Brown, 1980

date' (Wawersik, 1968). Jaeger and Cook (1979) justly believed that failure criteria based on the actual mechanism of fracture, which are more sophisticated than the theories of Coulomb, Mohr and Griffith, have yet to be developed, since some empirical equations fit the experimental results better.

To meet the immediate needs of the practical rock engineer, attention should be directed to empirical criteria for estimating the triaxial strength of rock. Such criteria can be selected by fitting a suitable equation into experimental data and they need not have a theoretical basis. They serve to meet the requirements of adequate prediction, simplicity of use and speed of application.

The requirement for a triaxial strength criterion is that, from the knowledge of the uniaxial compressive strength of a given rock material, values of the major principal stress σ_1 should be predicted, using $\sigma_2 = \sigma_3$ as an input value (the influence of the intermediate principal stress σ_2 can be neglected for practical purposes). The aim is to predict a Mohr strength envelope for a rock material from which one can also obtain its cohesion and friction data. Failure criteria may be applicable to rock materials only or also to rock masses.

Failure criteria for rock materials

A study of the literature reveals that the empirical criteria proposed by Murrell (1965) and by Hoek (1968) are particularly suitable for estimating the triaxial strength of rock materials. These criteria are not contradictory, and the choice of one instead of the other depends solely on practical convenience.

In 1965, Murrell proposed the following equation:

$$\sigma_1 = F\sigma_3^A + \sigma_c \tag{8.1}$$

where

σ_1 is the major principal stress;
σ_3 is the minor principal stress;
σ_c is the uniaxial compressive strength;
A and F are constants.

In normalized form, the above equation can be rewritten as follows:

$$\sigma_1/\sigma_3 = k(\sigma_3/\sigma_c)^A + 1 \tag{8.2}$$

where k is a constant.

Normalized form means the expression of the stresses as dimensionless ratios of the uniaxial compressive strength of the material. This has the advantage that, since effects such as specimen size, environmental conditions, and testing techniques are presumably similar in both numerator and denominator, they are eliminated upon normalization. Furthermore, the direct comparison of a number of tests on the same plot is possible.

In Figure 8.6, the triaxial strength results are plotted as σ_1/σ_c vs. σ_3/σ_c for five rock types, the two parameters of equation (8.2) are determined from the experimental data and the criterion given by this equation is fitted for each rock type.

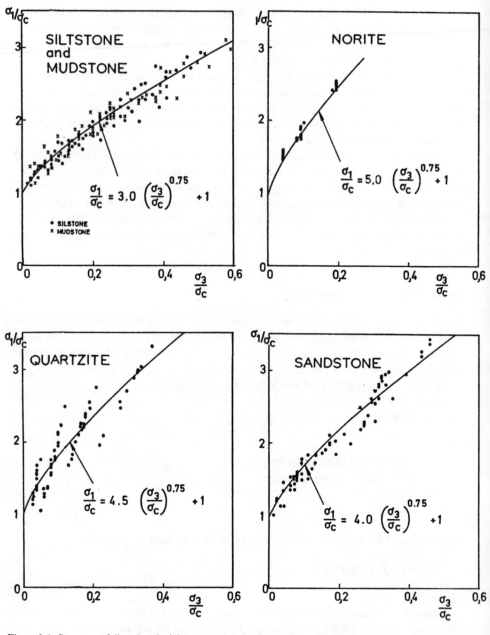

Figure 8.6. Stresses at failure in triaxial compression for five rock materials.

A particularly useful form for an empirical criterion was proposed by Hoek(1968) as follows:

$$\frac{\tau_m - \tau_0}{\sigma_c} = B\left[\frac{\sigma_m}{\sigma_c}\right]^C \tag{8.3}$$

where τ_m is the maximum shear stress and σ_m the mean normal stress given by:

$$\tau_m = \frac{\sigma_1 - \sigma_3}{2} \qquad \sigma_m = \frac{\sigma_1 + \sigma_3}{2} \tag{8.4}$$

and B, C and τ_o are constants. For practical purposes, $\tau_o = \sigma_t$ (uniaxial tensile strength).

The τ_m and σ_m quantities are given physical interpretation as the maximum shear stress acting in the specimen at failure and the normal stress acting on the plane of the maximum shear stress. They are the radius of a Mohr stress circle at failure and the distance from the origin to its center. A failure criterion expressed in this way defines the locus of points at the top of Mohr failure circles and is referred to as the maximum shear stress locus.

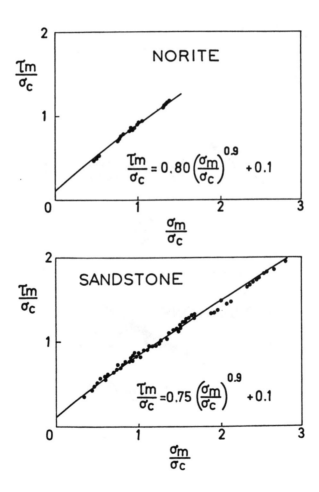

Figure 8.7. Relationship between the maximum shear and mean normal stresses at failure for norite and quartzite.

For the complete evaluation of the constants, the value of τ_o must be known and, as this is equal to σ_t, the ratio of σ_t/σ_c must be specified in equation (8.3). However, for practical purposes in rock mechanics, the uniaxial tensile strength σ_t is usually one-tenth of the uniaxial compressive strength σ_c. Equation (8.3) can thus be rewritten as:

$$\frac{\tau_m}{\sigma_c} = B \left[\frac{\sigma_m}{\sigma_c} \right]^C + 0.1 \qquad (8.5)$$

One reason for the choice of the maximum shear stress τ_m and the mean normal stress σ_m in the place of shear and normal stresses is that the construction of τ_m and σ_m circles and the fitting of a Mohr envelope is a simple and reliable graphical operation. This is not the case when fitting an envelope by eye to a set of experimentally determined Mohr circles. Such an envelope often does not include the scatter of experimental values because it is usually fitted to the circles of maximum diameter.

In Figures 8.7 and 8.8, the triaxial results are plotted as τ_m/σ_c versus σ_m/σ_c for five rock types and the two parameters of equation (8.5) are determined from the

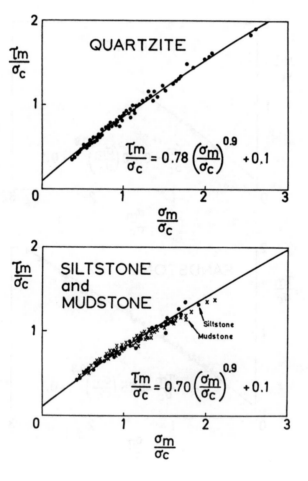

Figure 8.8. Relationship between the maximum shear and mean normal stresses at failure for sandstone, siltstone and mudstone.

Table 8.2. Parameters for two failure criteria for rock materials

Criterion	$\dfrac{\sigma_1}{\sigma_c} = A\left[\dfrac{\sigma_3}{\sigma_c}\right]^{0.75} + 1$			$\dfrac{\tau_m}{\sigma_c} = B\left[\dfrac{\sigma_m}{\sigma_c}\right]^{0.9} + 0.1$		
Norite	$A = 5.0$	Error:	3.6%	$B = 0.80$	Error:	1.8%
Quartzite	$A = 4.5$		9.2%	$B = 0.78$		3.2%
Sandstone	$A = 4.0$		5.8%	$B = 0.75$		2.3%
Siltstone	$A = 3.0$		5.6%	$B = 0.70$		4.2%
Mudstone	$A = 3.0$		6.1%	$B = 0.70$		6.6%
All types	$A = 3.5$	Prediction error: 10.4%		$B = 0.75$	Prediction error: 8.3%	

experimental data and the criterion given by this equation is fitted for each rock type.

The parameters for equations (8.2) and (8.5) are summarized in Table 8.2 as determined from 412 test specimens on five rock types. Also included are the average prediction errors for each rock type. These prediction errors were calculated as the difference between observed σ_1 and the predicted σ_1 expressed as a positive percentage of the predicted value. It is clear that both types of criteria – equation (8.2) or equation (8.5) – are acceptable for practical engineering purposes. Equation (8.2) is more convenient to use when the individual values of σ_1 are required for a given σ_3 while equation (8.5) should be employed whenever a full Mohr envelope is required (Bieniawski, 1974). Note that equation (8.2) is valid for compression only.

Failure criterion for rock masses

Despite a considerable research effort in the last two decades, a basic rock-mass strength criterion suitable for general practical application in rock mechanics has not as yet been developed. The latest most promising development is an empirical strength criterion for rock and rock masses for use in rock excavation design. Proposed by Hoek and Brown (1980) and discussed in Chapter 5, equation (5.7), the criterion is of the following form:

$$\frac{\sigma_1}{\sigma_c} = \frac{\sigma_3}{\sigma_c} + \sqrt{m\frac{\sigma_3}{\sigma_c} + s} \tag{8.6}$$

where
    σ_1 is the major principal stress at failure;
    σ_3 is the minor principal stress applied to the specimen;
    σ_c is the uniaxial compressive strength of intact rock;
    m and s are empirical constants which depend upon the properties of the rock and
        the extent to which it has been broken by being subjected to σ_1 and σ_3.

Priest and Brown (1983) provide a method for estimating m and s for rock masses using rock mass classifications.

For mining applications, Budavari (1974) discussed criteria for the design of underground excavations. Pointing out the complexity of mine workings and the lack of basic design data, he listed design criteria based on comparative studies of alternative designs regarding the states of stress or energy changes. These criteria do not allow the complete determination of the state of stability for rock structures. It must be noted, however, that the requirements regarding the stability of underground mining excavations are different from those in civil engineering tunneling. The main reason is that partial or local rock failure and deformations of small magnitudes are acceptable in mining. The design criteria applicable for underground mining are as follows:

1. Design criterion on the basis of comparative studies (comparison of potential fracture zones).

2. Design criterion based on the consideration of rock strength (strength of mine pillars).

3. Design criterion of limited deformation (mining in rock salt).

4. Design criterion using the principle of energy changes (critical energy release rate for rockbursts).

VALIDATION OF ANALYTICAL MODELING

In essence, analytical design methods are useful as modeling techniques to study the influence of the various parameters of the overall design of a rock structure and to enable a comparison of alternative designs. Analytical techniques suffer from the lack of validation experiments and as such mainly serve for parametric or comparative studies. The success of any analytical method is dependent on the input data that are used. In addition, the use of a realistic failure criterion describing the strength behavior of rock masses is essential for the successful application of analytical techniques. Brady and St. John (1982) identify some common deficiencies in rock mechanics applications of computational methods and propose ways of eliminating them.

Case history

In order to check prediction by the finite element method, a well documented case history was selected (Bieniawski, 1978). In this project, a test enlargement was constructed to the full size of the tailrace tunnel in a large underground hydroelectric project. The tunnel enlargement was instrumented with multiple-position borehole extensometers, convergence measuring devices, load cells, Glötzl pressure pads and piezometers. Rock stress measurements were carried out using two methods: the CSIR triaxial strength cell and circular flat jacks. Modulus of deformation measurements were conducted using small flat jacks, the Goodman borehole jack, tunnel relaxation and the petite sismique technique. Detailed engineering geological mapping was performed and geotechnical core logging was conducted on core from the instrumentation boreholes and from boreholes drilled from the surface. Groundwater conditions were assessed by a network of piezometers and by water pressure testing in boreholes. With the in situ stress field and the rock mass modulus of deformation

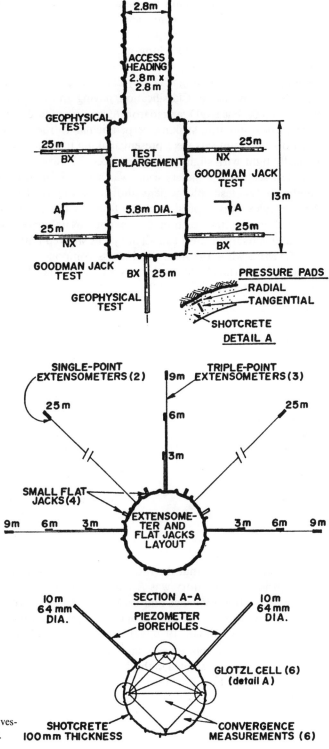

Figure 8.9. Rock mechanics investigations in a test enlargement.

known, a comparison could be made between the measured parameters and those predicted by the finite element method.

The test enlargement was located in a phyllite rock mass, 102 meters below the surface, and was 13 meters long and between 5.8 to 6 meters in diameter. It was excavated in two stages, by top heading and bench, using the smooth blasting technique of post-splitting. The phyllite rock mass was of a fair quality in accordance with the Geomechanics Classification, having an average rock mass rating RMR = 57 (range 48–60). The RQD ranged from 65%–75%. The dominant discontinuity set was a near vertical foliation striking perpendicular to the axis of the test enlargement. In addition, two joint sets were present striking normal to the foliation. The joints were typically tight with slightly wavy surfaces. The excavation was generally dry.

A test section, 2.5 meters wide, was selected for instrumentation purposes in the middle of the test enlargement shown in Figure 8.9. A shortcrete lining, up to 200 mm thick, was applied in stages to cover the Glötzl cells but no rockbolts were installed in the test section so as not to influence the instrumentation. Stress measurements by means of small flat jacks showed that the vertical stress component was 5.5 MPa while the horizontal stress component was 3.5 MPa. The modulus of deformation of the phyllite rock mass was determined by a number of methods and the results are listed in Table 8.3.

Table 8.3. Modulus of deformation for phyllite rock

Test method	Number of tests	Range GPa	Mean GPa	Standard deviation GPa
Small flat jacks	9	25.2–47.9	31.8	6.9
Goodman jack	6	6.0–20.0	12.0	6.2
Tunnel relaxation	4	9.7–39.6	20.0	13.4
Petite sismique	25	12.3–21.5	15.4	4.6
Quality index: RMR	7	15.1–22.4	20.1	2.6
Average in situ value (used for design)			19.8	
Laboratory tests	7	46.0–69.0	56.0	11.9

It should be noted that the ratio of the modulus of the rock mass to the modulus obtained in the laboratory was $E_M/E_L = 0.35$.

The excavation sequence and rock mass behavior were modeled, for comparison purposes, by two finite element programs, namely: a jointed rock model and a linear-elastic model (Goodman, 1979, van Heerden and Kovacs, 1979).

The measured displacements and pressures are shown in Figure 8.10. The finite element predictions depicted in this figure are for the jointed rock mass model as well as the elastic model. For convenience of comparison the results are summarized in Table 8.4. It may be concluded that the finite element methods gave a reasonable prediction of the displacements and pressures in the rock mass. As expected, the jointed rock model predicted larger displacements (in the roof and the floor) than the elastic model.

Table 8.4. Comparison of measured and predicted data

Position	Displacements, mm			Tangential Pressures, MPa	
	Measured (MPBX)	FEM jointed	FEM elastic	Measured (Flat jacks)	FEM jointed
Mid-roof	1.085	1.24	1.19	4.7 (3.5–6.0)	5.22
Left 45° roof	0.25	0.59	0.89	9.9 (4.3–14.0)	9.75
Right 45° roof	1.45	0.71	0.93	N/A	7.52
Left wall	0.50*	0.34	0.57	13.0 (11.4–15.9)	13.18
Right wall	0.12*	0.31	0.54	21.0 (8.1–15.9)	13.34
Mid-floor	**	1.28	0.91	4.7 (2.9–6.7)	5.45

*Convergence measurements showed shortening of 0.9 mm.
**Not measured by extensometers but convergence measurements yielded 1.3 mm

The highest compressive stress determined by the finite element method jointed rock model was 20.4 MPa in the sidewall as compared with the uniaxial compressive strength of the phyllite rock material of 57 MPa. It should be noted, however, that the strength of the phyllite rock mass would be substantially lower. Thus, the in situ compressive strength could possibly be exceeded by the compressive stresses in the sidewalls.

The maximum tensile stress determined by the jointed rock finite element analysis was 3.82 MPa in the roof and 2.6 MPa in the floor. This should be compared with the estimated uniaxial tensile strength of the phyllite material of 5 MPa. In Figure 8.11, the elements under tension are depicted together with the elements which showed shear failure on joints.

To check on the depth of loosening in the rock mass, analyses were conducted to determine the potential fracture zones using the method proposed by Hoek (1967). The principal stress distributions were obtained by the finite element method while the rock mass failure criterion was as follows (in MPa): $\sigma_1 - \sigma_3 = 0.58\,(\sigma_1 + \sigma_3) + 3$.

In Figure 8.12, the potential fracture zones in accordance with the jointed rock finite element method are given. It may be seen that the jointed rock finite element model predicts a zone of loosening from 0.5 to 2.0 meters. This finding may be compared with the data from the seismic refraction surveys which have indicated a possible zone of loosening between 2–3 meters around the test enlargement which was also confirmed by the triple-point extensometers. The elastic finite element method predicted a much smaller potential fracture zone.

It may be concluded from this discussion that the predictions by the finite element method were found to be sufficiently realistic for practical rock engineering purposes.

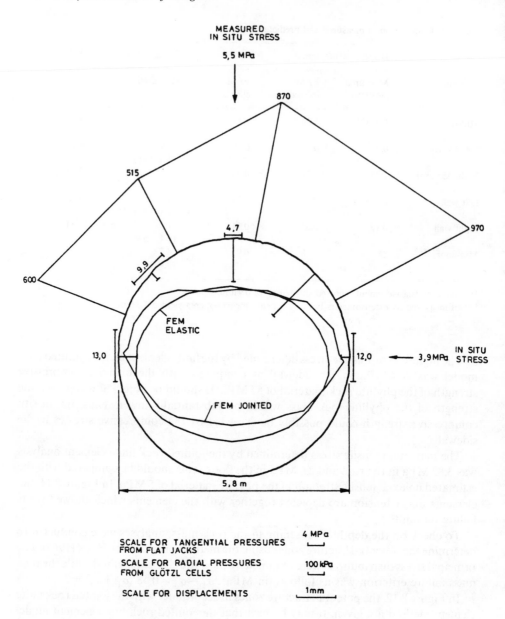

Figure 8.10. Comparison of measured displacements with those predicted by the finite element method.

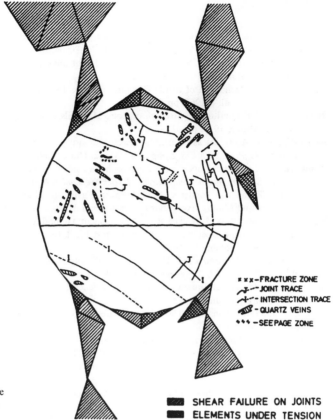

××× –FRACTURE ZONE
⌐ –JOINT TRACE
╤ – INTERSECTION TRACE
▱ – QUARTZ VEINS
♦♦♦ –SEEPAGE ZONE

▨ SHEAR FAILURE ON JOINTS
▬ ELEMENTS UNDER TENSION

Figure 8.11. Results from finite
element analyses using a jointed rock model.

▦ ELEMENTS UNDER TENSION

▨ SHEAR FAILURE ON JOINTS

■ MAXIMUM COMPRESSION

Figure 8.12. Potential fracture
zones based on finite element
analyses (jointed rock model).

SCALE
⊢———⊣
1 m

REFERENCES

Agbabian Associates. Application of a three-dimensional finite element analysis for the design of a large underground intersection. *NSF Report No. DAR*76–80044, El Sequndo, CA, 227 p.

Barron, K. and Larocque, E. Development of a model for mine structure. *Proc. Can. Rock Mech. Symp.*, McGill Univ., Montreal, 1962, pp. 145–190.

Bieniawski, Z. T. Mechanism of Brittle Fracture of Rock. *International Journal of Rock Mechanics and Mining Sciences*, Vol. 4, 1967, pp. 395–423.

Bieniawski, Z. T. Estimating the Strength of Rock Materials. *Journal of the S. A. Institute of Mining and Metallurgy*, March, 1974, pp. 312–320.

Bieniawski, Z. T. A critical assessment of selected in situ tests for rock mass deformability and stress measurements. *Proc. 19th U.S. Symp. Rock Mech.*, Univ. of Nevada, Reno, 1978, pp. 523–535.

Bieniawski, Z. T. Analytical modeling as a geomechanics aid for mine design applications in the USA. *Proc. 7th Plenary Session, International Bureau of Rock Mechanics*, A. A. Balkema, Rotterdam, 1981, pp. 7–22.

Bieniawski, Z. T. and Van Tonder, C. P. G. A Photo-Elastic Model Study of Stress Distribution and Rock Fracture Around Mining Excavations. *Experimental Mechanics*, Vol. 9, 1969, pp. 75–81.

Brady, B. H. G. and Bray, J. W. The Boundary Element Method for Determining Stresses and Displacements Around Long Openings in a Triaxial Stress Field. *International Journal of Rock Mechanics and Mining Sciences*, Volume 15, 1978, pp. 21–28.

Brady, B. H. G. and St. John, C. M. The role and credibility of computational methods in engineering rock mechanics. *Proc. 23rd U.S. Symposium on Rock Mechanics*, AIME, New York, 1982, pp. 571–586.

Brady, B. T. A Mechanical Equation of State for Brittle Rock. *International Journal of Rock Mechanics and Mining Sciences*, Volume 10, 1973, pp. 291–309.

Bray, J. W. and Goodman, R. E. The theory of base friction models. *Int. J. Rock Mech. Min. Sci.*, Vol. 18, No. 6, 1981, pp. 453–469.

Brebbia, C. A. and Walker, S. Introduction to the boundary element method, *Recent Advances in Boundary Element Methods* (C. A. Brebbia, ed.), Pentech Press, London, 1978, pp. 1–44.

Brook, N. Model studies of mine roadway deformation. *Mining Engineer*, Vol. 136, No. 191, 1977, pp. 375–384.

Budavari, S. Rock mechanics aspects of the design of underground mine workings, *Australian Mining*, October 1974, pp. 15–27.

Cook, N. G. W. and Schumann, E. H. R. *An electrical resistance analogue for planning tabular mine excavations*. Chamber of Mines Res. Rep. No. 72165, Johannesburg, 1965, 21 p.

Crouch, S. L. Solution of plane elasticity problems by the displacement discontinuity method. *Inter. J. Numer. Methods Eng.*, Vol. 10, 1976, pp. 301–343.

Cundall, P. A. Explicit finite-difference methods in geomechanics. *Proc. 2nd International Conference on Numerical Methods in Geomechanics*, American Society of Civil Engineers, New York, Vol. 1, 1976, pp. 132–150.

Desai, C. S. Some Aspects of Constitutive Models for Geologic Media, *Proceedings Third International Conference on Numerical Methods in Geomechanics*, Aachen, A. A. Balkema, Rotterdam, 1979, pp. 299–308.

Desai, C. S. and Christian, J. T. Introduction, numerical methods and special topics. *Numerical Methods in Geotechnical Engineering* (C. S. Desai and J. T. Christian, eds.) McGraw-Hill, New York, 1977, pp. 1–64.

Dolezalova, M. The Influence of Construction Sequence on the Stability of Underground Openings, *Proceedings Third International Conference on Numerical Methods in Geomechanics*, Aachen, A. A. Balkema, Rotterdam, 1979, pp. 561–570.

Egger, P. A new development in the base-friction technique. *Proc. Int. Colloquium on Physical Geomechanical Models*, ESMES, Bergamo, 1979, pp. 67–81.

Ertekin, T. and Farouq Ali, S. M. Numerical simulation of the compaction-subsidence phenomenon in a reservoir for two-phase nonisothermal flow conditions. *Proc. 3rd Int. Conf. Numerical Methods in Geomechanics*, Aachen, 1979, pp. 263–274.

Everling, G. Model tests concerning the interaction of ground and roof supports in gate roads. *Int. J. Rock Mech. Min. Sci.*, Vol. 1, No. 1, 1964, pp. 319–326.

Franklin, J. A. Triaxial strength of rock materials. *Rock Mechanics* Vol. 3, 1971, pp. 86–98.

Gercek, H. Stability of Intersections in Room-and-Pillar Coal Mining Ph.D. Thesis, The Pennsylvania State University, 1982, 186 pp.

Gergiannopoulos, N. G. and Brown, E. T. The Critical State Concept Applied to Rock. *International Journal of Rock Mechanics and Mining Sciences*, Vol. 15, 1978, pp. 1–10.

Goodman, R. E. *Methods of Geological Engineering*, West Publishing Co., St. Paul, 1976, 472 p.

Goodman, R. E. and St. John C. M. Finite Element Analysis for discontinuous rocks. *Numerical Methods in Geotechnical Engineering* (C. S. Desai and J. T. Christian, eds), McGraw-Hill, New York, 1977, pp. 148–155.

Griffith, A. A. The phenomenon of rupture and flow in solids. *Philosophical Transactions*, Vol. 222, 1921, pp. 163–198.

Griffith, A. A. Theory of rupture. *Proc. 1st Int. Congr. Applied Mechanics*, J. Waltman, Jr. Press, Delft, 1924, pp. 53–66.

Heuze, F. E. and Barbour, T. G. Stability Analysis for Rock Structures, *Proceedings 19th U.S. Symposium on Rock Mechanics*, University of Nevada, Reno, 1978, pp. 1–8.

Hobbs, D. W. Scale model studies of strata movement around mine roadways. *Int. J. Rock Mech. Min. Sci.*, Vol. 5, 1968, pp. 219–235.

Hoek, E. Experimental study of rock stress problems in deep level mining. *Proc. 1st Int. Congr. on Experimental Mechanics*, Pergamon, New York, 1963, pp. 177–193.

Hoek, E. Potential Fracture Zones in Rock Structures. *Proceedings 8th U.S. Symposium on Rock Mechanics*, AIME, Minneapolis, 1967, pp. 94–112.

Hoek, E. Brittle fracture of rock. *Rock Mechanics in Engineering Practice*, John Wiley & Sons, London, 1968, pp. 93–124.

Hoek, E. and Bieniawski, Z. T. Brittle fracture propagation in rock under compression. *Int. J. Fracture Mechanics*, Vol. 1, No. 3, 1965, pp. 139–155.

Hoek, E. and Brown, E. T. *Underground Excavations in Rock*, Institution of Mining and Metallurgy, 1980, pp. 87–182.

Ingraffea, A. R. and Heuze, F. E. Finite Element Models for Rock Fracture Mechanics. *International Journal for Numerical and Analytical Methods in Geomechanics*, Vol. 4, 1980, pp. 25–43.

Irwin, G. R. Fracture mechanics. *Structural Mechanics*, Pergamon Press, New York, 1960, pp. 557–592.

Jaeger, J. G. and Cook, N. G. W. *Fundamentals of Rock Mechanics*, Chapman and Hall, London, 3rd edition, 1979, pp. 88–106.

Kovamoto, T. and Saito, T. Stress and Stability Analyses of Underground Openings Taking Post-Failure Behavior of Rock into Consideration. *Numerical Methods in Geomechanics*, A. A. Balkema, Rotterdam, Volume 3, 1979, pp. 791–801.

Kovari, K. The Elasto-Plastic Analysis in the Design Practice of Underground Openings, *Finite Element in Geomechanics*, Edited Gudehus, G., John Wiley & Sons, 1975, pp. 377–412.

Kovari, K. Models for the Interpretation of Plastic and Brittle Behavior of Rocks, *Proceedings Third International Conference on Numerical Methods in Geomechanics*, Aachen, 1979, pp. 533–544.

Kovari, K., Hagedorn, H. and Fritz, P. Parametric studies as a design aid in tunneling. *Proc. 2nd Int. Conf. on Numer. Method in Geomechanics*, Blacksburg, Va., June 1976, pp. 1–18.

Krauland, N. The behavior of a prototype and a model mine tunnel. *Proc. Conf. on Technology and Potential of Tunneling*, Johannesburg, 1970, Vol. 1, pp. 135–140.

Lawrence, D. Effects of horizontal and vertical pressure in scale models of mine roadways. *Int. J. Rock Mech. Min. Sci.*, Vol. 10, No. 3, 1973, 173–183.

Mark, C. A Physical Model Study of Coal-Mine Roof using the Base-Friction Technique, M. S. Thesis, The Pennsylvania State University, 1982, 139 p.

McClain, W. C. The evaluation of mined room stability. *Proc. 1st Conf. on Mechanical Behavior of Salt*, The Pennsylvania State University, 1981, Trans Tech Publications, Clausthal, 1983.

McClintock, F. A. and Walsh, J. Friction on Griffiths's cracks in rocks under pressure. *Proc. 4th U.S. National Congr. Appl. Mech.*, Berkeley, 1962, pp. 1015–1021.

Muller, M. Numerical Design Method for Tunnel Structures of the Budapest Underground Railways, *Proceedings Third International Conference on Numerical Methods in Geomechanics*, Aachen, A. A. Balkema, Rotterdam, 1979, pp. 571–580.

Murrell, S. A criterion for brittle fracture of rocks and concrete under triaxial stress and the effect of pore pressure on the criterion. *Proc. 5th U.S. Rock Mech. Symp.*, Minneapolis, Minnesota, 1963, pp. 563–573.

Murrell, S. A. The effect of triaxial stress system on the strength of rock at atmospheric temperatures. *Geophys. J. Roy. Astr. Soc.*, Vol. 10, 1965, pp. 231–281.

Nadai, A. *Theory of Flow and Fracture of Solids*. McGraw-Hill Book Co., New York, 1950, pp. 207–228.

Panek, L. The combined effects of friction and suspension in bolting bedded mine roof. *Bureau of Mines RI*6139, 1962, 31 p.

Pariseau, W. G., Voight, B. and Dahl, H. D. Finite Element Analyses of Elastic-Plastic Problems in the Mechanics of Geologic Media. *Proceedings Second International Congress on Rock Mechanics*, ISRM, Belgrade, 1972, Paper 3–75.

Petukhov, I. M. and Linkov, A. M. The Theory of Post-Failure Deformations and the Problem of Stability in Rock Mechanics. *International Journal of Rock Mechanics and Mining Sciences*, Vol. 16, 1979, pp. 57–76.

Priest, S. D. and Brown, E. T. Probabilistic stability analysis of variable rock slopes. *Trans. Inst. Min. Metall.*, London, Vol. 92, 1983, pp. A1–12.

Roberts. W. J. and Einstein, H. H. Numerical modeling in rock joints. *Proc. 20th U.S. Symp. on Rock Mechanics*, University of Texas, Austin, 1979, pp. 233–241.

Salamon, M. D. G. Theoretical Considerations in Tunnel Design, *Tunneling in Rock*, edited Z. T. Bieniawski, CSIR, 1974, pp. 179–185.

Salamon, M. D. G. and Oravecz, K. I. The electrical analogue solution for determining the elastic response of strata surrounding tabular mining excavations. *Proc. 2nd Int. Congress on Rock Mech.*, ISRM, Belgrade, 1970, p. 4–18.

Smelser, T. W., Dar, S. M., Pettibone, H. C. and Bolstad, D. D. Modeling and field verification of roof-bolt systems, *SME-AIME Annual Meeting*, Dallas, 1982, Preprint No. 82–121.

Stimpson, B. Laboratory techniques for demonstrating rock mass behavior. *Int. J. Rock Mech. Min. Sci.*, Vol. 18, 1981, pp. 535–537.

Stimpson, B. Modeling materials for engineering rock mechanics. *Int. J. Rock Mech. Min. Sci.*, Vol. 7, 1970, pp. 77–121.

St. John, C. M. Christianson, M., Petersen, D. L. and Hardy, M. P. Geotechnical analysis of underground mining methods for the copper-nickel orebodies of N. E. Minnesota. *Proc. U.S. 20th Symp. Rock Mech.*, University of Texas, Austin, 1979, pp. 87–94.

Swoboda, G. Finite Element Analysis of the New Austrian Tunnelling Method. *Third International Conference on Numerical Methods in Geomechanics*, A. A. Balkema, Rotterdam, 1979, pp. 581–586.

Terzaghi, K. Rock defects and loads on tunnel support *Rock Tunneling with Steel Supports*, Commercial Shearing Co., Youngstown, Ohio, 1946, pp. 15–99.

U.S. National Committee for Rock Mechanics. *Rock Mechanics Research Requirements*, National Academy of Sciences, Washington, DC, 1981, pp. 184–188.

Van Heerden, W. L. and Kovacs, I. K. A. Two-dimensional finite element stress analysis of jointed rock – computer program ROCKJNT. *Rep. Coun. Sci. Ind. Res.*, Pretoria, No. ME1601/4, February 1979, 50 p.

Wawersik, W. R. Detailed analysis of rock failure in laboratory compression tests. Ph.D. Thesis, university of Minnesota, Minneapolis, 1968.

Weibull, W. A survey of statistical effects in the field of material failure. *Appl. Mech. Review*, Vol. 5, 1952, pp. 449–451.

Wittke, W. and Pierau, B. 3-D Stability Analysis of Tunnels in Jointed Rock. *Numerical methods in Geomechanics*, A. A. Balkema, Rotterdam, Volume 3, 1979, pp. 1401–1418.

Zienkiewicz, O. C. *The finite element method (3rd edition)*, McGraw-Hill, London, 1977, 785 pp.

CHAPTER 9

Integrated designs

College is where you learn how to learn.

Socrates (470–399 B.C.)

Integrated designs are those design procedures into which a number of concepts have been incorporated to make a design approach distinctive on its own. Generally, design methods such as empirical, observational and analytical should not be used separately to the exclusion of another method but all three should be utilized to provide a cross-check on the design assumptions and the design recommendations. In some instances, this has met with considerable success and has led to the development of a new design philosophy or procedure which systematically integrates various design concepts into one design approach. Three examples of integrated designs can be given:

1. The New Austrian Tunneling Method (NATM) – integrating observational and monitoring techniques with the fundamentals of rock-support interaction to provide a sound practical philosophy for tunnel design.

2. The German Strata Control System (Gebirgsbeherrschung) – integrating many design concepts for practical coal mining design.

3. The design of mine pillars – integrating the design of mine roofs, mine pillars and the selection of appropriate safety factors into an overall pillar design procedure.

Mining and civil engineers can learn much from each other concerning integrated designs. Yet, the NATM is virtually unknown in mining while the Strata Control System is a mystery to civil engineers. This chapter describes the Strata Control System and the design of pillars, while the New Austrian Tunneling Method is discussed in Chapter 7.

THE STRATA CONTROL SYSTEM FOR GERMAN COAL MINING (SYSTEM ZÜR GEBIRGSBEHERRSCHUNG)

The German Strata Control System (Jacobi, 1980) is an integrated planning and design system developed to serve the coal mining industry by the West German national research institution, Steinkohlenbergbauverein. They system was developed over the years by Dr.-Ing. Oskar Jacobi and his group but it was only in 1981 that Jacobi's book entitled *Praxis der Gebirgsbeherrschung* (*Practical Strata Control*) was published in 1981.

Coal mining in West Germany is exclusively by the longwall method. The present average depth of mining is about 900 meters, with some coal mines already operating at 1,400 meters. Accordingly, rock pressures are becoming increasingly more hazardous for coal mine operators. The combination of increasing working depth and concentration of longwalls under inhabited areas, has led to systematic consideration of the effects of rock pressures. The results of this effort are embodied in what is now known as 'The Strata Control System'.

The system is best described with reference to Figure 9.1. Two control loops are evident which are based on the results of appropriate analyses. One loop is directed to the planning and design operations while the other one is concerned with the practical support and mining operations directly involved in strata control. Much of the strata control system is directed to roof stability since, on average, 16 percent of the exposed roof results in falls. Each year more than 500 kilometers of tunnels (gateroads) are driven in West German coal mining. Although 90 percent of all gateroads are supported with modern yielding arches, on average they undergo closure to a third of

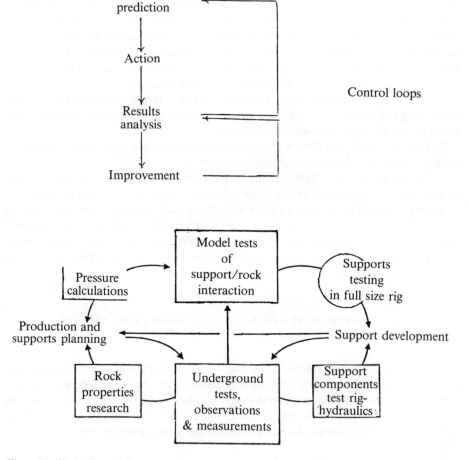

Figure 9.1. Strata Control System: contemporary concept (after Jacobi, 1980).

their original height. This causes interruptions in the transport of materials and men as well as in ventilation. All things considered, the cost of keeping the German workings open amounts to 16 percent of the total mining costs (Grotowsky, 1982).

The Strata Control System is coordinated through the Mine Support and Rock Mechanics Research Station in Essen, established in 1960. Over the years, a number of major advances were made in understanding the behavior of rock and coal strata in Germany. The starting point was a study of rock and support interaction by means of underground measurements as well as extensive modeling experiments.

With reference to Figure 9.1, rock pressure effects are simulated by model studies for obtaining information on the behavior of the strata and the supports. In the 1:10 scale face model, the effects of fracture in the roof are studied in relation to different types of support systems. Conclusions are drawn from these investigations with regard to the necessary support resistance. In a roadway model, also on a 1:10 scale, investigations are made into different types of support as well as the necessary measures to achieve the minimum convergence and roadway closures. In addition, the actual supports are evaluated in test rigs under very high loads such as those expected in the actual operation underground. The test rigs thus simulate actual operational conditions and provide useful feedback towards improving design.

The knowledge gained from the analytical, laboratory and underground methods has led to a number of design guidelines which emerged from the application of the Strata Control System in Germany. One of the most important aspects is to ensure that mine workings are sited in low pressure zones. Rules have been compiled and successfully applied for planning of mine tunnels (roadways). The rules cover the following points: the most favorable position of the roadways; the most suitable sequence of mining; the correct direction of face advance; the correct distance when overmining or undermining tunnels; the optimum layout of mining excavations.

In essence, the Strata Control System provides the following closely related objectives (Jacobi, 1980):

1. Calculating or evaluating rock pressures;
2. Planning the mine workings for placing long-term roadways in low pressure zones and competent strata;
3. Planning the layout of faces and support selection to minimize the rock pressure;
4. Establishing the service behavior of roof supports on the test rig under simulated conditions with the objective of detecting and eliminating defects before the supports are transported underground;
5. Monitoring of support and rock strata in-situ;
6. Collecting and storing of information and experience in the central data bank;
7. Solving special problems arising in coal mines.

The implementation of the Strata Control System is made possible through the interaction of various expert committees chaired by members of the mining technology main committee at Steinkohlenbergbauverein. The technical expert committees are composed of managers of coal mines or their representatives. One of the main tasks of the operation is to ensure that the results are made available to the coal mines with a minimum of delay. This means that the main committee has to coordinate the activities of the coal mines, the Research Station and the manufacturers of the equipment.

In order to handle the various aspects of the problem, the technical expert committees are set up in four areas: rock mechanics, face supports, roadway supports

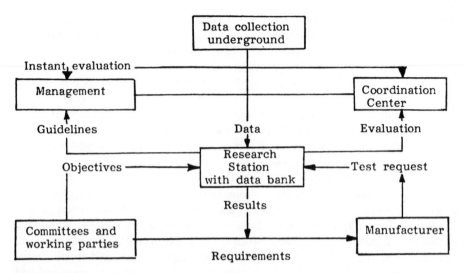

Figure 9.2. Strata Control System: cooperation between coal mines, the Research Station and equipment manufactures (after Jacobi, 1980; Grotowsky, 1982).

and support engineering. Each coal mine has at least one support engineer and he belongs to the regional working group which in turn coordinates the work relating to the coal mines.

Cooperation between the coal mines and the Research Station is on the basis depicted in Figure 9.2 (Grotowsky, 1982). This means that:

1. Underground operations data are evaluated for all coal mines;

2. Faces and roadways free of problems are also instrumented for the record so as to assist in determining stable behavior;

3. All data are routed to the Research Station for comprehensive evaluation and compilation;

4. These evaluations are used for planning and direct application at management levels, for designing supports by the equipment manufacturers, and for formulating further objectives for the technical committee.

The Research Station may be called for information and advice in cases where the mine engineers concerned with support are unable to provide immediate satisfactory solutions to the problems of rock pressure.

In summary, the concept of the Strata Control System operates as indicated diagrammatically in Figure 9.1. This is done along the following lines: Rock samples are taken in the course of in-situ measurements. Strata pressures and stresses are studied in special model test rigs and the rock strength is determined in the laboratory. The results are compared with in-situ observations. The supports are manufactured and tested in a rig to determine the behavior of single props as well as several support units. Note that strata-support interaction is evaluated both by means of large scale physical model tests as well as by means of numerical modeling. Although the Strata Control System has provided a new dimension by applying recent results for the direct benefit of the mining industry, Jacobi (1980) and his co-workers believe that during the next few years the basis for the planning and design of mining engineering projects will have to be refined and expanded. The challenges will be directed along four lines:

1. To produce documentation and methods for mine planning and design;
2. To compile operational observations as a basis for automation;
3. To develop new coal mining methods with a view to improved coal extraction, and;
4. To reduce dust at the faces and in the gateroads.

DESIGN OF MINE PILLARS

The rock mechanics research effort devoted to the design of pillars has been evident for many years. The first pillar strength formula was proposed in the USA as early as 1900 for anthracite after laboratory tests made for the Scranton Engineers Club. During the last two decades, research efforts have led to significant progress and today the design of pillars can be approached in a rational manner.

Nevertheless, no single design approach or pillar strength formula has been accepted as the most reliable one, even for coal mine pillars which have received the most research attention.

Uses of pillars

Although pillars are thought to be associated mainly with room and pillar coal mining, it is seldom that minerals have been or are being extracted underground without employing pillars either as main support elements or in some secondary role. There are three main categories of mine pillars:

1. Support pillars;
2. Protective pillars;
3. Control pillars.

Support pillars are found in those situations where the main support to the roof strata is provided by a system of pillars, usually laid out in a systematic manner. Room and pillar mining is the best example of the use of support pillars.

Protective pillars are used to protect either surface structures or underground mining excavations or to separate one mine from its neighbor. These pillars are also referred to as barrier pillars, shaft pillars, boundary pillars, or protection pillars (of buildings, highways, railroads, etc.) The main consideration in designing protective pillars is to ensure the integrity of the structures to be protected. Hence, consideration is given to the stresses and displacement induced by mining in the immediate vicinity of the structures for which protection is intended.

Control pillars are found in deep mining of tabular deposits in hard rock where the rockburst hazard can become severe. By introducing a systematic layout of pillars it is possible to control the energy changes induced by mining and alleviate the rockburst problem.

Pillars in coal mining

While pillars in coal mines are predominantly associated with room-and-pillar systems, their use as support elements in development entries for longwall and

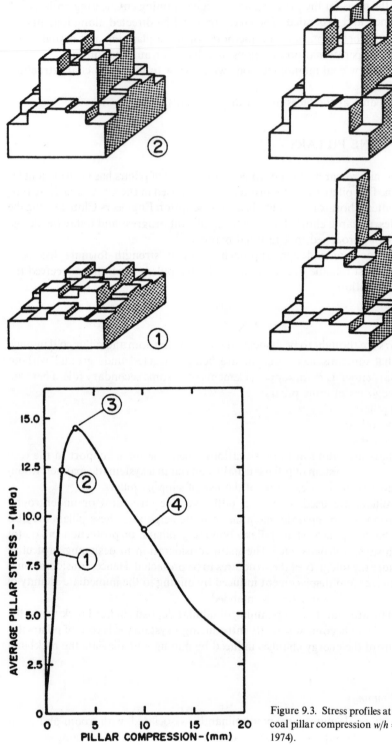

Figure 9.3. Stress profiles at various stages of a coal pillar compression $w/h = 2$ (after Wagner, 1974).

shortwall systems will continue to be of practical importance. These development entries, being service entries for such vital services as ventilation, power distribution, escapeways and haulage, represent the umbilical cord of a coal mine and must be maintained in a safe and adequate manner.

Coal pillars may or may not be extracted after mining. Room or chain pillars (located between entries) are more or less square or rectangular in shape for supporting and maintaining the rooms and entries. However, diamond-shape pillars are also frequently employed so that mining machines can negotiate the turn from entries to crosscuts with ease. Barrier pillars are located on both sides of each main entry or between sections to separate mined-out sections from neighboring virgin sections. Nevertheless, the world 'pillar' usually refers to room or chain pillars because they are so numerous.

The design of pillars involves determining the proper sizes of pillars for a given locality in line with the expected load. There are two approaches to coal pillar design. The ultimate strength approach contends that pillars will fail as soon as the applied load reaches the ultimate strength of the pillars. It presumes that the load-bearing capacity of a pillar reduces to zero the moment its strength is exceeded. The progressive failure approach emphasizes the existence of defects or a non-uniform stress distribution in the pillar. Failure initiates at the most critical point and propagates gradually to ultimate failure. Overall stability can be maintained despite the local failure.

In the ultimate-strength approach, a global or average safety factor is obtained for the entire pillar, whereas, in the progressive-failure approach, local safety factors are the prime aim of the calculations. The global safety factor is based on an average pillar strength and load; consequently, it is constant across the entire pillar. In contrast, the local safety factor relies on the pillar strength and load at a given point. Since pillar strength and load vary across an actual pillar, a local safety factor better represents reality.

It should be noted that in the United States, the 1969 Coal Mine Health and Safety Act prescribes the prevailing safety concept for underground structures (i.e., entries and pillars), namely, that the structural elements (roof, floor and ribs) of the opening must be kept in perfect or nearly perfect condition to be safe for use. It is obvious that the U.S. safety concept uses failure initiation as the criterion rather than ultimate failure as has been practiced in other countries. Accordingly, the design of pillars that form the ribs of the opening has to consider not only the stability of the pillars themselves, but also their interaction with the roof and floor.

In Figure 9.3, the results of underground tests on coal pillars, conducted by Wagner (1974), are presented. He measured the stress distribution across pillars at various stages of deformation. It was found that the perimeter of a pillar is capable of carrying relatively little stress but this portion of the pillar provides lateral confinement which enhances the strength of the center of the pillar. These tests have also indicated that pillars of rectangular cross-section are up to 40 percent stronger than square pillars of the same width and height because of the relatively smaller perimeter of square pillars. Experimental results show (Cook and Hood, 1978) that long rectangular pillars (barrier pillars) having a width greater than 10 times their height are unlikely to fail except for punching into the roof or the floor.

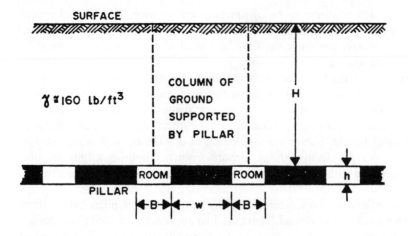

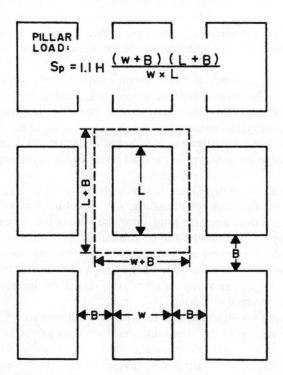

Figure 9.4. Tributary area concept for pillar loading.

Pillar-load considerations

A number of approaches are available for estimating the 'pillar load' or, more correctly, the average pillar stress. The two major ones are the tributary area approach and the elastic-deflection theory.

Tributary-area approach
This approach expresses the pillar load for rectangular pillars in the following manner (see Figure 9.4):

$$S_p = \frac{0.025\,H(w+B)(L+B)}{w \times L} \tag{9.1}$$

where
S_p = pillar load or the average pillar stress (in MPa);
H = depth below surface (in meters);
w = pillar width (in meters);
L = pillar length (in meters);
B = entry width (in meters).

The term $0.025\,H$ can be replaced by the virgin vertical pressure, S_v, for a more general expression. The term S_v is derived from the overburden weight above the seam, γH, where γ is the unit weight of the overburden. The pressure can be considered to increase at a rate of 0.025 MPa per meter of depth.

For square pillars, that is when $w = L$, equation (9.1) becomes

$$S_p = 0.025\,H\left[\frac{w+B}{w}\right]^2 \tag{9.2}$$

If the term 'extraction', e, is introduced ($100e$ is percentage extraction) which is defined as the ratio of the mined-out area to total area, then for square pillars:

$$e = 1 - \left[\frac{w}{w+B}\right]^2 \tag{9.3}$$

Thus, equation (9.2) may also be rewritten as:

$$S_p = \frac{0.025\,H}{1 - e} \tag{9.4}$$

This approach incorporates the following assumptions:
1. The seam is subjected only to vertical pressure which is constant over the mined area. However, stress transfer occurs where stiff abutments exist in underground workings. Thus, this vertical pressure may be relieved partially.
2. Each pillar supports the column of rock over an area which is the sum of the cross-sectional area of the pillar plus a portion of the room area, the latter being equally shared by all neighboring pillars. However, this is certainly not valid if the area of development is small since the pillars in the center of the excavation are under more stress than the pillars near the sides. It is usually only accepted as valid if the mined-out area is greater than the depth below surface.
3. It is assumed that the load is uniformly distributed over the cross-sectional area of the pillar. However, research has shown that:

a) The stress is not evenly distributed over the cross-section of an individual pillar, the maximum stress occurring at the corners formed by the intersection of three orthogonal planes, namely, two sidewalls of the pillar and the roof or the floor.

b) The stress on pillars increases with percentage extraction; and

c) The stress distribution in pillars depends upon the ratio of pillar width to pillar height.

Clearly, the assumptions made in the formulation of this approach lead to a conservative estimate of the pillar load. Therefore, it represents the upper limit of the average pillar stress. In fact, measurements have shown (Hustrulid, 1981) that this approach overestimates the pillar load by about 40%. The simplicity and conservatism of this theory results in its present popularity.

Elastic-deflection theory

Salamon (1964, 1967), Coates (1966), and Oravecz (1977) studied the concept of pillar-load based on the theory of elasticity. The most important consideration is that of seam compression between a relatively stiff roof and floor. Coates (1966) derived a complicated equation listed in Table 9.1 for incremental loading due to mining. The value of ΔS_p is then entered into $S_p/S_v = \Delta S_p/S_v + 1$ to obtain the total pillar stress. S_v represents the virgin vertical stress acting on the seam. Coates' elastic solution results in average pillar loadings that are 40 percent lower than the values from the tributary-area-theory. Elastic deformations of the structural elements produce this stress reduction.

Oravecz (1977) studied pillar loading using an electrical-resistance analog model to simulate seam convergence and obtain pillar-load distributions. The results of three field-convergence comparisons with the model predictions revealed a good correlation

Table 9.1. Coates' elastic pillar-load formula

$$S_p/S_v = \Delta S_p/S_v + 1$$

where

S_p = total pillar load;
S_v = virgin vertical stress;

and

ΔS_p = pillar load due to mining which is described as:

$$\Delta S_p = \frac{2R - kh(1-w)(1-x^2+h) - wp(khn)}{hn + \pi(1-R)(1+1/N)(1+h/1-x^2)/2 + 2Rb'(1-w)\pi}$$

where, for plane strain:

$M = E/(1-v^2)$	$b' = b/L$
$w = v/(1-v)$	$x = x^*/l^*$
$k = \sigma_h/\sigma_v$	$h = h^*/l^*$
$n = M/M_p$	

(p subscript denotes pillar rock value);
E = Young's modulus of the roof rock (psi);
v = Poisson's ratio;
σ_h = Horizontal stress acting on the seam (psi);
σ_v = Vertical stress acting on the seam (psi);
b = Width of the pillar (feet);

L = Breadth of the mining zone (feet);
x^* = Displacement in x direction (feet);
h^* = Pillar height (feet);
l^* = Pillar length (feet);
N = Number of pillars;
R = Radial distance from center (feet).

between pillar-load magnitudes and distributions and an appropriate in-situ elastic-modulus selection. These field tests consisted of convergence measurements using a surface-mounted extensometer that extended down to the seam. This system enabled Oravecz (1977) to measure the very small displacements which often occur in coal mining. Oravecz outlined modeling assumptions which affect the applicability of this theory. These assumptions are:

1. The analog solution is based on the existence of a homogeneous medium;
2. The mine-panel geometry must be uniform;
3. The depth of cover must be uniform;
4. The displacements increase linearly in the vicinity of the seam.

The first three assumptions correlate to those made in the tributary-area approach. However, rigid elements and, more importantly, restrictions on stress distributions across the pillar and panel are eliminated and replaced with more realistic in-situ characteristics.

Oravecz concluded that the analog technique described adequately the stress displacement distribution across a pillar and supported the elastic-theory approach of Coates rather than the tributary-area-theory approach. However, despite this agreement between the theory and the field measurements, the tributary-area-theory is still used in practical mining applications due to its simplicity and conservative results.

Pillar-strength considerations

The strength of mine pillars, that is the ultimate load per unit area is dependent upon three elements: (i) the size or volume effect (strength reduction from a small laboratory specimen of rock to full size mine pillars); (ii) the effect of pillar geometry (shape effect); (iii) the properties of the pillar material.

The size effect
As discussed in Chapter 5, experimental results from tests on rock show that there is a strength reduction with increasing specimen size (see Figures 5.14 and 5.15).

The concept of the 'critical size' strength (Bieniawski, 1968) for rock masses is very important in practical design. The critical size is defined as that specimen size at which a continued increase in specimen width causes no significant decrease in strength. Other authors (Jahns, 1966, Lama, 1971, and Pratt et al., 1972) confirmed that this critical-size phenomenon exists in various rock types as shown in Figure 5.15.

For South African coal, Bieniawski (1968) concluded that 1.5 m (5 ft) cubic specimens constitute the critical-size value. Pariseau, in 1977, reported that the critical size for western coal is 0.9 m (3 ft). Hustrulid (1976) pointed out that a critical size of 3 ft would be generally applicable to coal for practical engineering purposes. This is evident from Figure 9.5 where his data for the Pittsburgh coal are depicted. Wang, et al. (1976) utilized the critical size given by Bieniawski in his research program. Peng (1978) and Singh (1981) compiled the data relating specimen size to specimen strength from many investigations which presented a strong argument for the critical-size property for coal (see Figure 5.14 in Chapter 5).

The significance of the phenomenon of 'critical size' is, of course, that the strength values at the critical size are directly applicable to full size pillars.

The size effect characterizes the difference in the strength between the small size

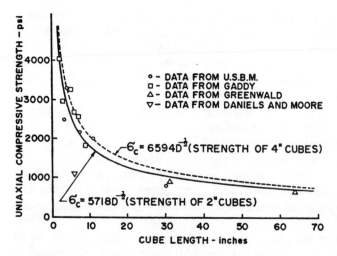

Figure 9.5. Compressive strength as a function of cube size for Pittsburgh coal (after Hustrulid, 1975).

specimens tested in the laboratory and the large size pillars mined in situ. Research has shown (Hustrulid, 1976) that the scaling of coal properties from laboratory measured data to field values can be satisfactorily achieved by the following equations:

$$\sigma_1 = \frac{k}{\sqrt{36}} \tag{9.5}$$

applicable to cubical pillars having the height $h > 36$ inches (0.9 m) or

$$\sigma_1 = \frac{k}{\sqrt{h}} \tag{9.6}$$

applicable to cubical pillars having the height less than 0.9 m.

In the above equations, the constant k must be determined for the actual pillar material and is obtained as shown by Gaddy (1956):

$$k = \sigma_c \sqrt{D} \tag{9.7}$$

where σ_c is the uniaxial compressive strength of rock specimens tested in the laboratory having a diameter or cube size dimension D (in inches). It should be noted that although there is a difference in laboratory results depending on whether cylindrical or cubical specimens are used, for practical engineering purposes this difference is not significant within the range of D between 50 mm to 100 mm – see Figure 9.5.

The 'critical size' strength of the rock mass (σ_1) may also be obtained by other methods described in Chapter 5 including the use of empirical equations such as the Protodyakonov formula and the Hoek-Brown criterion. Large scale in situ tests (Bieniawski and van Heerden, 1975) have also been used for this purpose but, since they are expensive and time consuming, the empirical equations may be preferable.

The shape effect
Extensive laboratory and in-situ investigations have been conducted throughout the world aimed at estimating the strength of mine pillars. As a result, numerous pillar

strength formulae were proposed describing the effect of the pillar shape on the strength. In fact, although no less than 12 different approaches can be distinguished, two types of pillar strength expressions are predominant:

$$\sigma_p = \sigma_1 \left(A + B\frac{w}{h} \right) \tag{9.8}$$

and

$$\sigma_p = K \frac{w^\alpha}{h^\beta} \tag{9.9}$$

where σ_p is the pillar strength, σ_1 is the strength of a cubical pillar at the critical specimen size (scaled strength incorporating the size effect); K is a constant characteristic of a pillar rock while α and β are constants. This shape effect is valid from laboratory size specimens up to the full-size pillars at which point the pillars may become indestructible at high w/h ratios. Figure 9.6 shows a rapid strength increase for sandstone specimens with increasing width-to-height ratios, particularly for $w/h > 5$.

1. *Obert–Duvall/Wang formula*
Obert and Duvall (1967) derived from laboratory tests on hardrock and elasticity

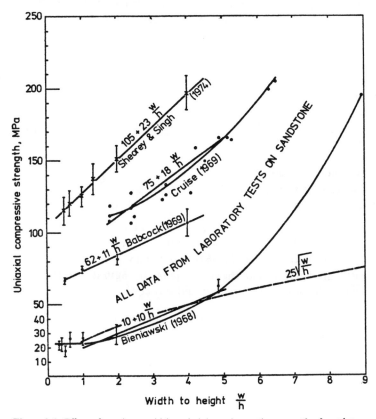

Figure 9.6. Effect of specimen width-to-height ratio on the strength of sandstone.

considerations the same relationship as did Bunting in 1911. This formula is given as:

$$\sigma_p = \sigma_1\left(0.778 + 0.222\frac{w}{h}\right)$$

where

σ_p is the pillar strength;
σ_1 is the uniaxial compressive strength of a cubical specimen ($w/h = 1$);
w and h are the pillar dimensions.

According to Obert and Duvall, this equation is valid for w/h ratios of 0.25 to 4.0 assuming gravity-loading conditions. Through back calculations from mining case histories and utilization of laboratory rock properties, safety factors of 2 to 4 were derived for short and long-term pillar stability, respectively. Essentially, this safety factor accounts for strength scaling from laboratory (or rock-material) strength to in-situ (or rock-mass) strength.

In 1975, Wang, Skelly, and Wolgamott of the Colorado School of Mines (CSM) conducted in-situ tests on one coal pillar located in West Virginia (Wang et al., 1976). The tests consisted of reducing pillar dimensions until failure occurred and then determining the pillar strength. The authors proposed the same formula as above and defined σ_1 as the ultimate strength of a cubical specimen of critical size or greater.

The CSM research was important for a number of reasons. First, equation (9.10) was applied to coal strata. Second, the term σ_1 was defined acknowledging the existence of a critical-size phenomenon. Third, the equation was stated as being valid for w/h ratios up to 8.

2. *Holland-Gaddy formula.* Holland (1964) extended the work by Gaddy (1956) and proposed the following formula:

$$\sigma_p = \frac{k\sqrt{w}}{h} \tag{9.11}$$

where

k is the Gaddy factor from equation (9.7);
w and h are the pillar dimensions in inches;
σ_p is the pillar strength in lb/sq. in.

Holland recommended a safety factor between 1.8 and 2.2 for the design of coal pillars, with a recommended value of 2.0. The width-to-height ratio, for which the Holland formula is valid, ranges from 2 to 8. Holland (1962) stated that w/h ratios of 9 to 10 can be used, but the result will underestimate the in-situ pillar strength due to significant confinement effects which his formula derivation did not consider.

3. *Holland formula.* In a paper published in 1973, Holland provided a diferent expression for the strength of coal pillars, namely:

$$\sigma_p = \sigma_1\sqrt{\frac{w}{h}} \tag{9.12}$$

where σ_1 is the strength of cubical pillars ($w = h = 1$). In effect, σ_1 can be interpreted as the strength at the 'critical size' of coal specimens and is to be determined from equation (9.5).

4. *Salamon-Munro formula* (1967). Salamon and Munro (1967) conducted a survey of failed and standing coal pillars in South Africa. Based on the studies of Holland (1964) and Greenwald et al. (1939), they selected the following form of pillar strength to apply to square pillars:

$$\text{Strength} = Kh^{\alpha}w^{\beta}$$

The constants for the above equation were derived from a statistical survey of the data reflecting the actual mining experience. In all, 125 case histories were used, of which 98 were standing pillars and 27 were failed pillars (collapsed at the time of the analysis). In deriving a pillar strength formula it was assumed that those pillars which were still intact had safe dimensions while the collapsed pillars were too small. The following pillar strength formula was proposed:

$$\sigma_p = 1320 \frac{w^{0.46}}{h^{0.66}} \tag{9.13}$$

where the strength σ_p is in lb/sq. in. and the pillar dimensions w and h are in feet. The recommended safety factor for this formula is 1.6, the range being 1.31 to 1.88.

In metric units, equation (9.13) becomes:

$$\sigma_p = 7.2 \frac{w^{0.46}}{h^{0.66}}$$

where the strength σ_p is in MPa while w and h are in meters.

This statistical formula is applicable to South African conditions and it represents the average strength data for coal pillars in that country. Since there are considerable variations in coal strength between the various mines in South Africa (Bieniawski and van Heerden, 1975), the Salamon-Munro formula is currently being modified in South Africa in two respects: (i) incorporating the actual strength of coal in a mine rather than the average coal strength in the country, and (ii) extending its use for a w/h ratio of five and over (Wagner, 1982). The first aspect can be simply achieved by the use of equation (9.5) or (9.6).

As with any statistical formulae, they should be applied within the range of values which were used for the analyses. The following range of parameters is applicable to the Salamon–Munro formula.

Range of parameters used by Salamon and Munro (1967)

Group	Standing pillar cases	Failed pillar cases
Number of cases	98	27
Depth (meters)	20–220	21–192
Seam height (meters)	1.2–5.0	1.5–5.5
Pillar width (meters)	2.7–21	3.4–16
Extraction percent	37%–89%	45%–91%
Width-to-height ratio	1.2–8.8	0.9–3.6
Shape of pillars	Square	Square

Table 9.2. Summary of strength formulae proposed from large-scale in situ tests

Year and country	Investigators	Coal seams	Specimen cross-section	Width (m)	Height (m)	Width/height ratio	No. of tests	Formula	Remarks
1933–1939 USA	H. P. Greenwald H. C. Howarth I. Hartmann	Pittsburgh	Square	0.81–1.61	0.78–1.61	0.50–1.03	5	$\sigma_p = 700\sqrt{w/h}$ (psi)	
1939–1941 USA	H. P. Greenwald H. C. Howarth I. Hartmann	Pittsburgh	Square	0.30–1.07	0.74–0.77	0.41–1.68	7	$\sigma_p = 2800(\sqrt{w}/\sqrt{h^5})$ (psi)	
1965–1966 South Africa	Z. T. Bieniawski	Witbank	Square	0.61–1.22	0.61–1.22	0.50–2.00	19	$\sigma_p = 7.6\,w^{0.16}/h^{0.55}$ (MPa) with w and h in meters	Valid for w/h < 1 and w < 1.5 m
1967–1968 South Africa	Z. T. Bieniawski	Witbank	Square	1.50–2.00	0.60–2.00	1.00–3.10	16	$\sigma_p/\sigma_1 = 0.64 + 0.36(w/h)$	Valid for: w/h > 1 and w > 1.5 m
1970–1972 South Africa	N. G. W. Cook H. Wagner	Usutu	Square and rectangular	0.60–2.00	0.86–2.00	0.60–2.20	12	$\sigma_p = \sqrt{w/h}$ (MPa)	$\sigma_p = 7 + 4w/h$ (MPa) also fits the data
1973 South Africa	W. L. van Heerden	New Largo	Square	1.40	0.41–1.24	1.14–3.39	10	$\sigma_p = 10 + 4.2\,w/h$ (MPa)	
1977 USA	F. Wang J. Wolgamott W. A. Skelley	Pocahontas #3	Square	7.90–24.00	1.76	4.48–13.60	1	$\sigma_p/\sigma_1 = 0.78 + 0.22\,w/h$	

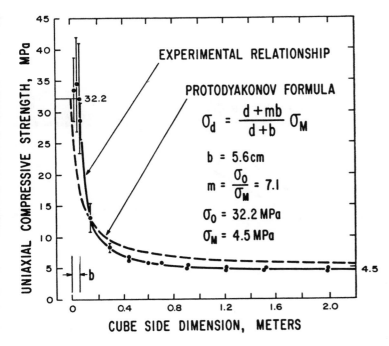

Figure 9.7. Comparison of experimental data from large scale in situ tests on coal with the Protodyakonov formula (after Bieniawski, 1969).

5. *In situ test methods.* Large scale in situ tests on coal pillars were first undertaken in the United States by Greenwald et al. (1939) during the period 1933–1941. Extensive tests were conducted in South Africa during 1965–1973 by Bieniawski (1967, 1969), Wagner (1974) and Bieniawski and van Heerden (1975). In 1977, Wang et al. (1977) conducted in the USA the largest test of all involving one full size coal pillar measuring 24 m in width. All these investigations led to the various pillar strength formulae summarized in Table 9.2. In Figure 9.7, the experimental data from the in situ large scale tests are compared with the Protodyakonov formula for the size effect (see also Figure 5.13 in Chapter 5). In Figure 9.8, the shape effect for coal is demonstrated on the basis of in situ tests in the USA and South Africa.

To make the in situ test results generally applicable (i.e. not only to the locality where the actual tests were carried out), the pillar strength formula should be expressed in a normalized form. For example, the original formula for the Witbank coalfield (Bieniawski, 1967) was of the form:

$$\sigma_p(psi) = 400 + 220\frac{w}{h}$$

This can be represented dimensionlessly as:

$$\sigma_p = 620\left(0.64 + 0.36\frac{w}{h}\right)$$

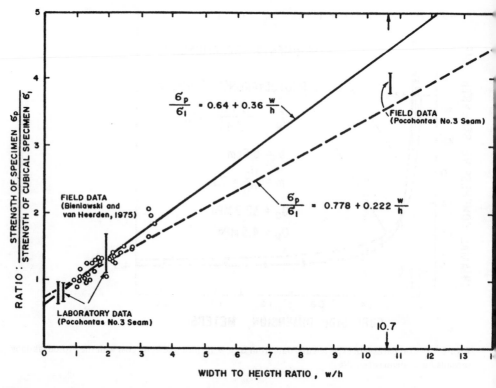

Figure 9.8. The effect of specimen width-to-height ratio on strength of coal (after Wang et al., 1977, and Bieniawski and van Heerden, 1975).

where $\sigma_1 = 620$ *psi* is the 'critical size' strength for the Witbank coalfield. Thus the general normalized form of this equation is:

$$\sigma_p = \sigma_1 \left(0.64 + 0.36 \frac{w}{h} \right) \qquad (9.14)$$

where

σ_p = the pillar strength;
w = the pillar width;
h = the pillar height;
σ_1 = the strength of a cubical specimen of critical size or greater (e.g. about 1 m for coal).

Bieniawski (1969) and Bieniawski and van Heerden (1975) confirmed this relationship by large-scale in-situ tests on 66 coal specimens of width-to-height ratios from 0.5 to 3.4.

The formula is valid for w/h ratios up to 5. Although the formula was developed in South African coal mines, Holland (1973) suggested that a safety factor of two is adequate for U.S. applications of this formula.

For U.S. coal fields, Wang et al. (1977) suggested the following formula from in-situ tests on the Pocohantas No. 3 seam in southern West Virginia (see Figure 9.8):

$$\sigma_p = \sigma_1 \left(0.78 + 0.22 \frac{w}{h} \right)$$

Note that this same equation was proposed by Bunting in 1911 and by Obert and Duvall in 1946.

6. *British approach.* Wilson (1972) emphasized the concept of soft rock mechanics applicable to coal strata in England. In soft rocks, the failure occurs progressively and the immediate strata around the excavation is in a condition of yield. Thus the problem of rockbursts or bumps in the stronger rocks is replaced with that of closure in the weaker rocks such as coal.

The Wilson concept is based on the premise that a pillar is divided into two zones: a central inside core subjected to triaxial stress conditions (known as the pillar core) which is solid and behaves elastically, and the 'yield zone' which is fractured and which tends to constrain the pillar core. The benefit of this hypothesis is that it enables the determination of coal pillar sizes and the assessment of the entry or cross-cut stability.

Wilson defined his concept as a 'supposition made as a basis for reasoning, not necessarily based on fundamentally correct theory and only approximate to the truth but one ultimately giving the correct answer'. This correct answer is that the pillar width is equal to one-tenth of the overburden depth plus 15 yards. In fact, although his original paper was published in 1972, the hypothesis was subsequently modified (Wilson, 1977) and described in its latest form in 1983 (Wilson, 1983).

The basis of Wilson's hypothesis is that the strength of coal can be represented by an equation as follows:

$$\sigma_1 = \sigma_c + \sigma_3 \tan \beta$$

In this equation σ_c is the uniaxial compressive strength and $\tan \beta$ is the triaxial stress factor assumed to be equal to 4, which is an approximation derived from laboratory tests on coal conducted in England. This means in essence that the relationship for coal between the confining pressure and the stress at failure is assumed to be a straight line, the slope of which is $\tan \beta$. Wilson also assumed that $\tan \beta$ is a material constant which does not change with the state of the rock. In other words, $\tan \beta$ is the same for intact rock as well as for fractured rock. Note that for in situ applications σ_c is taken as one-fifth of the laboratory strength determined from a small sample in the laboratory.

To check the validity of the above assumption, $\tan \beta$ may be determined by means of the triaxial test. Alternatively, the borehole shear tester of the U.S. Bureau of Mines is a very useful device as it enables determination in the field of the values of σ_c as well as tan β (Panek, 1980).

The next assumption in Wilson's hypothesis is that for coal measure rocks σ_c is small compared to $4\sigma_3$. It is assumed that at the edges of pillars the coal is already fractured and in the core of the pillar the confining pressures are very high. This led Wilson to the conclusion that for most coal measure rocks at depth, regardless of their unconfined strength or state of fracture, the stress required to cause failure is about four times the confining pressure.

Therefore, to check Wilson's hypothesis, it is necessary to conduct stress measurements across coal pillars to establish whether the stress distribution across the pillars confirms the presence of the solid core and the yield zone. Furthermore, it would also be necessary to determine the boundary between the yield zone and the core.

The third assumption in the hypothesis is that virgin hydrostatic conditions of in situ stress are in existence. However, the Bureau of Mines has found that in the USA, in many cases the horizontal stresses are much greater than the vertical stresses (Aggson, 1978). Consequently, at any test sites, it will be necessary to establish the virgin stress conditions.

The fourth aspect of the hypothesis is that it applies if the roof and floor are of moderate strength. If either are exceptionally weak the triaxial stress factor, tan β, will be significantly less than 4 and new formulae would have to be used with a lower triaxial stress factor. If the roof contains exceptionally strong and massive strata, the yield zone would be small or nonexistent. This means that attention must also be directed to the quality of the floor and roof strata.

The triaxial stress factor is considered by Wilson as one of the most important parameters in assessing the behavior of soft rocks around an excavation. It is the rock mechanics counterpart of a well known soil mechanics function, the angle of internal friction ϕ, and can be shown (Wilson, 1977) to be related by the equation:

$$\tan \beta = k = \frac{1 + \sin \phi}{1 - \sin \phi}$$

Wilson (1977) proposed a formula for the width of the yield zone x_b alongside wide excavations. Thus, the minimum coal pillar width w will equal to twice the yield zone x_b plus a constant C:

$$w = 2(x_b + C) \tag{9.15}$$

The width of the yield zone x_b is given by:
a) For weak stratum between strong roof and floor:

$$x_b = \frac{h}{F_k} \ln \frac{\gamma H}{p} \tag{9.16}$$

where

$$F_k = \frac{k - 1}{\sqrt{k}} + \frac{(k - 1)^2}{k} \tan^{-1} \sqrt{k}$$

b) For weak rock in roof, seam and floor:

$$x_b = \frac{h}{2} \left[\left(\frac{\gamma h}{p} \right)^{1/(k - 1)} - 1 \right] \tag{9.17}$$

The peak abutment pressure for both cases is given by:

$$\sigma_y = k \gamma H$$

where
      h is the seam height;
      H is the depth below surface;
      γ is the weight per unit volume;
      k is the triaxial stress factor (tan β);
      p is the horizontal restraint at the ribside (support resistance plus strength of broken rock ~ 0.1 MPa).

Note that the values quoted for p are between 0.05 MPa ($0.5 \, t/ft^2$) and 0.4 MPa ($3.7 \, t/ft^2$) and they should be compared with an approximation used by Wilson in 1972, that is, $x_b = 0.005hH$ (in meters) or $0.0015hH$ (in feet).

7. *Canadian approach.* Based on laboratory tests in triaxial compression conducted on intact and fractured samples of various sizes of siderite rock, up to 24 cm in diameter, Herget and Unrug (1974) estimated the strength of a mine pillar in Canada. The Mohr envelopes obtained showed the size effect over the whole range of confining pressure employed. The prediction of the pillar strength by a log-volume/log-strength relationship was considered unrealistically low. Instead, it was found that the mean uniaxial compressive strength of broken and sound samples converged with increasing size and this convergence was used to estimate the strength of the full size pillar (21.3 m wide) which was found to be 78.6 MPa by comparison with the strength of NX size samples of 206 MPa.

8. *Australian approach.* In Australia, pillar sizing in room-and-pillar coal mines is based on prescribed legislative regulations in accordance with §53BA of Mining Act No. 51 of 1974. These guidelines are given below:

Depth	Minimum pillar width	Minimum percentage extraction
< 60 m	8 m	50%
60–150 m	11 m	40–50%
150–300 m	17 m	30–40%
> 300 m	24 m	15–30%

Note: Room width: max. 5.5 m; Room height: max. 4.0 m if seam height > 5 m.

9. *Analytical studies.* Pariseau (1977) conducted a study directed towards assessing in-situ pillar strength. The research included laboratory, field and analytical work on Utah coal. Pariseau concluded that numerical methods using limit-stress analysis are reliable tools for pillar design. He added that data input remains a problem and that laboratory values were sufficient for the present stage of development. The finite-element method, incorporated into a limit-design approach, enabled the prediction of progressive failure from local spalling to pillar collapse (Pariseau and Sorensen, 1979). Both local and global safety factors were proposed as indicators of pillar stability. Upper and lower bounds of pillar stability were obtained using elastic perfectly-plastic and elastic-brittle failure criterion, respectively.

10. *Similitude studies.* Panek (1980) proposed an approach based on similitude modeling of the in-situ pillar. His equation has the following form:

$$\frac{\sigma_P}{E} = K_0 \left[\frac{d_1}{w}\right]^{C_1} \left[\frac{w}{h}\right]^{C_2} \left[\frac{l}{w}\right]^{C_3} \left[\frac{E_r}{E_s}\right]^{C_4} \left[\frac{E_f}{E_s}\right]^{C_5} \left[\mu_{s/r}\right]^{C_6} \left[\mu_{s/f}\right]^{C_7}$$

$$\times \left[\frac{1}{v_r}\right]^{C_8} \left[\frac{1}{v_f}\right]^{C_9} \left[\frac{1}{v_s}\right]^{C_{10}} \left[\frac{d_1}{d_2}\right]^{C_{11}} \left[\frac{d_1}{d_3}\right]^{C_{12}} \tag{9.18}$$

where

l, w, h = pillar dimensions, length, width, and height;
d_1, d_2, d_3 = discontinuity spacing in each direction;
v_s, v_r, v_f = Poisson's ratio for the seam, roof, and floor;
$\mu_{s/r}, \mu_{s/f}$ = coefficient of friction at roof and floor contact of the seam;
E_s, E_r, E_f = Young's Modulus of seam, roof and floor;
σ_p = pillar strength;
K_0, C_i = constants.

The method incorporates size effect, shape effect and mechanical properties of the roof seam and floor. Unfortunately, these properties are not easy to obtain with sufficient accuracy.

11. *Barrier-pillars formula*. Barrier pillars are left to support main entries or separate unmined and mined-out panels (sections).

The Mine Inspector's formula developed in Pennsylvania by Ashley (1930) serves to estimate the width of the barrier pillar, W_{bp}, in feet:

$$W_{bp} = 20 + 4h + 0.1H \qquad (9.19)$$

where H is the depth below surface and h is the seam height, both in feet.

A rule-of-thumb used by British coal operators is that the width of a barrier pillar should be one-tenth of the overburden depth plus 45 ft:

$$W_{bp} = H/10 + 45$$

12. *Pressure-arch theory*. The concept of a 'pressure arch' is sometimes used for pillar-sizing. This concept is not limited to a single entry but entails the entire panel width. It relies on the formation of yielding pillars, that is pillars that deform in a controlled fashion, and the subsequent transferral of overburden stress to the abutments (Stefanko, 1983). Yield-pillar size guidelines are dependent on seam depth, seam thickness, and entry width.

While not providing a pillar strength formula, the pressure-arch concept facilitates pillar dimensioning and is thus included for completeness.

From observations in the European coal-fields, the maximum span of the pressure arch increases with depth as follows:

$$W_{pa} = 0.15H + 60 \qquad (9.20)$$

where W_{pa} is the width of the pressure arch in feet while H is the depth below surface in feet.

The recommended pressure arch span is:

$$W_R = 0.75 W_{pa} \qquad (9.21)$$

Once the pressure arch span is determined, if the entry roof spans are selected and the number of entries is known, the pillar width can be established. However, it must be emphasized that the pressure arch concept is a rule-of-thumb, useful only for rough estimates in simplified cases.

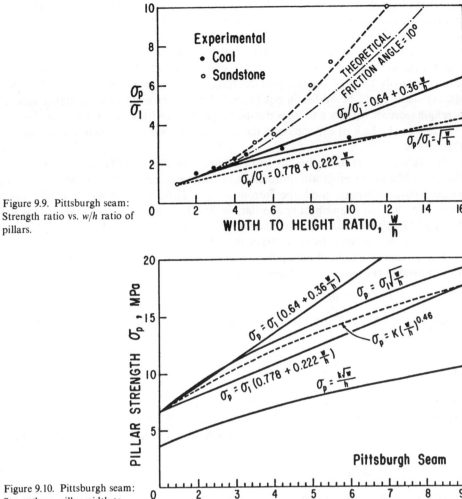

Figure 9.9. Pittsburgh seam: Strength ratio vs. *w/h* ratio of pillars.

Figure 9.10. Pittsburgh seam: Strength vs. pillar width to height ratio.

COMPARISONS OF PILLAR STRENGTH FORMULAE

From all the available pillar strength formulae, five expressions are most commonly used.

In Figure 9.9, the selected formulae are plotted (using the Pittsburgh coal seam properties) as the strength ratio versus the width-to-height ratio. In Figure 9.10, the strength is plotted versus the width-to-height ratio for five formulae.

It is apparent from these figures that for higher width-to-height ratios the Holland-Gaddy formula predicts the lowest strength while equation (9.14) predicts the highest strength. At the same time, the form of the Holland formula is such that it will become very conservative at large width-to-height ratios. The higher strength values predicted by equation (9.14) are consistent with the fact that for high width-to-height ratios there is a very rapid strength increase (see Figure 9.6). In fact, pillars are thought to be almost indestructible for width-to-height ratios greater than 10 (Cook and Hood, 1978).

A detailed study of this aspect conducted at Penn State (Bauer, 1980) has revealed that the theoretical strength of coal pillars is considerably higher than that predicted by equation (9.14). Thus, at some stage of this research it was proposed (Belesky, 1981) that an exponent could be added in equation (9.14) thus incorporating a higher rate of strength increase with increasing width-to-height ratios. However, for the sake of safety and due to the lack of experimental data, it was decided not to pursue this concept (Bieniawski, 1982).

In addition, it is also obvious from Figure 9.10 that the Holland formula and Salamon-Munro formula are quite close in their predictions. This is not surprising since Salamon-Munro used the format of the Holland formula to derive their expression for the strength of coal pillars in South Africa. It is also evident that the Holland-Gaddy formula is quite conservative by comparison with the original Holland formula as well as with the other three formulae.

For improved design of coal pillars in the United States, the following formula is recommended (Equation 9.14) Bieniawski (1983):

$$\sigma_p = \sigma_1(0.64 + 0.36\,w/h)$$

where $\sigma_1 = 6.4\,\mathrm{MPa}$ (930 psi) for Pittsburgh coal ($k = 5580$) and, for general use,

$$\sigma_1 = k/\sqrt{36}$$

It should be stated that the above formula is valid for pillar sizes greater than the critical size which is about 3 ft (1 m) for coal and for width-to-height ratios equal to and greater than unity. Other formulas are available for $w/h < 1$ and for smaller specimen sizes (Hustrulid, 1976, Bieniawski and van Heerden, 1975). Furthermore, for width-to-height ratios of 10 and greater, the formula will underestimate the strength of pillars.

Survey of U.S. coal mining conditions

A national survey of coal pillar and roof dimensions in the United States was conducted with the aim of identifying factors of safety for room-and-pillar design applicable to the United States coal fields (Bieniawski, 1982). Any pillar design formula requires an input of a factor of safety, defined as a ratio of pillar strength to pillar load (pillar stress), to assure that the pillar will not fail during the mining process. This safety factor provides a margin of pillar strength to account for uncertainties in the design process and the variability of geologic conditions and structural dimensions encountered in the mining area.

Work on coal pillars performed in South Africa by Salamon and Munro in 1967 was used as a foundation for the survey. They established safety factors by surveying stable and failed coal pillars in South Africa with the assumption that accumulated mining experience and practice has led to appropriate factors of safety. Thus, a statistical formula for pillar design was developed which rationalized accumulated experience and practice. The form of the pillar design formula selected in South Africa was based on earlier research conducted in the United States by Greenwald et al. (1939) and by Holland (1964).

Table 9.3. Range of room-and-pillar parameters used in U.S. coal mining (174 cases)

	Range	Typical
Depth below surface	25–480 m	150 m
Seam or pillar height	1–4.5 m	2 m
Entry width	3.6–8 m	4.9–6.1 m
Pillar width	5–23 m	15 m
Pillar length	6–27 m	20 m
Width to height ratio	2–16	8.0
Width to length ratio	1–3	1.25
Percentage extraction	25%–85%	50%
Shape of pillars	Rectangular	Rectangular

It should be noted, however, that the objective of the U.S. survey was not to develop a new pillar strength formula. Unlike South Africa, in the United States a number of pillar design formulae have been developed and used since 1911. The aim here was to collect enough field data to rationalize pillar design, incorporating improved procedures and appropriate safety factors for economical yet safe mining.

In total, 174 cases were available for stability analyses of coal pillars plus 58 cases of roof falls for analyzing roof spans. The pillar cases, summarized in Table 9.3, included only three instances of pillar failure in the United States. However, 20 pillar failure cases were collected from other countries for comparison purposes.

The survey included a comprehensive study of such parameters as the depth below surface, seam thickness, roof spans, pillar height, pillar width, pillar length, width-to-height ratios, percentage of extraction and the method of design. The results are depicted in Figure 9.11.

A major conclusion from this survey was that there was no universally accepted design code for U.S. coal mining and no systematic design procedures were observed. In fact, regression analyses were performed to establish possible correlation between the various parameters and this proved to be inconclusive.

Selection of factors of safety

A factor of safety is defined as the ratio of the strength of a pillar to the load acting on it. Thus:

$$F = \frac{\sigma_p}{S_p} \qquad (9.22)$$

A factor of safety is necessary because to derive the load and strength formulae presented in the previous section, certain assumptions had to be made.

A structure is defined as stable when $F > 1$. In engineering practice the factor of safety used is smaller when the conditions are well explored and understood. Sarcastically the factor of safety may be called a 'factor of ignorance'. Its values, which are derived from experience, take into consideration the likely accuracy of the predicted value of the strength and that of the expected load.

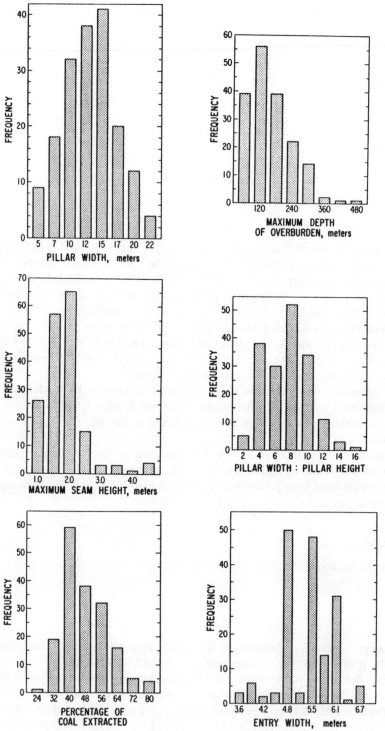

Figure 9.11. Penn State University survey of room-and-pillar parameters in U.S. coal mining.

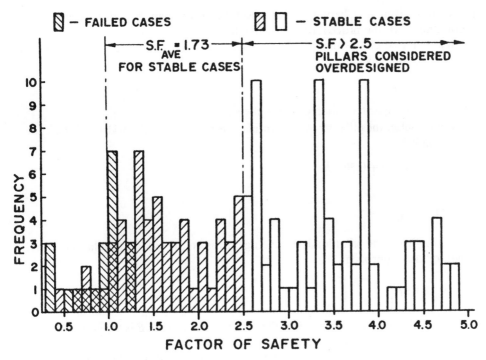

Figure 9.12. Histogram of safety factors for the strength formula given by equation (9.14).

It is important to note that if the factor of safety is unity, the probability of failure is 50%. The factor of safety should be greater than unity to achieve a low probability of failure. What probability of failure is acceptable in coal mining?

The data from the U.S. survey were used in conjunction with the various pillar strength formulae. A histogram of the safety factors for equation (9.14) is given in Figure 9.12, for 174 case histories from the United States which included three failure cases. Also included, are 20 case histories involving failed pillars in other countries.

It is concluded from Figure 9.12, that factors of safety ranging from 1.5 to 2.0 are appropriate for U.S. coal mining conditions when using equation (9.14). It must be emphasized, however, that this range should be used as a guide only and local mining experience as well as requirements for long-term or short-term pillar stability should be taken into consideration.

INTEGRATED DESIGN PROCEDURE

The following step-by-step procedure is recommended when planning new mines:

Step 1: From geological data, borehole logs and rock and coal specimen testing (54 mm core or cubes), tabulate the following: uniaxial compressive strength of roof rock and coal, σ_c; spacing, condition and orientation of geological discontinuities and groundwater conditions.

Step 2: Determine rock mass rating (RMR) for roof rock in accordance with the procedures given in Chapter 6 and select the roof span B and roof support in accordance with the procedures given in Chapter 10.

Step 3: Based on the uniaxial compressive strength of coal, σ_c, determine the value of k for the mine locality:

$$k = \sigma_c \sqrt{D}$$

where D is the specimen diameter or cube size.

Step 4: Select the pillar strength formula to estimate the pillar width w, for a known seam height h:

$$\sigma_p = \sigma_1 (0.64 + 0.36 w/h)$$

where

$$\sigma_1 = \frac{k}{\sqrt{36}}$$

Step 5: Select the pillar load (the average stress on the pillar) formula based on the tributary area approach:

$$S_p = 1.1 H \left[\frac{w + B}{w} \right]^2$$

where S_p is the pillar load in psi, H is the depth below surface, B is the entry span from Step 2 and w is the width of square pillars.

To simplify the design procedure, it may be assumed that the pillars are of a square cross-section which will result in an underestimated pillar strength.

Step 6: Select a factor of safety F (usually ranging between 1.5 and 2.0) and equate $\sigma_p/F = S_p$. Solve for pillar width w. For convenience, use Design Table I or II, or Figure 9.13 or 9.14.

Step 7: For economic considerations, check whether the percentage extraction ($100e$) is acceptable for profitable mining:

$$e = 1 - \left[\frac{w}{w + B} \right]^2$$

Step 8: If the percentage extraction is not acceptable and needs to be increased by decreasing the pillar width w, select from Step 7 a pillar width which would give the required coal extraction and determine whether this is acceptable for mine stability. This requires calculation of the factor of safety:

$$F = \sigma_p / S_p$$

where σ_p is the pillar strength from Step 4 while S_p is the pillar load from Step 5. The safety factors should be between 1.5 and 2.0.

Step 9: Cross-check the results by using the Holland formula, the Obert–Duvall formula or the Salamon–Munro formula.

Step 10: Exercise engineering judgment by considering a range of mining and geological parameters, to assess the various options for mine planning. Consider the effect of the floor condition.

Note: To assess the stability of an existing mining operation, all the mining dimensions are known and the acceptable factor of safety can be determined for use in future design.

Design Table I. Design of Room and Pillar Coal Mining: square pillar sizes (ft) and coal extraction (%) Pittsburgh Seam

Safety factor	Seam height (ft)	Entry width (ft)	Depth below surface (ft)				
			200	400	600	800	1000
	4	16	$w = 12.8$	19.3	24.8	30.0	34.8
			% 80.2	70.1	63.0	57.4	53.0
		18	$w = 13.8$	20.6	26.3	31.6	36.6
			% 81.1	71.5	64.7	59.4	55.0
		20	$w = 14.7$	21.8	27.8	33.3	38.4
			% 82.0	72.8	66.1	60.9	56.7
	6	16	$w = 14.8$	23.1	30.5	37.5	44.2
			% 76.9	65.0	56.9	50.8	46.0
1.5		18	$w = 16.0$	24.6	32.3	39.4	46.3
			% 77.8	66.6	58.7	52.8	48.1
		20	$w = 17.1$	26.1	34.0	41.3	48.3
			% 78.7	67.9	60.3	54.6	49.9
	8	16	$w = 16.4$	26.4	35.5	44.2	52.7
			% 74.3	61.2	52.4	46.0	41.1
		18	$w = 17.7$	28.1	37.5	46.5	55.1
			% 75.4	62.8	54.3	48.0	43.1
		20	$w = 19.0$	29.8	39.4	48.6	57.4
			% 76.2	64.1	56.0	49.8	45.0
	4	16	$w = 15.1$	23.0	30.0	36.4	42.6
			% 76.4	65.2	57.4	51.7	47.1
		18	$w = 16.2$	24.5	31.6	38.3	44.6
			% 77.5	66.7	59.4	53.7	49.2
		20	$w = 17.3$	25.9	33.3	40.1	46.5
			% 78.4	68.1	60.9	55.4	51.1
	6	16	$w = 17.7$	28.1	37.5	46.3	55.0
			% 72.4	59.3	50.8	44.7	39.9
2.0		18	$w = 19.1$	29.8	39.4	48.5	57.3
			% 73.4	61.1	52.8	46.8	42.0
		20	$w = 20.3$	31.4	41.3	50.6	59.6
			% 74.6	62.6	54.6	48.6	43.9
	8	16	$w = 19.9$	32.5	44.2	55.5	66.6
			% 69.2	55.0	46.0	39.7	34.9
		18	$w = 21.4$	34.4	46.5	57.9	69.2
			% 70.4	56.9	48.0	41.8	37.0
		20	$w = 22.8$	36.3	48.6	60.3	71.7
			% 71.6	58.4	49.8	43.6	38.8

Design Table II. Design of Room and Pillar Coal Mining; square pillar sizes (m) and coal extraction (%) Pittsburgh Seam

Safety factor	Seam height (m)	Entry width (m)	Depth below surface (m) 50	100	150	200	250	300	500
	1.2	4.9	$w =$ 3.5	5.2	6.7	8.0	9.3	10.5	15.0
			% 82.7	73.4	66.7	61.5	57.2	53.6	43.1
		5.5	$w =$ 3.8	5.6	7.1	8.5	9.8	11.0	15.7
			% 83.5	74.7	68.3	63.2	59.0	55.5	45.2
		6.1	$w =$ 4.0	5.9	7.5	8.9	10.3	11.6	16.3
			% 84.2	75.8	69.6	64.7	60.6	57.2	47.0
	1.8	4.9	$w =$ 4.0	6.2	8.1	9.9	11.6	13.3	19.7
			% 79.7	68.8	61.1	55.3	50.5	46.7	35.9
1.5		5.5	$w =$ 4.3	6.6	8.6	10.4	12.2	13.9	20.4
			% 80.6	70.2	62.8	57.1	52.5	48.6	38.0
		6.1	$w =$ 4.6	7.0	9.1	11.0	12.8	14.5	21.1
			% 81.3	71.3	64.2	58.7	54.2	50.4	39.8
	2.4	4.9	$w =$ 4.4	7.0	9.3	11.6	13.7	15.8	24.0
			% 77.5	65.4	57.0	50.7	45.7	41.7	31.0
		5.5	$w =$ 4.8	7.5	9.9	12.2	14.4	16.5	24.9
			% 78.4	66.8	58.7	52.5	47.7	43.7	32.9
		6.1	$w =$ 5.1	7.9	10.4	12.8	15.0	17.2	25.6
			% 79.2	68.0	60.2	54.2	49.4	45.5	34.7
	1.2	4.9	$w =$ 4.1	6.2	8.0	9.7	11.3	12.8	18.6
			% 79.2	68.8	61.5	55.9	51.4	47.7	37.3
		5.5	$w =$ 4.4	6.6	8.5	10.2	11.8	13.4	19.3
			% 80.1	70.2	63.2	57.8	53.4	49.7	39.4
		6.1	$w =$ 4.7	7.0	8.9	10.7	12.4	14.0	20.0
			% 81.0	71.5	64.7	59.4	55.1	51.5	41.2
	1.8	4.9	$w =$ 4.8	7.5	9.9	12.2	14.4	16.5	24.8
			% 75.6	63.5	55.2	49.2	44.4	40.5	30.3
2.0		5.5	$w =$ 5.2	8.0	10.4	12.8	15.0	17.2	25.6
			% 76.6	65.0	57.1	51.1	46.4	42.6	32.2
		6.1	$w =$ 5.5	8.4	11.0	13.4	15.7	17.9	26.4
			% 77.5	66.4	58.7	52.8	48.2	44.4	34.0
	2.4	4.9	$w =$ 5.3	8.6	11.6	14.4	17.2	20.0	30.7
			% 72.9	59.5	50.7	44.3	39.4	35.5	25.6
		5.5	$w =$ 5.7	9.1	12.2	15.1	18.0	20.7	31.6
			% 74.0	61.1	52.5	46.2	41.4	37.5	27.4
		6.1	$w =$ 6.1	9.6	12.8	15.8	18.7	21.5	32.5
			% 74.9	62.5	54.2	48.0	43.2	39.3	29.1

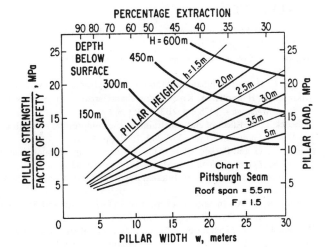

Figure 9.13. Design chart for Pittsburgh seam showing pillar strength versus pillar width for different pillar heights and different depths (roof span 5.5 m, factor of safety $f = 1.5$).

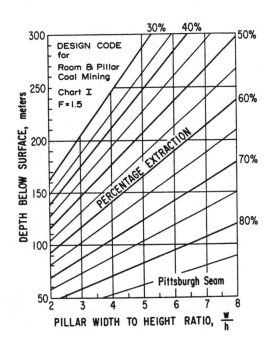

Figure 9.14. Design chart for room and pillar coal mining in the Pittsburgh seam showing depth below surface vs w/h ratio for different percentage of coal extraction and factor of safety $f = 1.5$.

REFERENCES

Adler, L. and M-C. Sun. Ground control in bedded formations. *VPI Bulletin No.* 28, Research Division, March 1976, pp. 77–108.

Aggson, J. R. Coal mine floor heave in the Beckley coal bed – an analysis. *Bureau of Mines, RI* 8274, 1978, 32 p.

Ashley, G. H. Barrier pillar legislation in Pennsylvania. *Trans. AIME*, Coal Division, 1930, pp. 76–96.

Atkinson, R. H. and H. -Y. Ko. Strength characteristics of U.S. coals, *Proceedings of the 18th Symposium on Rock Mechanics*, 1978, pp. 2B3–1:2B3–6.

Babcock, C. O. Effect of end constraint on the compressive strength of model rock pillars. *Trans. Society Mining Engineers AIME*, Vol. 344, 1963, pp. 45–48.

Barrientos, G. and Parker, J. Use of the pressure arch in mine design at White Pine, *Trans. AIME Society of Mining Engineers*, Vol. 255, March 1974, pp. 75–82.

Bauer, J. A. *Limit Stress Theory*. Internal Report on Strata Control, The Pennsylvania State University, 1980, 21 p.

Belesky, R. M. An In Situ Assessment of Deformability and Strength of Coal Pillars. M.S. Thesis, the Pennsylvania State University, 1981, 275 p.

Bieniawski, Z. T. Mechanism of Brittle Fracture of Rock. D.Sc.(Eng.), University of Pretoria, 1967, 226 p.

Bieniawski, Z. T. The effect of specimen size on the strength of coal. *Int. J. Rock Mech. & Min. Sci.*, Vol. 5, 1968, pp. 325–335.

Bieniawski, Z. T. In situ strength and deformation characteristics of coal. *Engineering Geology*, Vol. 2, 1968, pp. 325–340.

Bieniawski, Z. T. In situ large scale testing of coal. *Proceedings Conference in Situ Investigations in Soils and Rocks*, British Geotechnical Society, London, 1969, pp. 67–74.

Bieniawski, Z. T. Time dependent behavior of fractured rock, *Rock Mechanics*, Vol. 2, 1970, pp. 123–137.

Bieniawski, Z. T. *Improved design of room-and-pillar coal mining*. Final Report, U.S. Dept. of Energy, Grant #DE–FG01–78ET–11428, June 1982, 164 p.

Bieniawski, Z. T. New design approach for room-and-pillar coal mines in the U.S.A., *Proc. 5th International Congress on Rock Mechanics*, ISRM, Melbourne, Australia, 1983, pp. E27–36.

Bieniawski, Z. T. and van Heerden, W. L. The significance of in situ tests on large rock specimens. *International Journal of Rock Mechanics, Mining Science*, Vol. 12, 1975, pp. 101–113.

Borecki, M. and Kidybinski, A. Coal strength and bearing capacity of coal pillars. *Proceedings of the 2nd International Congress on Rock Mechanics*, ISRM, Belgrade, 1970, Vol. 2, paper 3–21.

Brady, B. T., Hooker, V. E. and Agapito, J. F. T. Laboratory and in situ mechanical behavior studies of fractured oil shale pillars, *Rock Mechanics*, Vol. 7, 1975, pp. 101–120.

Bunting, D. Chamber pillars in deep anthracite mines. *Trans. American Institute of Mining Engineers*, Vol. 42, 1911, pp. 236–245.

Carpenter, G. W., Rockaway, J. D., Stephenson, R. W. and Speck, R. C. Geotechnical evaluation of sub-coal strata for coal pillar support, *Illinois Mining Institute*, 1976, pp. 92–102.

Coates, D. F. Pillar loading – a new hypothesis. *Canada Department of Mines and Technical Surveys*, Mines Branch Research Reports R168/170/180, February 1966.

Cook, N. G. W. and Hood, M. The stability of underground coal mine workings. *Proc. Int. Symp. on Stability in Coal Mining*, Vancouver, Canada, 1978, pp. 135–147.

Cook, N. E., H. -Y. Ko and Gerstle, K. H. Variability and anisotropy of mechanical properties of the Pittsburgh coal seam, *Rock Mechanics*, Vol. 11, 1978, pp. 3–18.

Couedtic, J. M. and Barron, K. Plate-load testing as a method of assessing the in situ strength properties of western Canadian coal, *International Journal of Rock Mechanics, Mining Sciences*, Vol. 12, 1975, pp. 303–310.

Crouch, S. L. and Fairhurst, C. Mechanics of coal mine bumps. *Trans. AIME Society of Mining Engineers*, Vol. 256, December 1974, pp. 317–323.

Cruise, J. A. The Determination of the Strength Characteristics of Wide Pillars. University of the Witwatersrand, Johannesburg, M.S. thesis, 1969, 45 p.

Denkhaus, H. G. A critical review of the present state of scientific knowledge related to the strength of mine pillars. *Journal of South African Inst. Min. Metall.*, Vol. 63, 1962, pp. 59–75.

Djahanguiri, F. Rock mechanics for a longwall mine design; Carbon County Coal Company, Wyoming, *Proceedings of the 18th Symposium on Rock Mechanics*, 1977, pp. 1C5–1:12.

Evans, I., Pomeroy, C. D. and Berenbaum, R. The compressive strength of coal. *Colliery Engineering*, Vol. 38, 1961, pp. 126–128.

Everling, G. and Jacobi, O. Rock pressure and design of mine layouts. *Proc. 6th Int. Strata Control Conference*, CANMET, Banff, 1977, pp. 1/2–1/16.

Gaddy, F. L. A study of the ultimate strength of coal as related to absolute size of the cubical specimens tested. *VPI Bulletin*, Series No. 112, August 1956, pp. 1–27.

Greenwald, H. P., Hawarth, H. C. and Hartmann, I. Experiments on strength of small pillars of coal in the Pittsburgh bed. *U.S. Bureau of Mines*, Technical Paper 605, 1939.

Grotowsky, U. The Strata Control System and its application in West German coal mining. *Proc. 7th Int. Strata Control Conf.*, INIEX, Liege, September, 1982.

Hogood, D. Design of pillars for overburden support in coal mines, *The Mines Magazine*, Colorado School of Mines, March 1975, pp. 14–17.

Hardy, M. F. and Agapito, J. F. T. Pillar design in underground oil shale mines, *Design Methods in Rock Mechanics*, (Proc. of 16th U.S. Symposium on Rock Mechanics), ASCE, New York, 1977, pp. 257–266.

Hazen, G. and Artler, L. Practical coal pillar design problem. *Mining Congress Journal*, June 1976, pp. 86–92. See also reference 53.

Hazen, G. A., Lewis, H., Artler, L. and Middaugh, I. Practical pillar design problem encountered under deep cover and with different block geometric pillar. *USBM Final Report*, Grant No. G0144139, Department of Civil Engineering, Ohio University, July 1975, 44 p.

Herget, G. and Unrug, K. In situ prediction of mine pillars based on laboratory tests. *Proceedings of the 3rd International Congress on Rock Mechanics*, ISRM, Denver, 1974, Vol. 1B, pp. 150–155.

Heuze, F. E. and Goodman, R. E. The design of room and pillar structures in competent jointed rock: the Crestmore Mine, California, *Proceedings of the 2nd International Congress on Rock Mechanics*, ISRM, Belgrade, 1970, Vol. 2, paper 1–10.

Holland, C. T. Design of pillars for overburden support. *Mining Congress Journal*, Part I – March 1962, pp. 24–32; Part II – April 1962, pp. 66–71.

Holland, C. T. Pressure Arch Techniques, *Mechanization*, Vol. 27, No. 3, 1963, pp. 45–48.

Holland, C. T. The strength of coal in mine pillars. *Proceedings of 6th Symposium on Rock Mechanics*, University of Missouri, Rolla, 1964, pp. 450–466.

Holland, C. T. Mine pillar design, *SME Mining Engineering Handbook*, Vol. 1, Section 13–8, AIME, New York, 1973, pp. 97–118.

Holland, C. T. Pillar design for permanent and semi-permanent support of the overburden in coal mines. *Proceedings of the 9th Canadian Rock Mechanics Symposium*, Montreal, December 1973, pp. 114–139.

Hustrulid, W. A. A review of coal pillar strength formulas. *Rock Mechanics*, Vol. 8, 1976, pp. 115–145. Discussion by Z. T. Bieniawski, *Rock Mechanics*, Vol. 10, 1977, pp. 107–110.

Hustrulid, W. A. and Rames, G. The split-platen technique for determining load-deformation behavior of model coal mine pillars, *Proceedings of the 19th Symposium on Rock Mechanics*, University of Nevada, Reni, 1978, pp. 130–136.

Hustrulid, W. A. and Swanson, S. R. *Field verification of coal pillar strength prediction formulas*, Final Report to Bureau of Mines, Contract #H0242059, April, 1981.

Jacobi, O. The Strata Control System – retrospect and prospects. *Gluckauf Translation*, Vol. 116, November, 1980, pp. 454–460.

Jahns, H. Measuring the strength of rock in situ at an increasing scale. *Proc., 1st Int. Congr. on Rock Mech.*, ISRM, Lisbon, Vol. 1, 1966, pp. 477–482.

Kalia, H. N. Improving the design of coal mines by borehole logging, rock mechanics and related data. Trans. AIME Society of Mining Engineers, Vol. 260, March 1976, p. 17–20.

Lama, R. D. in situ and laboratory strength of coal. *Proc. 12th U.S. Symp. on Rock Mech.*, AIME, New York, 1971, pp. 265–300.

Langland, R. T. Three-dimension FE analysis of a room and pillar coal mine (a comparison with experiment), *Numerical Methods in Geomechanics*, ed., C. S. Desai, ASCE, New York, 1976, Vol. 2, pp. 802–820.

Maniev, G. and Avramova-Tacheva, E. On the evaluation of strength and resistance condition of the rocks in natural rock massif, *Proceedings of the 2nd International Congress on Rock Mechanics*, ISRM, Belgrade, 1970, Vol. 2, paper 4–41.

National Coal Board. Report on the effects of working in adjacent seams upon new developments. *Transactions, Institute of Mining and Metallurgy*, London, Vol. 113, 1954, pp. 398–415.

Obert, L. and Duvall, W. I. *Rock Mechanics and the Design of Structures in Rock*. John Wiley & Sons, New York, 1967, pp. 542–545.

Oravecz, K. Analogue modelling of stresses and displacements in bord and pillar workings in coal mines.

International Journal of Rock Mechanics and Mining Sciences, Vol. 14, No. 1, 1977, pp. 7–23.

Panek, L. A. Estimating mine pillar strength from compression tests. *Trans. SME-AIME*, Vol. 268, 1980, pp. 1749–1761.

Pariseau, W. G. Limit design of mine pillars under uncertainty. *Proceedings, 16th Symposium on Rock Mechanics*, Minneapolis, ASCE, New York, 1977, pp. 287–301.

Pariseau, W. G. and Sorensen, W. K. 3D mine pillar design information from 2D FEM analysis. *International Journal for Numerical and Analytical Methods in Geomechanics*, Vol. 3, 1979, pp. 145–157.

Parker, J. The logical way to design pillars. *Engineering and Mining Journal*, February 1974, pp. 67–71.

Peng, S. S. *Coal Mine Ground Control*. John Wiley & Sons, New York, 1978, pp. 174–207.

Petersen, G. B., Plumeau, D. B. and Parker, J. Yielding pillar and pressure arches, *Engineering and Mining Journal*, May 1979, pp. 122–130.

Pratt, H. R., Black, A. D., Brown, W. S. and Brau, W. F. The effect of specimen size on the mechanical properties of unjointed diorite. *International Journal of Rock Mechanics and Mining Sciences*, Vol. 9, 1972, pp. 513–529.

Protodyakonov, M. M. On the scale effect in rock and coal. *Proceedings, 4th International Conference on Strata Control and Rock Mechanics*, Henry Krumb School of Mines, New York, 1964, Addendum.

Salamon, M. D. G. Elastic analysis of displacements and stresses induced by the mining of seam or reef deposits. *J. S. Afr. Inst. Min. Metall.*, Vol. 65, 1964, pp. 319–338.

Salamon, M. D. G. Stability, instability and design of pillar workings, *International Journal of Rock Mechanics, Mineral Science*, Vol. 7, 1970, pp. 613–631.

Salamon, M. D. G. and Munro, A. H. A study of the strength of coal pillars. *Journal of South African Inst. Min. Metall.*, Vol. 68, 1967, pp. 55–67.

Sheorey, P. R. and Singh, B. Strength of rectangular pillars in partial extraction. *International Journal of Rock Mechanics and Mining Science*, Vol. 11, 1974, pp. 41–44.

Singh, M. M. Strength of rock. *Physical Properties of Rock and Minerals*. McGraw-Hill, New York, 1981, pp. 81–121.

Starfield, A. M. and Fairhurst, C. How high-speed computers advance design of practical mine pillar system, *Engineering and Mining Journal*, May 1968, pp. 78–84.

Starfield, A. M. and Wawersik, W. R. Pillars as structural components in room-and-pillar mine design, *Basic and Applied Rock Mechanics* (Proc. 10th Symp. on Rock Mechanics, 1968), University of Texas, Austin AIME, New York, 1971, pp. 793–809.

Stefanko, R. *Coal Mining Technology – Theory and Practice*. Society of Mining Engineers, AIME, New York, 1983, 402 p.

Townsend, J. M., Jennings, W. C., Haycocks, C., Neall, M. G. and Johnson, L. P. A relationship between the ultimate compressive strength of cubes and cylinders for coal specimens, *Proceedings of the 18th Symposium on Rock Mechanics*, 1978, pp. 4A6–1:6.

van Heerden, W. L. In situ determination of complete stress-strain characteristics of large coal specimens. *J. South African Inst. Min. Metall.*, Vol. 75, No. 8, 1975, pp. 207–217.

Wagner, H. Determination of the complete load-deformation characteristics of coal pillars, *Proceedings of 3rd International Congress on Rock Mechanics*, ISRM, Denver, 1974, Vol. 2B, pp. 1076–1082.

Wagner, H. The introduction of high percentage extraction methods in South Africa. *Proc., 7th Int. Conf. on Strata Control*, IMIEX, Liege, 1982, Paper 7/3.

Wang, F. D., Skelly, W. A. and Wolgamott, J. In situ coal pillar strength study. *Colorado School of Mines*, Contract Report No. H0242022, November 1976. See also: *Proceedings of 18th Symp. on Rock Mechanics*, 1977, pp. 2B5–1.

Wardell, K. and Eynon, P. Structural concept of strata control and mine design, *The Mining Engineer*, August 1968, pp. 633–645.

Whittaker, B. N. and Singh, R. N. Design and stability of pillars in longwall mining, *The Mining Engineer*, Vol. 139, No. 214, July 1979, pp. 59–73.

Wilson, A. H. Research into determination of pillar size. A hypothesis concerning pillar stability. *The Mining Engineer*, Vol. 131, No. 141, June 1972, pp. 409–417.

Wilson, A. H. The effect of yield zones on the control of ground. *Proceedings of the 6th International Strata Control Conference*, Banff, Canada, 1977, Section 1, paper 1–3, pp. 1–25.

Wilson, A. H. The stability of underground workings in the soft rocks of the coal measures. *Int. J. of Mining Engineering*, Vol. 1, no. 2, 1983, pp. 91–187.

Zahary, G. Alternative room-and-pillar patterns proposed for bigger, safer or take, *Engineering and Mining Journal*, August 1975, pp. 112–175.

CHAPTER 10

Guided design

All men by nature desire to learn.

Aristotle

Guided design is a new educational concept developed in the United States (Wales, 1978) to provide an improved educational strategy for learning the engineering design process and decision making. Guided design makes it possible for professors to accomplish two goals:1) teaching the subject matter, and 2) developing decision-making skills for the solution of real-life engineering problems. Using guided design, the professor shows the students how the material they study can be used to make better decisions. A by-product of this process is increased motivation which improves the students' retention of the subject matter.

The process of guided design is directed to devising solution for a series of carefully open-ended problems. The emphasis on problem-solving makes this approach close to 'real life' experience, where many different opinions and values must be considered and reconciled in the decision-making process. In sum, the students not only acquire knowledge within the discipline under the guided design approach but also develop the ability to learn on their own, think logically, gather the information they need to make intelligent decisions, make value judgments, and communicate their ideas to others.

Guided design was conceived and developed in 1970 at West Virginia University by Professor Charles E. Wales assisted by R. A. Stager. Although it was designed as a better way of teaching engineering, it quickly became apparent that it could be adapted to many disciplines. This growth was accelerated between 1973 and 1978 by the Exxon Education Foundation Program which provided small grants to college faculty who wanted to try guided design. This led to the publication of a book by Wales (1977) entitled *Guided Design* and to a national conference on Guided Design in 1980. In addition, Ronald E. Eck (1979), also of West Virginia University, applied the guided design concept to the solution of civil engineering design problems with considerable success and reported his findings at a number of meetings of the American Society for Engineering Education. Encouraged by these developments, the author applied the principles of guided design to teaching advanced rock mechanics design in mining and tunneling at the Pennsylvania State University (Bieniawski, 1980).

In summary, the concept of guided design provides step-by-step procedures for selected engineering problems requiring solution by decision-making and judgment. Moreover, it is a principle of guided design that the problems are of an open-ended type, meaning that there are a number of possible solutions.

217

For the purposes of rock-mechanics design in mining and tunneling, guided design will be applied to the broad topic of 'roof support in underground excavations' but in three different areas, namely, civil engineering tunneling, hard rock (metal) mining and coal mining. By treating the topic of roof support design in these three areas, it will be possible to compare the design approaches in mining and in civil engineering. This is particularly important, as an exchange of knowledge between mining and civil engineers seldom takes place in spite of many similarities in objectives. The topic of roof support design is considered ideal for such comparison purposes.

GENERAL CONSIDERATIONS FOR SUPPORT DESIGN

Hoek and Brown (1980) have rightly emphasized that the principal objective in the design of underground support is to help the rock mass to support itself. They provide an excellent discussion of the rock-support interaction analysis together with a number of worked examples. In addition, their book should be consulted for the practical aspects of the use of rockbolts, shotcrete and mesh as the principal elements of the support systems.

Other sources such as the U.S. Army Corps of Engineers (1980), the U.S. Bureau of Mines (Lang and Bischoff, 1981), the Canadian Ontario Hydro (1979) and the Norwegian Geotechnical Institute (1979) provide information on general empirical rules which are useful as a check for bolt lengths and spacings. These rules are as follows:

Minimum bolt length
Greatest of:
a) Twice the bolt spacing.
b) Three times the width of critical and potentially unstable rock blocks defined by the average discontinuity spacing in the rock mass.
c) For spans less than 6 m (20 ft), bolt length of one half the span. For spans from 18 m to 30 m (60 to 100 ft), bolt length of one quarter of the span. For spans from 6 m to 18 m – interpolate between 3 m and 5 m lengths, respectively. For excavations higher than 18 m (60 ft), sidewall bolts are one fifth of wall height.

Maximum bolt spacing
a) One half the bolt length.
b) One and one-half the width of critical and potentially unstable rock blocks.
c) 2 m (6 ft) – greater spacing than 2 m makes attachment of chain link or weld mesh difficult.

Minimum bolt spacing: 0.9 m (3 ft)
Note: Where discontinuity spacing is close and the span is relatively large, the superposition of two bolting patterns may be appropriate, e.g. long, heavy bolts on wide centers to support the span and shorter thinner bolts on closer centers to stabilize the surface against raveling due to close jointing.

The above empirical rules should only be considered as general guidelines because the appropriate support system for a particular underground excavation depends on many factors such as the characteristics of the rock mass, in situ stress field, the expected loading history, safety regulations, availability and cost of different types of support.

Hoek and Brown (1980) recommend that, once support estimates have been made, one should prepare a working sketch depicting the layout of rockbolting superimposed on the excavation cross-section and the structural features.

ROOF SUPPORT DESIGN IN CIVIL ENGINEERING TUNNELING

A water-supply tunnel was constructed in a major city in the eastern United States (Bieniawski, 1979, Blackey, 1979, Bieniawski et al., 1980). The function of the tunnel is flood control by diverting overflow of water from one river to another. The inside diameter of the tunnel is 6.7 meters and it extends 2,800 meters between the intake and the outlet. It is excavated through shale and basalt rock at a maximum depth of 61 meters below the surface. The tunnel, which is located beneath a business district in the city, is of an inverted siphon shape. The tunnel invert at the outlet is 15.9 meters below the intake invert with the tunnel sloping at about 0.6%. A minimum rock thickness of approximately 15.3 meters remains above the crown excavation at the outlet.

The bid prices for the tunnel ranged from $33.37 million for the drill-and-blast option to $23.25 million for machine boring with precast lining. The unit cost was $8,303 per meter based on TBM bid prices in 1978.

Tunnel geology

Figure 10.1 shows a longitudinal geological section of the tunnel. The rocks along the alignment are primarily easterly-dipping red shales/siltstones interrupted by a basalt dike and two fault zones.

Three major geological zones were distinguished along the tunnel route during preliminary investigations (Blackey, 1979):

1. Shale and basalt zones, constituting 88% of the tunnel.
2. Fractured rock zones (very blocky and seamy), between stations 23 + 10 and 31 + 10.
3. Two fault zones, one near station 57 + 50 and the other between stations 89 + 50 and 95 + 50.

Bedding and jointing are generally north/south which is perpendicular to the tunnel axis (tunnel runs west to east). The bedding is generally dipping between 15° and 20° while the joints are steeply dipping between 70° and 90°. The joints in the shale have rough surfaces and many are very thin and healed with calcite.

Groundwater levels measured prior to construction of the tunnel indicated that the piezometric level in the bedrock was normally 47 to 58 m above the invert of the tunnel.

Geological investigations

Site investigations included diamond core drilling, various tests in the boreholes and a seismic survey. Tests in the boreholes featured borehole photography, water pressure testing, piezometer installation, observation wells and pump tests.

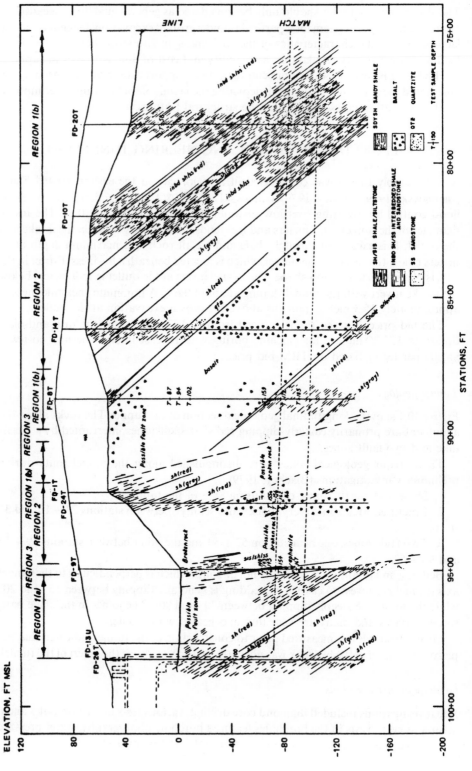

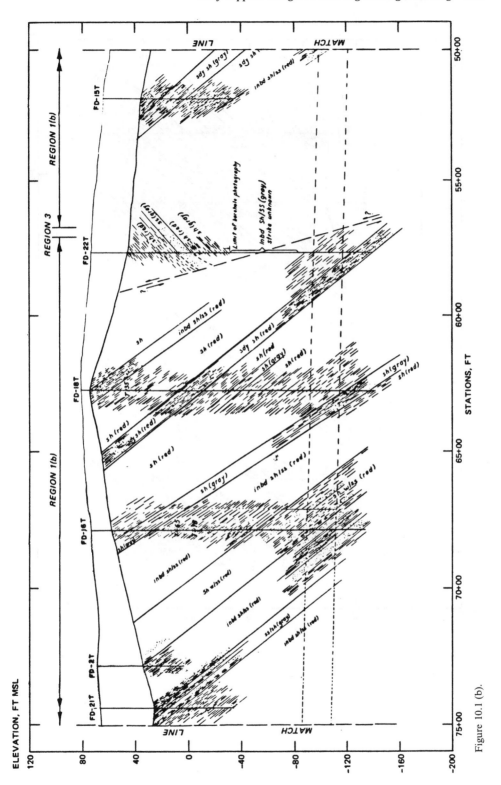

Figure 10.1 (b).

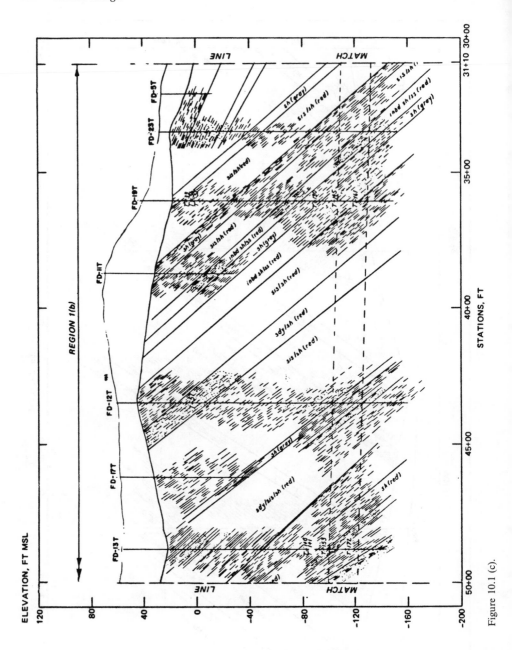

Figure 10.1 (c).

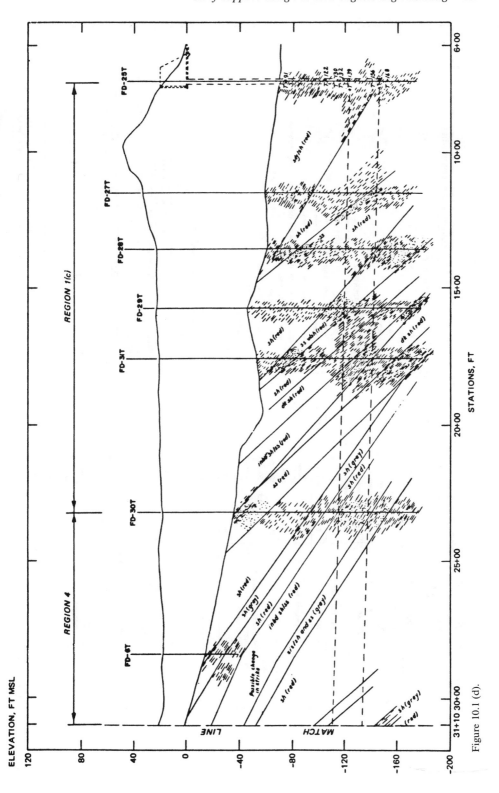

Figure 10.1 (d).

Name of project: *Park River Tunnel*

Site of survey: *Hartford, Conn.*

Conducted by: *G. A. N.*

Date: *July 15, 1978*

STRUCTURAL REGION	ROCK TYPE AND ORIGIN
23+10-7+10+	*Shale with interbedded sandstone*

DRILL CORE QUALITY R.Q.D.*

Excellent quality:	90 - 100%	
Good quality:	75 - 90%	✓
Fair quality:	50 - 75%	✓
Poor quality:	25 - 50%	
Very poor quality:	<25%	

*R.Q.D. = Rock Quality Designation

GROUND WATER

INFLOW per 10 m of tunnel length	litres/minute	*Dripping*
or		
WATER PRESSURE	kPa	
or		
GENERAL CONDITIONS (completely dry, damp, wet, dripping or flowing under low/medium or high pressure:		

WALL ROCK OF DISCONTINUITIES

Unweathered	
Slightly weathered	✓
Moderately weathered	
Highly weathered	
Completely weathered	
Residual soil	

STRENGTH OF INTACT ROCK MATERIAL

Designation	Uniaxial compressive strength, MPa	OR	Point-load strength index, MPa
Very high:	Over 250		>10
High:	100 - 250		4-10
Medium high:	50 - 100	✓	2-4
Moderate:	25 - 50	✓	1-2
Low:	5 - 25		<1
Very low:	1 - 5		

SPACING OF DISCONTINUITIES

	Set 1	Set 2	Set 3	Set 4
Very wide:	Over 2 m			
Wide:	0.6 - 2 m			
Moderate:	200 - 600 mm	✓		
Close:	60 - 200 mm			
Very close:	<60 mm			

NOTE: These values are obtained from a joint survey and not from borehole logs.

STRIKE AND DIP ORIENTATIONS

	Strike:				Dip:	
Set 1	*N23E* (from *N5E*) to (*N35E*)				*20*	*SE* (direction)
Set 2	*N47E* (average) (from *N40E*) to (*N60E*)				(angle) *20*	*SE*
Set 3	Strike: (from) to)				Dip:	
Set 4	Strike: (from) to)				Dip:	

NOTE: Refer all directions to magnetic north.

CONDITION OF DISCONTINUITIES

PERSISTENCE (CONTINUITY)		Set 1	Set 2	Set 3	Set 4
Very low:	<1 m				
Low:	1 - 3 m	✓			
Medium:	3 - 10 m		✓		
High:	10 - 20 m				
Very high:	> 20 m				

SEPARATION (APERTURE)					
Very tight joints:	<0.1 mm				
Tight joints:	0.1 - 0.5 mm	✓			
Moderately open joints:	0.5 - 2.5 mm		✓		
Open joints:	2.5 - 10 mm				
Very wide aperture	> 10 mm				

ROUGHNESS (state also if surfaces are stepped, undulating or planar)

Very rough surfaces:				
Rough surfaces:	✓			
Slightly rough surfaces:		✓		
Smooth surfaces:				
Slickensided surfaces:				

FILLING (GOUGE)

Type:

Thickness:

Uniaxial compressive strength, MPa

Seepage:

MAJOR FAULTS OR FOLDS

Several small fracture zones were found in core logs. Zones range from 100 mm to 0.3 m in thickness and occur between sta. 16+00-13+50.

Describe major faults and folds specifying their locality, nature and orientations.

GENERAL REMARKS AND ADDITIONAL DATA

Random joints present

NOTE:
(1) For definitions and methods consult ISRM document: 'Quantitative description of discontinuities in rock masses.'
(2) The data on this form constitute the minimum required for engineering design. The geologist should, however, supply any further information which he considers relevant.

Figure 10.2 Input data sheets. Region 1(c) of the Park River Tunnel

Rock cores from 29 boreholes were used to determine the tunnel geology. Of these, 18 were NX (54 millimeters in diameter) and 11 were 100 millimeters in diameter. Ten boreholes did not reach the tunnel level. All cores were photographed in the field immediately upon removal from the core barrel and the core was logged, classified, and tested.

Borehole photography was employed in 15 boreholes to determine the discontinuity orientations and rock structure.

Core samples were selected from 21 localities within the tunnel, near the crown and within one-half diameter above the crown to determine the density, uniaxial compressive strength, triaxial strength, modulus of elasticity, Poisson's ratio, water content, swelling and slaking, sonic velocity and joint strength. The results are given in Table 10.1.

In situ stress measurements were conducted in vertical boreholes involving 15 tests but only three yielded successful results. Eight tests could not be completed due to core breakage, two failed due to gage slipping and two more due to equipment malfunction. The measured horizontal stress was found to be 3.1 MPa $\pm$ 0.9 MPa. For the depth of 36.6 meters, the vertical stress was calculated as 0.91 MPa. This gave the horizontal to vertical stress ratio as 3.4.

Input data for rock mass classifications

Input data to enable rock-mass classifications have been compiled for all the structural regions anticipated along the tunnel route, and, as an example, are depicted for the outlet region in Figure 10.2. It should be noted that all the data entered on the classification input sheets have been derived from the boreholes, including the information on discontinuity orientation and spacing. This was possible because borehole photography was employed for borehole logging, in addition to the usual core-logging procedures.

Table 10.1. Summary of rock properties

Rock material	No. of tests	Uniaxial compressive strength (MPa)	No. of tests	Modulus of elasticity (GPa)
Shale	19	22.4–90.3 ave. 53.5	7	1.38–34.5 ave. 14.5
Basalt	11	38.2–94.8 ave. 70.8	9	6.14–68.9 ave. 31.9
Sandstone	2	64.5–65.8 ave. 65.1	–	–

Tunnel design features

Three different tunnel sections were designed and offered as bid options:

1. Drill and blast with a reinforced variably thick cast-in-place liner designed to meet three ranges of rock loading;

Table 10.2. Tunnel design rock loads and support based on Terzaghi's method

Rock condition	Length of zone (ft)	Drill and blast construction: diameter 26 ft			Machine boring: diameter 24 ft			Water inflow (gpm)
		Rock load (tsf)	Temporary support	Permanent lining	Rock load (tsf)	Temporary support	Permanent lining	
Best average quality: massive, moderately jointed RQD > 80	8000	1.1	11 ft bolts at 4½ ft shotcrete 1 in. thick	Reinforced concerete 14 in. thick plus 8 in. overbreak	0.5	10 ft bolts occasionally at 6 ft shotcrete 2 in. if needed	Reinforced precast line 9 in. thick grouted	1
Worst average quality: very blocky, seamy RQD = 40	800	2.2	11 ft bolts at 2 ft shotcrete 2 in. thick	Reinforced concrete 15 in. thick plus 8 in. overbreak	1.4	10 ft bolts at 3 to 5 ft shotcrete 2 in. if needed	As above	4
Fault zones: completely crushed RQD = 30	300	4.8	W8 steel beams at 2 to 4 ft shotcrete 3 in. thick	Reinforced concrete 22 in. thick plus 8 in. overbreak	3.5	10 ft bolts at 3 ft shotcrete 3 in. thick	As above	50

2. Machine excavation with a reinforced cast-in-place lining;
3. Machine excavation with a reinforced pre-cast lining.

The recommended support and rock-loads are given in Table 10.2 based on the Terzaghi method.

The support recommendations were also prepared from other rock mass classification systems and are included in Table 10.3 (Bieniawski, 1979). The main conclusion to be drawn from this table is that the Terzaghi method recommends the most extensive support measures which seem clearly excessive by comparison with the recommendations of the other three classification systems. The reason for this is three-fold:

Firstly, the current permanent lining design does not account fully for the action of the temporary support which in itself may be sufficient for the structural stability of the tunnel.

Secondly, the original modifications to the Terzaghi method by Deere et al. (1970) were based on 1969 technology which is now outdated.

Thirdly, not enough use is made in the Terzaghi method of the ability of the rock to support itself. The Terzaghi method uses such qualitative rock mass descriptions as 'blocky and seamy', which do not utilize fully all the quantitative information available from the site exploration program.

Tunnel instrumentation was planned to provide for design verification, future design applications, and monitoring of construction effects (Engels et al., 1981). Ten test sections at locations based on different geologic conditions were selected in the tunnel (see Figure 10.1). These test sections consisted of extensometers (MPBX's) installed from the surface; as well as pore pressure transducers, rockbolt load cells, convergence points, and surface and embedded strain gages installed within the tunnel. Further, in-situ stress measurements were also considered. The test sections were arranged to provide the greatest amount of data based on the planned construction schedule of a TBM with precast liners. Since the precast liners were designed for the worst ground conditions (10% of the tunnel) but were utilized throughout the tunnel, they were in effect overdesigned for the major portion of the tunnel. The purpose of the instrumentation program was to validate design assumptions, and to refine the calculations for future designs.

Construction

The greatest number of bids was made on the precast liner option with five of the seven acceptable bids ranging in price from $23,248,185 to $28,551,497. The highest bid for the drill-and-blast option was $33,374,140 (Blackey, 1979).

The tunnel was advanced upgrade from the outlet shaft. Upon completion of the outlet shaft, approximately the first 72 m of the tunnel was advanced using drill and blast excavation techniques to form a U-shaped chamber about 7.9 × 7.9 m in cross-section. The roof of the tunnel in the drill-and-blast section of the project was supported with 3 m long fully resin-bonded rock bolts installed on approximately 1.2 m to 1.5 m centers and shotcreted.

After completion of the drill and blast section, the tunnel boring machine (TBM) was assembled in the excavated chamber and the tunnel advance using the TBM began. The TBM was a fully shielded, rotary hard-rock machine manufactured by The Robbins Company of Seattle and which cut a 7.4 m diameter bore. The temporary support and final lining were provided by four-segment precast concrete liner rings which were

Table 10.3. Comparison of support recommendations

Rock conditions	Support system			
	Terzaghi's method	RSR concept	Geomechanics Classification	Q-system
Best average conditions: Regions 1 and 2	Rock load: 1.1 tsf Reinforced concrete 14 in. thick plus 8 in. overbreak Temporary: 11 ft bolts at $4\frac{1}{2}$ ft, shotcrete 1 in. thick	RSR = 76 Permanent: N/A Temporary: None	RMR = 72 Locally rockbolts in roof 10 ft long at 8 ft spacing plus occasional mesh and shotcrete 2 in. thick	Rock load: 0.5 tsf Q = 20 Untensioned spot bolts 9 ft long spaced 5–6 ft. No shotcrete or mesh.
Worst average conditions: Sta 23+00 to 31+00	Rock load: 2.2 tsf Reinforced concrete 15 in. thick plus 8 in. overbreak Temporary: 11 ft bolts at 2 ft, shotcrete 2 in. thick	RSR = 26 Permanent: N/A Temporary: 8W40 steel ribs at 2 ft	RMR = 37 Systematic bolts 12 ft long at 5 ft spacing with wire mesh plus shotcrete 5 in. thick	Rock load: 1.1 tsf Q = 2.2 Untensioned systematic 9 ft long bolts at 3 ft spacing plus shotcrete 1–2 in. thick. Primary: spot bolts
Fault zones: Region 3	Rock load: 4.8 tsf Reinforced concrete 22 in. thick plus 8 in. overbreak Temporary: steel ribs: W8 ring beams at 2–4 ft, shotcrete 3 in.	RSR = 23 Permanent: N/A Temporary: 8W40 steel ribs at 2 ft	RMR = 16 Steel ribs at $2\frac{1}{2}$ ft, 15 ft with wire mesh plush shotcrete 8 in thick	Rock load: 2.7 tsf Q = 0.14 Reinforced concrete 8–16 in. thick plus tensioned 9 ft bolts at 3 ft. Primary: shotcrete 6–10 in. with mesh

erected in the tail shield of the TBM about 11 to 12 m behind the cutter face. Each of the four segments was 22.9 cm thick and about 1.8 m wide. A completed ring provided a finished inside diameter of 6.7 m. Circumferential sponge rubber O-rings were provided between rings, and neoprene pad gaskets and a hydraulic cement sealant were used between segments (Engels et al., 1981).

GUIDED DESIGN PROBLEM

Design a 50-meter long section of the tunnel based on the geological and engineering information discussed above.

The section to be designed is an extension of the tunnel due to relocation of the tunnel outlet. Positioned near the outlet, the section is 20 meters below the surface.

Perform the following tasks:

1. Classify the rock mass conditions in accordance with:
   a) Terzaghi method,
   b) RSR concept,
   c) Geomechanics Classification (RMR),
   d) Q-system.

2. Calculate the rock loads by means of each of the above four methods and for two alternatives: drill-and-blast tunnel and machine bored tunnel.

3. Determine the self-supporting span and the maximum span possible for the encountered rock mass conditions.

4. Estimate the stand-up time, rock mass deformability and the friction and cohesion of the rock mass.

5. Select the tunnel support in accordance with the four methods specified in Item 1.

6. Select the final lining.

7. Tabulate the results for Items 1 to 6 in a manner suitable for a convenient comparison of the alternatives.

8. Recommend the method of excavation and decide on the type of support.

9. Estimate the cost of the tunnel section.

10. Draw a tunnel cross-section showing the layout of support and any recommended monitoring instrumentation.

SOLUTION

Item 1: Classification of rock mass conditions

a) Terzaghi: 'Moderately blocky and seamy' (RQD = approx. 72%)

b) RSR concept:
- Rock type: soft sedimentary rock;
- Slightly faulted and folded;
- Parameter $A = 15$;
- Spacing: moderate to blocky;
- Strike approx, perpendicular to tunnel axis, dip 0–20°;
- Parameter: $B = 30$;
- Water inflow: moderate;
- Joint conditions: fair (moderately open, rough and weathered);
- For: $A + B = 45$, parameter $C = 16$;
- Therefore: $RSR = 15 + 30 + 16 = 61$.

c) Geomechanics Classification (RMR):
- Intact rock strength, $\sigma_c = 50$ MPa
  Rating = 4;
- Drill core quality, $RQD = 55–85\%$; Ave. 72%
  Rating = 13;
- Spacing of discontinuities, range: 50 mm to 0.9 meters
  Rating: 10;

- Condition of discontinuities: separation 0.8 mm to 1.1 mm, slightly weathered, rough surfaces
  Rating: 25;
- Groundwater: dripping water, low pressure, flow 25–125 liters/min.
  Rating 4;
- Basic RMR: $4 + 13 + 10 + 25 + 4 = 56$ without adjustment for orientation of discontinuities;
- Discontinuity orientation: strike perpendicular to tunnel axis, dip $20°$;
  Fair orientation. Adjustment: –5,
  Adjusted RMR $= 56–5 = 51$;
- RMR $= 51$, represents Class III: Fair rock mass.
d) Q-System:
- RQD $= 72\%$ (average);
- $J_n = 6$, two joint sets and random;
- $J_r = 1.5$, rough, planar joints;
- $J_a = 1.0$, unaltered joint walls, surface staining only;
  $J_w = 0.5$, possible large water inflow;
- SRF $= 1.0$, medium stress, $\sigma_c/\sigma_1 = 50/0.91 = 55$.

$$Q = \frac{RQD}{J_n} \times \frac{J_r}{J_a} \times \frac{J_w}{SRF} = \frac{72}{6} \times \frac{1.5}{1} \times \frac{0.5}{1} = 9.0$$

Fair rock mass

Summary:

Classification	Result	
Terzaghi	Moderately blocky & seamy	
RSR	61	
RMR	51	Fair rock mass
Q	9.0	Fair rock mass

Item 2: Rock loads
Drill-and-blast diameter: 7.4 m + 0.6 m overbreak $= 8.0$ m
Machine-bored diameter: 7.4 m
Shale density: 2660 kg/m³ (166 lb/ft³)

Method	Drill-and-blast	TBM
Terzaghi	$h_p = 0.35C = 0.7B = 0.7 \times 8.0 = 5.6$ m Rock load $P = \gamma h_p = 0.146$ MPa (1.52 t/ft²)	$h_p = 0.45B = 3.3$ m $P = 0.09$ MPa (0.9 t/ft²)
RSR = 61	From Fig. 6.3, $P = 0.067$ MPa (1.4 kip/ft²)	TBM adjustment, Fig. 6.2 RSR $= 69.5$, $P = 0.034$ MPa (0.7 kip/ft²)
RMR = 51	$h_p = \dfrac{100 - 51}{100} B = 3.92$ m $P = \gamma h_t = 0.102$ MPa	TBM adjustment via conversion to RSR (eqn. 6.12) and Fig. 6.2 RMR $= 74$, $P = 0.049$ MPa
Q = 9.0	$P = \dfrac{2.0}{J_r} Q^{-1/3} = \dfrac{2.0}{1.5}(9)^{-1/3} = 0.64$ kg/cm² $= 0.0628$ MPa or $\quad P = \dfrac{2 J_n^{1/2}}{3 J_r} Q^{-1/3} = \dfrac{2\sqrt{6}}{3\,1.5}(9)^{-1/3}$ $= 0.52$ kg/cm² $= 0.0513$ MPa	TBM adjustment via conversion to RSR (eqn. 6.13) and Fig. 6.2. Q $= 54$ $P = 0.0321$ MPa

Summary of rock-loads in kPa (1 MPa = 1000 kPa)

Method	Drill-and-blast	TBM
Terzaghi	146	90
RSR	67	34
RMR	102	49
Q	63	32

Item 3 : Self supporting span and maximum span : by RMR and Q system
Fig. 6.7: Span vs stand-up time

	RMR = 51	Q = 9 (ESR = 1.6)
Self supporting span	2.4 m	8 m
Maximum span	10.5 m	80 m $[D = 2(1.6 \times 9)^{0.4}]$

Item 4 : Stand-up time, deformability and c, ϕ values
– RMR = 51 and Span = 8 m
  Stand-up time: approximately 100 hours or 4–5 days
  Deformability. RMR = 56 (no adjustment for joint orientations)
  $E = 2$ RMR $- 100 = 12$ GPa $(1.74 \times 10^6$ psi)
  $c = 192$ kPa
  $\phi = 39°$ [Table 6.9].

Item 5: Support recommendations

Terzaghi	Drill and blast – light to medium steel sets spaced 1.5 m. Concrete lining
RSR	Drill and blast – 6H25 ribs on 2 m centers plus final lining
RMR	Drill and blast – systematic bolts 3.5 m long – spaced 1.5 m, shotcrete 50 to 100 mm in roof and 30 mm on walls, were mesh in crown
Q system	Drill and blast – 3 m long rockbolts spaced 1.5 m and 50 mm thick shotcrete

Item 6: Final lining
100 mm thick fiber-reinforced shotcrete. See item 8.

Item 7 : Tabulation of results from Items 1–6

Item	Terzaghi	RSR	RMR	Q
Shale quality	Moderately blocky and seamy	61	51	9.0
Rock load height	5.6 m	N/A	3.9 m	N/A
Rock load	146 kPa	67 kPa	102 kPa	63 kPa
Stand-up time	N/A	N/A	4–5 days	N/A
Support	Ribs at 1.5 m Concrete lining	Ribs at 2 m Final lining	3.5 m bolts at 1.5 m, shotcrete 50 to 100 mm, wire mesh	3 m bolts at 1.5 m, shotcrete 50 mm thick

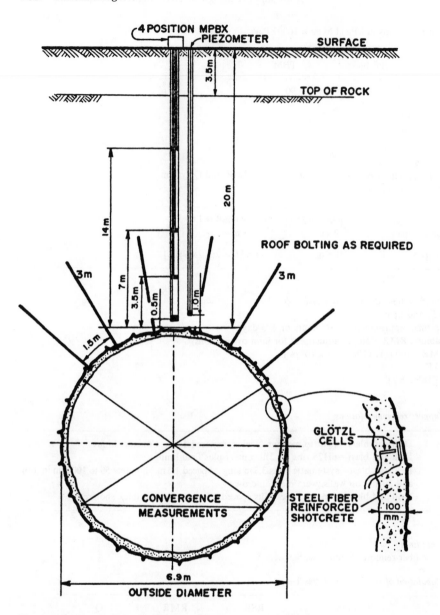

Figure 10.3. Tunnel support and instrumentation.

Item 8: Method of excavation
Pre-split blasting. Machine boring not economical for a short distance of 50 m. Hence, fiber-reinforced
shortcrete could be used as final lining. This would be acceptable on structural and hydraulic grounds.

Item 9: Estimated cost
The 1978 bid prices for this tunnel ranged from $11,220/m for drill-and-blast construction to $8,300/m for
machine boring. Inflation since 1978 to date amounted to 30%. The $11,220/m cost included cast-in-place
concrete lining. This cost will be reduced by using steel-fibre shotcrete as the final lining.
   Estimated cost of constructing the 50 m long section by drilling and blasting is:

$9,500/m (1978 base year) × 50 m =	$475,000
Increase due to inflation: 30%	142,500
Mobilization, etc.	60,000
Supervision	22,500
Total for 50 m section	$700,000

Item 10: Tunnel cross-section.
See Figure 10.3

ROOF SUPPORT DESIGN IN HARD ROCK (METAL) MINING

Recently, a design procedure has been developed for estimating support requirements
for drifts in metal mines using caving methods, such as depicted in Figure 10.4
(Cummings et al., 1982, Kendorski et al., 1983). This new method is based on the rock

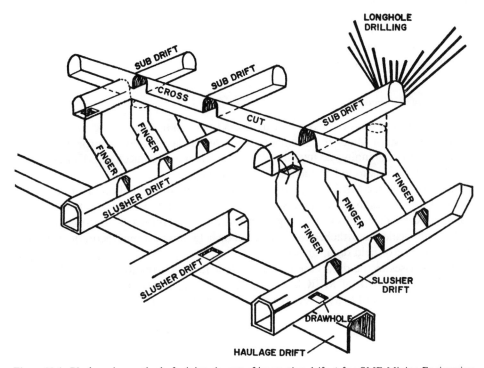

Figure 10.4. Block caving method of mining: layout of interacting drifts (after SME Mining Engineering
Handbook, 1973).

mass classification approach and has been named the MBR (standing for modified basic RMR) system, since it follows closely the Geomechanics Classification (RMR) system (Bieniawski, 1979) and incorporates some ideas of Laubscher (1981).

The MBR method is intended to aid planners, developers and operators of caving mining systems by providing rational recommendations for drift support. The method is useful for advanced planning during exploration, pre-development and expansion; for estimating support costs during feasibility studies; and for re-examining existing support philosophies in light of new geologic and engineering information. The MBR system is not a substitute for detailed mine design.

The MBR system was adopted and modified from existing concepts in use for civil engineering tunneling. These modifications were necessary because the development of a caving mine is radically different from driving a tunnel. In developing the modifications and adaptations for the MBR system, use was made of the current support philosophy and observed support effectiveness in a number of United States mines using block, panel or mass caving. Data collected at these mines encompassed a spectrum of geological conditions and engineering factors.

In using this approach, it is necessary to distinguish between the initial cave deformations and deformations due to production by caving. The former deformations are unloading and abutment phenomena which depend directly on rock mass conditions and the geometry of the mine layout. The latter deformations are very strongly dependent on operational factors which are the continuity of production (mainly) and the spacial distribution of draw rates. It has been assumed that the draw control practices are adequate to keep peak rock mass strains during production at levels below those occurring during abutment loading. This translates into 'good draw control' and 'effective undercutting', using mining jargon. The supports recommended are not as conservative as would be specified for civil projects, in recognition of the temporary life of most mine openings.

Overview of the method

The MBR system was developed by Engineers International, Inc. under contract with the U.S. Bureau of Mines to examine how a ground classification approach could be used fruitfully in planning caving mine drift supports. The Geomechanics Classification (RMR system) was found to have the greatest potential.

In developing the MBR system, the basic data required were collected for numerous block caving mines in the United States. Original field data were generated wherever possible. Key factors affecting drift performance were identified as adjustment factors and a rating scale was attached to each, based on field observations, theoretical analysis in the absence of field data, or both.

Rock masses in the data base range in MBR ratings from about 20 to almost 70. Development in rock of MBR less than 20 is ordinarily avoided and is never very extensive, and rock of MBR over 70 would be very difficult to cave, so the data base is fairly representative of the likely mining conditions. Depths ranged from about 200 meters to well over 600 meters. Mining experience at depths greater than 760 meters was limited.

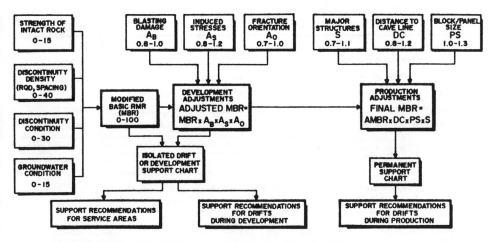

Figure 10.5. Organization of the MBR system (after Kendorski et al., 1983).

Description

The MBR (modified basic RMR) is depicted in Figure 10.5. It uses the basic RMR approach of Bieniawski (1979) with some of the concepts of Laubscher (1981). Key differences lie in the arrangement of the initial rating terms and in the adjustment sequence. In the MBR system, the inputs are selected and arranged so that a rational rating is still possible using very preliminary geotechnical information from drillholes. The MBR is also a multi-stage adjustment; the output at each stage can be related to support for various mining conditions. The MBR rating is the result of the initial stage and is the simple sum of the raw ratings.

The MBR is an indicator of rock mass competence, without regard to the type of opening constructed in it. This MBR value is used in the same fashion as the RMR and other systems for determining support requirements by consulting support charts or tables. The MBR recommendations are for isolated single tunnels that are not in areas geologically different from production areas.

The second stage is the assignment of numerical adjustments to the MBR that adapt it to the ore block development process. With regard to support, the principal differences between production drifts and civil tunnels (in development only) are the excavation techniques and the need for multiple, parallel openings. Unfavorable fracture orientation may also strongly influence stability. Input parameters relate to excavation (blasting) practice, geometry (vicinity, size and orientation of openings), depth, and fracturing orientation. The adjustment values are obtained from tables and charts, and the MBR is multiplied by the decimal adjustment to obtain the adjusted MBR. Drift support charts are again consulted to give a range of supports for drift development (initial support). The user may select support according to the performance period desired, since lighter support will be adequate in some rock for short periods. The objective is to stabilize initially the opening during development so that the permanent support may use its full capacity to resist the abutment loading increment.

Project Name _____ Site of Survey _____ By _____ Date_____

1. Geologic Region: _____ Rock Type _____ Location _____

2. Compressive Strength: Average _____ Range _____ Method _____ Comment _____

3. Core Recovery: Interval _____ Average _____ Range _____

4. RQD: Interval _____ Average _____ Range _____

5. Discontinuity Spacing: Average _____ Range _____ Comment_____

6. Discontinuity Condition   Wall Roughness   Wall Separation   Joint Filling   Wall Weathering
         Most Common
         Intermediate
         Least Common
         Consensus

7. Water Condition   Dry   Damp   Wet   Dripping   Flowing

8. Fracture Orientations   Set 1   Set 2   Set 3   Set 4   Set 5
         Strike
         Dip/Dir
         Rank

9. Major Structures   Strike   Dip   Dip Dir.   Width   Location/Comment
   Name: _____   Location/Comment
   Name: _____
   Name: _____

10. Stress Field σ_1: Direction _____   Magnitude _____   Measured? _____
                 σ_3: Direction _____   Magnitude _____   Measured? _____

11. Source of Geological Data _____

Figure 10.6. Input form: Geological data (after Kendorski et al., 1983).

Project Name _____ Site of Survey _____ By _____ Date_____

1. Type of Drift(s) _____   2. Orientation(s) _____   3. Design Life _____

4. Design Dimensions   Width _____   Width variation _____
                       Height _____   Height variation _____

5. Drift Spacing (Horizontal) _____
   Other Openings   Type _____   Size _____   Spacing _____

6. Extraction Ratio
      Multiple Openings: Excavated Area _____   Unexcavated _____ e_r_____
      Single Opening: 1.5 (width) _____   Excavated _____ Unexcavated _____ e_r_____

7. Distance below undercut – drift floor to undercut floor _____
                             drift crown to undercut floor _____

8. Method of Excavation: Machine bored   Controlled D & B   Conventional D & B

9. Excavation conditions:
      Perimeter Hole Traces _____
      Rib or Crown Looseness _____
      New or Existing Cracks _____
      Overbreak & Barring-Down _____
      Other Criteria _____

10. Intersections, turnouts: Type _____   Location _____   Max. Span _____

11. Block Dimensions: Side _____   Orientation _____   End _____   Orientation _____

12. Cave Line   Direction _____   Direction of Progress _____

13. Drift Location (in block, with respect to major structures and their dips, with respect to cave)
    _____
    _____

Figure 10.7. Input form: Engineering data (after Kendorski et al., 1983).

The third and last classification stage deals with the additional deformations due to abutment loadings. As stated before, caving deformations will also be accounted for if proper undercutting and draw control practices are followed. The most significant identified factors influencing abutment load are the location and orientation of the drift with respect to the caved volume, the size of the caved volume, the ability of the rock mass to withstand stress, the tendency of the lining to attract stress, and the role of any major structural trends that may serve to localize or transfer the abutment deformations. Input variables relate to block or panel size, undercutting sequence, level layout, MBR, and general structural geology of the area. The adjustment values are obtained from tables and graphs and are used as multipliers to the adjusted MBR and result in the final MBR. This value, together with an assessment of repair acceptability (depending on the type of opening) is correlated with recommendations for permanent support at intersections and in drift sections.

Approach

The first step in using the MBR system is the collection of representative data on geology and mining alternatives. Data sheets, such as those in Figures 10.6 and 10.7, are helpful in organizing these data.

Once the basic data have been assembled, the analysis proceeds according to the flow chart presented in Figure 10.5. Ratings are applied to the intact rock strength, discontinuity density, discontinuity condition and groundwater conditions.

Intact rock strength is rated according to Figure 10.8. The shaded region permits adjustment of ratings to allow for a natural sampling and testing bias.

The discontinuity density is related to blockiness and is the sum of ratings for RQD and discontinuity spacing, and is depicted in Figure 10.9. If either type of data is lacking, it can be estimated through the use of Figure 10.10.

Table 10.4 is used for rating the discontinuity condition. The most representative conditions are assessed for this step. The degree or type of alteration can be a useful index for this as well.

The groundwater condition rating is determined by use of Table 10.5.

To obtain the MBR, the four ratings mentioned above are summed. The ranges of the input parameters are given in Figure 10.5. At this point, the development support chart, given in Figure 10.11, provides support for service areas away from production areas.

Having thus obtained the MBR and the applicable recommendations, the adjusted MBR is computed for development adjustments as follows:

First, the extraction ratio is computed for the mining layouts under study. For single drifts with multiple intersections or those that are otherwise affected by other openings, the extraction ratio may depend on the extent of the area considered. Only in such instances is the convention adopted that all openings within 1.5 drift diameters of each rib are considered in computing the extraction ratio. The ratio is computed at springline and therefore includes the horizontal planimetric area of the finger or transfer raises.

Blasting damage is next assessed according to the criteria of Table 10.6. Both the blasting damage adjustment A_B and the descriptive term (moderate, slight, severe, none) should be noted. The induced stress adjustment A_S is then determined. The

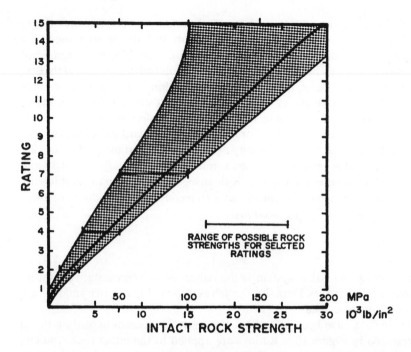

Figure 10.8. Ratings for intact rock strength (after Kendorski et al., 1983). The stippled area allows latitude in assigning ratings where biased test results from point load testing are suspected.

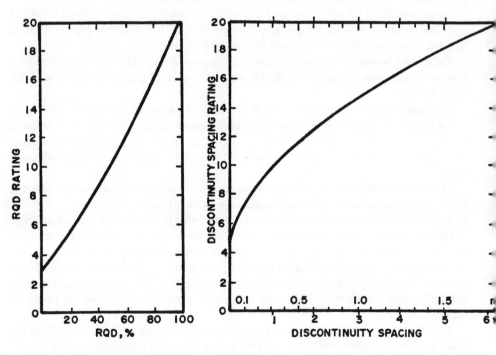

Figure 10.9. Ratings for discontinuity density (after Kendorski et al., 1983).

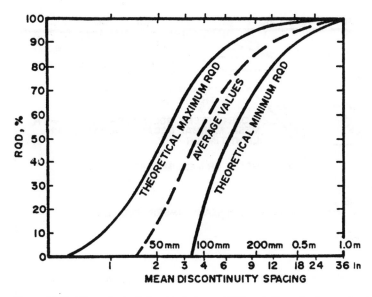

Figure 10.10. Theoretical relationship between RQD and discontinuity spacing (after Priest and Hudson, 1976).

Table 10.4. Discontinuity condition ratings

Description of discontinuity

	VR	R-SR	SR	SM-SK	SM
Wall roughness	VR	R-SR	SR	SM-SK	SM
Wall separation	None	Hairline	< 1 mm	1–5 mm	> 5 mm
Joint filling	None	None	Minor clay	Stiff clay, gouge	Soft clay, gouge
Wall weathering	F	SL	SO	SO	VS
Rating	30	25	20	10	0

Roughness:
VR = Very rough (coarse sandpaper);
R = Rough (medium or fine sandpaper);
SR = Smooth to slightly rough;
SM = Smooth but not polished;
SK = Slickensided, shiny;

Weathering (Alteration):
F = Fresh, unweathered, hard;
SL= Slightly weathered, hard;
SO = Softened, strongly weathered;
VS = Very soft or decomposed.

Table 10.5. Groundwater condition rating

Condition	Dry	Damp	Wet	Dripping	Flowing
Rating	15	10	7	4	0

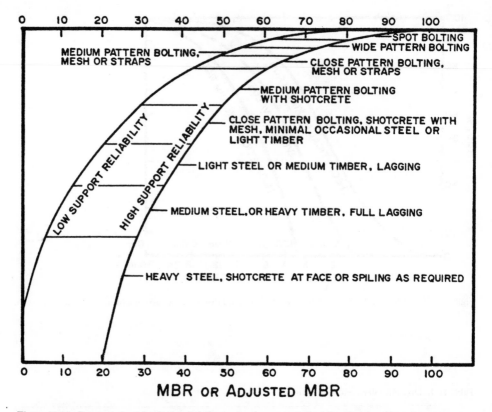

Figure 10.11. Support chart for isolated drifts or development drifts (after Kendorski et al., 1983).

Explanations of the support types in Figure 10.11

Spot bolting: Bolting to restrain limited areas or individual blocks of loose rock, primarily for safety.

Wide pattern bolting: Bolt spacing on 1.5 m to 1.8 m, or wider in very large openings.

Medium pattern bolting, with or without mesh or straps: Bolts spaced 0.9 m to 1.5 m, 23 cm wide straps or 100 mm welded wire mesh.

Close pattern bolting, mesh, or straps: Bolt spacing less than 0.9 m, 100 mm welded wire mesh, 0.3 m straps, or chain link.

Medium pattern bolting with shotcrete: Bolts spaced 0.9 m to 1.5 m and 80 mm (nominal) of shotcrete. Light mesh for wet rock to alleviate shotcrete adherence problems.

Close pattern bolting, shotcrete with mesh, minimal occasional steel or light timber: Bolt spacing less than 0.9 m with 100 mm welded wire mesh or chain link throughout, and nominal 100 mm of shotcrete. Localized conditions may require light wide-flange steel-sets or timber sets.

Light steel, medium timber, lagging: Bolting as required for safety at the face – full contact (grouted or Split Set) bolts only. Light wide-flange steel-sets or 0.25 m timber sets spaced 1.5 m, with full crown lagging and rib lagging in squeezing areas.

Medium steel, heavy timber, full lagging: Medium wide-flange steel-sets or 0.3 m timber sets spaced 1.5 m, fully lagged across the crown and ribs. Support to be installed as close to the face as possible.

Heavy steel, shotcrete at face or spiling as required: Heavy wide-flange steel-sets spaced 1.2 m, fully lagged on crown and ribs, carried directly to face. Spilling or shotcreting of face as necessary.

General: Bolting: bolts in spot bolting through close pattern bolting are considered to be 19 mm in diameter, fully grouted or resin-anchored standard rockbolts; mechanical anchors are acceptable in material of MBR > 60. Spilt-Set use is at the discretion of the operator.

horizontal (σ_h) and vertical (σ_v) components of the stress field must be computed or estimated, and the adjustment (A_S) can then be read from Figure 10.12 for the appropriate effective extraction ratio, depth and stress state. The extraction ratio is the area of rock, after development, being effective in carrying the load.

Next, the adjustment A_O for fracture orientation is computed. If drift exposures are available, Table 10.7 is used. If no drift exposures exist but fracturing trends are known, Table 10.8 can be used. The basis of Table 10.8 is that fractures perpendicular to the axis of the opening are more favorable than fractures parallel to it; that both development and support are facilitated by fractures that dip away from the heading rather than towards it; and that steep dips are preferable to shallow dips. If fracturing trends are not known but core is available for examination, fully interlocking core can be examined for the number of groups of discontinuities of similar inclinations in the core.

The three adjustments A_S, A_B, A_O, are multiplied, yielding for most situations a

Table 10.6. Blasting damage adjustment A_B

	Conditions/method	Applicable term	Adjustment A_B
1.	Machine boring	No damage	1.0
2.	Controlled blasting	Slight damage	0.94 to 0.97
3.	Good conventional blasting	Moderate damage	0.90 to 0.94
4.	Poor conventional blasting	Severe damage	0.90 to 0.80 (worst)
5.	No experience in this rock	Moderate damage	0.90 (nominal)

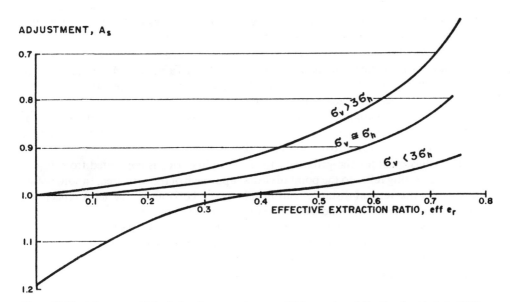

Figure 10.12. Adjustment AS for induced stresses due to multiple openings (after Kendorski et al., 1983).

Table 10.7. Fracture orientation rating A_o based on direct observation in drift

Number of fractures defining block	Number of non-vertical faces					
	1	2	3	4	5	6
3	—	0.95	0.80	—	—	—
4	—	0.95	0.85	0.80	—	—
5	1.0	0.95	0.90	0.85	0.80	—
6	1.0	1.0	0.95	0.90	0.85	0.80

Table 10.8. Fracture orientation rating A_o based on indirect observation of fracture statistics

Strike	Perpendicular				Parallel		Flat dip
Heading direction	With dip		Against dip				
Dip amount	45–90	20–45	45–90	20–45	45–90	20–45	0–20
Adjustment	1.0	0.95	0.90	0.85	0.80	0.90	0.85

decimal value between 0.45 and 1.0. The MBR is multiplied by this value or by 0.5 whichever is greater to yield the adjusted MBR.

The development support chart in Figure 10.11 is then again consulted for support recommendations. It should be decided what degree of support reliability is desired for development. It is recommended that the development support be selected as so as to stabilize the opening for as long as it will take to bring the block into production.

Next, the final MBR is computed. In this third and last stage, the role of abutment loadings is accounted for. This is addressed through considerations of structural geology and mining geometry ('production adjustments').

Faulted and shattered zones disrupt the mining-induced stress pattern and are dealt with through the adjustment for major structures, S(see Table 10.9). Although any zone of significantly less competence is eligible for adjustment, it is suggested that only the larger, nearby features are worthy of consideration. The limiting width-distance relationship will become clear for each mining property. Where information is too sparse or preliminary, it may be possible to characterize blocks of ground according to an expected or typical distribution of weakness zones.

The adjustment for the proximity to the cave line, DC, is computed from Figure 10.13. This rating refers to the point of closest approach of the cave area. In some cases, this means the vertical distance, and in others, the horizontal. The term reflects the dissipation of abutment load away from the point of application.

The block or panel size adjustment, PS, (see Figure 10.14) reflects the relationship between mangitude of abutment stress and size of caved volume. Smaller panel or block sizes are associated with lower abutment load levels because the caved volume is smaller. Blocks larger than 60 meters or so, as well as level-wide (mass) caving systems receive an adjustment of 1.0. PS may also be applied to blocks that are partially undercut.

These three adjustment values, S, DC and PS, are multiplied together and then multiplied by the adjusted MBR rating to yield the final MBR which is used to obtain permanent drift support recommendations. The range of values for the product of these adjustment ratings is 0.56 to 1.7; there are no other restrictions on this range. In practice, the high end of this range will seldom be reached because small caving blocks are uncommon in present practice.

The recommended support is then arrived at for drift sections or intersections through Figure 10.15. For spans of more than 6 meters the rating scale for intersections is used.

The degree of acceptable repair refers to the occurrence of cracking, spalling, slabbing, or other unacceptable deformation of the lining, that requires a production interruption while repairs are made. Repairs necessitated by damage resulting from excessive secondary blasting, wear, poor undercutting or draw control were not addressed in developing the support chart. A higher incidence of repair is tolerated in slusher or grizzly drifts than in fringe drifts of haulageways.

In selecting a support type based on final MBR, the user should have in mind the level of conservatism that was applied in selecting the development support. A high degree of support reliability in development will permit up to one repair category lighter support in production than might otherwise have been selected. For lower final MBR values, the support charts indicate a range of supports. This reflects the variability in conservatism among mine operators. Generally, the support used in such cases is the lightest in the range, although this will depend on the acceptable amount of repair.

Table 10.9. Major structures adjustment S.
Adjustments are > 1 if abutment stresses tend to be carried away from the excavation; S = 1 if stresses are concentrated

Fault strike vs. heading direction	Most nearly perpendicular						Most nearly parallel					
Fault dip direction with respect to works	Towards			Away			Towards			Away		
Amount of dip	Sh	M	St	Sh	M	St	Sh	M	St	Sh	M	St
Distance to nearest fault zone (*W* = zone width)												
<0.1 *W*	0.8	0.75	0.75	–	0.9	0.95	0.75	0.7	0.7	–	0.9	0.95
0.1 *W* to 1.0 *W*	0.85	0.8	0.8	0.90	0.9	1.0	0.8	0.75	0.9	0.85	1.0	0.95
1.0 *W* to 10.0 *W*	0.95	0.85	0.9	0.95	1.05	1.05	0.9	0.9	0.95	0.90	1.05	1.10
10.0 *W* to 50.0 *W*	1.0	0.95	1.0	1.05	1.05	1.0	1.0	1.0	1.0	1.0	1.10	1.0
> 50 *W*	1.0	1.0	1.0	1.0	1.0	1.0	1.0	1.0	1.0	1.05	1.0	1.0
Within zone	0.85	0.80	0.90	0.85	0.80	0.90	0.80	0.75	0.85	0.80	0.75	0.85

Sh = Shallow (< 30°)
M = Moderate (30° to 60°);
St = Steep (> 60°);

<0.1 *W* factor not to be applied for *W* < 3 m;
> 50 *W* factor not to be applied for *W* > 3 m.

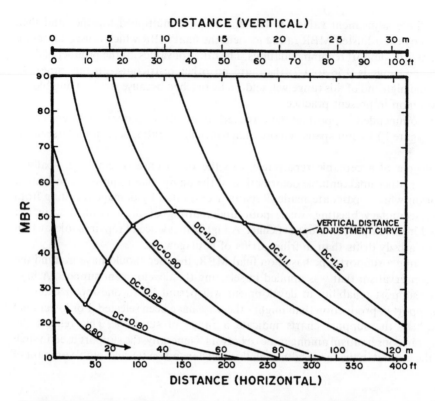

Figure 10.13. Adjustment DC for distance to cave line (after Kendorski et al., 1983).
For drifts beneath the caving area, the vertical distance is projected up to the single vertical distance adjustment curve; the rating is read by interpolating between the multiple curves. For workings horizontally removed from the caving area, the horizontal distance is projected up to the MBR value and the rating is interpolated at that point from the multiple curves. For working both beneath and to the side, ratings are computed both ways, and the lowest value is taken.

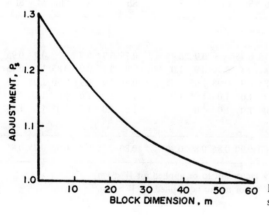

Figure 10.14. Adjustment PS for block/panel size (after Kendorski et al., 1983).

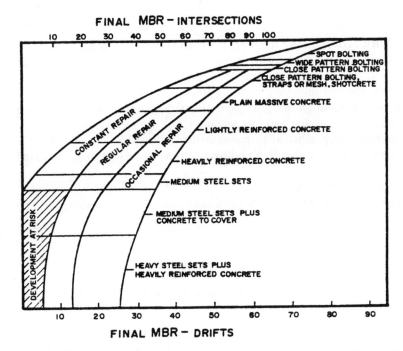

FINAL MBR – INTERSECTIONS

DEVELOPMENT AT RISK

SPOT BOLTING
WIDE PATTERN BOLTING
CLOSE PATTERN BOLTING
CLOSE PATTERN BOLTING,
STRAPS OR MESH, SHOTCRETE
PLAIN MASSIVE CONCRETE
LIGHTLY REINFORCED CONCRETE
HEAVILY REINFORCED CONCRETE
MEDIUM STEEL SETS
MEDIUM STEEL SETS PLUS
CONCRETE TO COVER
HEAVY STEEL SETS PLUS
HEAVILY REINFORCED CONCRETE

CONSTANT REPAIR
REGULAR REPAIR
OCCASIONAL REPAIR

FINAL MBR – DRIFTS

Figure 10.15. Permanent support chart for production drifts (after Kendorski et al, 1983).

Explanation of the support types in Figure 10.15

Spot bolting: Bolting to restrain limited areas or individual blocks of loose rock, primarily for safety.

Wide pattern bolting: Bolts on spaced 1.2 m to 1.8 m. May be wider in very large openings, when longer bolts are used.

Close pattern bolting: Bolts spaced less than 0.9 m to 1.2 m (practical limit 0.6 m).

Close pattern bolting, mesh or straps, shotcrete: Close pattern bolts with welded wire mesh or chain link in raveling ground, and nominal 100 mm of shotcrete.

Plain massive concrete: Cast-in-place massive concrete lining, 0.3 m to 0.45 m thick, may be applied over bolts or bolts and mesh when necessary. Prior shotcrete, if not damaged, may be considered part of this concrete thickness. Concrete should have a *minimum as-placed* 28-day compressive strength of 21 MPa (3000 lb/in^2).

Lightly reinforced concrete: Massive, cast-in-place concrete lining 0.3 m to 0.45 m thick as above, lightly reinforced with rebars on 0.6 m centers or continuous heavy chain link. Reinforcement mainly in brows, crown, corners, and intersections.

Heavily reinforced concrete: Massive, cast-in-place concrete lining as above, heavily reinforced with rebars on 0.6 m centers or less, on ribs and crown.

Medium steel sets: Medium wide-flange steel-sets on 1.2 m centers, fully lagged on the crown and ribs.

Medium steel sets plus plain concrete to cover: Medium wide-flange steel-sets on 1.2 m centers, with plain, cast-in-place concrete (minimum strength 21 MPa) of sufficient thickness to cover the sets.

Heavy steel sets plus heavily reinforced concrete: Heavy wide-flange steel-sets on 1.2 m centers, with minimum 0.3 m thick heavily reinforced concrete throughout.

General:

Concrete: it is assumed that proper concrete practice is observed: negligible aggregate segregation, full rock-concrete contact, adequate curing time.

Chain link or steel sets, from development support, are considered reinforcement if the concrete between the sets is also reinforced.

General

In essence, the MBR system allows the user to consider various mining layouts and procedures to obtain the lowest-cost workable support system. Ratings are improved by the following (which are within the control of mine operators):

1. Controlled blasting or improved blasting practice;
2. Widest possible separation of openings, both laterally and vertically, given the constraints of draw-point spacing and ore height;
3. Driving openings perpendicular to major structural trends;
4. Keeping critical openings (haulage and fringe drifts) well away from the caved volume;
5. Minimal undercut area; and
6. Avoidance of weakness zones and major discontinuities for all openings, where possible.

GUIDED DESIGN PROBLEM

Design drift support for a block caving mine based on the following geological and mining information.

Geology

The ore body is mined in several levels. The ore occurs in fractured and altered igneous rock. Ore deposition was associated with an intrusive porphyry; subsequent faulting has dissected and offset portions of the orebody and remobilized other portions. A wide fault zone dips moderately towards the production area.

The geologic data are given in Table 10.10. These data are an estimate of representative rock mass conditions observed in core and drift exposures. The drifts are to be designed in the porphyry rock masses which are quite competent. Although alteration and ore mineralogy have a strong bearing on rock mass competence, overall mining conditions are governed by the geologic structure.

Table 10.10. Geological data for guided design problem

Project Name *Example Mine*		Site of Survey *Upper Level*	By *ABC*	Date *2/25/83*

1. Geologic Region: *Altered Porphyry*   Rock Type *Alt.Gd.ppy,volcanics*   Location *Block1, access & elsewhere*
2. Compressive Strength: Average *9,300 psi* Range *4,500-12,600* Method *pt.load* Comment *Many fracture-cont.*
3. Core Recovery: Interval *90 ft-300 ft*   Average *83%*   Range *66% - 100%+*
4. RQD: Interval *-do-*   Average *39%*   Range *14% - 90%*
5. Discontinuity Spacing: Average *0.6 ft*   Range *0.2 ft-1.6 ft*   Comment *locally 1.5 ft-2 ft*

6. Discontinuity Condition

	Wall Roughness	Wall Separation	Joint Filling	Wall Weathering
Most Common	*Rough*	*hairline*	*None*	*Sl. weathered*
Intermediate	*Sl. rough*	*< 1/4"*	*FeOx*	*Softened*
Least Common	*Smooth*	*None*	*Clay*	*Severe*
Consensus	*R-SR*	*hairline*	*Non clay*	*SL*

7. Water Condition   (Dry)   Damp   Wet   Dripping   Flowing

8. Fracture Orientations

	Set 1	Set 2	Set 3	Set 4	Set 5
Strike	*NE*	*WNW*	*NE*	*NW*	*-*
Dip/Dir	*Vert*	*Str/NE*	*Mod/SE*	*Str/SW*	*-*
Rank	*1(56)*	*2(53)*	*3(32)*	*4(33)*	*-*

9. Major Structures

	Strike	Dip	Dip Dir	Width	Location/Comment
Name: *Fault Zone*	*NE*	*Mod*	*NW*	*+100ft*	*SE Boundary, Block 1, Distance=80 ft-100 ft*
Name: *-*	*-*	*-*	*-*	*-*	*-*
Name: *-*	*-*	*-*	*-*	*-*	*-*

10. Stress Field σ_1: Direction *Vert*   Magnitude *1100 psi*   Measured? *No*
    σ_3: Direction *Horiz*   Magnitude *800 psi*   Measured? *No*

11. Source of Geological Data   *Mainly core with limited underground exposures*

Table 10.11. Engineering data for guided design problem

Project Name _Example Mine_   Site of Survey _Upper Level_   By _ABC_ Date _____ _3/10/83_

1. Type of Drift(s) _slusher_ 2. Orientation(s) _NW/SE_   3. Design Life _about 1-1/2 yr. max._

4. Design Dimensions Width _10 ft_ Width variation _____ _none_ _____
   Height _11 ft_ Height variation _____ _none_ _____

5. Drift Spacing (Horizontal) _____ _35 ft C-C_ _____

   Other Openings   Type _fingers_   Size _5 ft x 5 ft_   Spacing _17.5 ft C-C_ _____

6. Extraction Ratio
   Multiple Openings: Excavated Area _225 ft^2_   Unexcavated _388 ft^2_ _____ e$_r$ _0.37_ _____

   Single Opening: 1.5 (width) _____ _--_   Excavated _____ _--_   Unexcavated _--_ _ e$_r$ _--_

7. Distance below undercut - drift floor to undercut floor _____ _15 ft_
   drift crown to undercut floor _____ _4 ft_

8. Method of Excavation: Machine bored   Controlled D & B   ⟨ Conventional D & B ⟩

9. Excavation conditions
   Perimeter Hole Traces _Few seen. No blast holes remaining._ _____
   Rib or Crown Looseness _Ribs drummy in places. Crown tight after barring down._ _____
   New or Existing Cracks _None new. Some old joints opened._ _____
   Overbreak & Barring-Down _O.B. = 1 ft-2 ft. Barring: Same, not major_ _____
   Other Criteria _____ _--_ _____

10. Intersections, turnouts: Type _Intersection_ Location _access, vent_   Max. Span _16 ft_

11. Block Dimensions: Side _200 ft_ Orientation _NW/SE_   End _200 ft_ Orientation _NE/SW_

12. Cave Line   Direction _ENE_ Direction of Progress _____ _NNW_ _____

13. Drift Location (in block, with respect to major structures and their dips, with respect to cave)
    Across block, beneath cave, fault zone structure across ends opposite slusher _____

Mining methods
The mine uses a panel cave method with undercutting. Ore is developed and caved in a blockwise fashion. Undercut pillars are longholed and shot; there is no drift widening.

Slushers are used to move ore from the drawpoints to a drop point, through which it falls directly into ore cars in the haulage level. There are no transfer raises. Drift life is 1.5 years or less, due to the relatively short ore columns (61 m or less). Slusher lanes are nominally 61 m in length, but may be less.

The type of drift considered in this example involves slusher lanes, which pose ongoing support problems. Key data for slusher drifts are given in Table 10.11.

SOLUTION

MBR determination for slusher drifts in altered porphyry

From data in Table 10.10, the ratings are as follows:

Intact rock strength
Average: 64 MPa.
From Fig. 10.8, rating: 5.

Discontinuity density
Wide range of RQD, 39% (average). Discontinuities average spacing 18.3 cm (0.6 ft). May not be representative.
From Fig. 10.9, rating 8 for RQD and rating 10 for spacing. From Fig. 10.10, a check: RQD = 39% relates to spacing of 15 cm. Discontinuity density rating = RQD rating + Spacing rating = 8 + 10 = 18.

Discontinuity condition
Wall roughness: 'R' to 'SR'
Wall separation: 'hairline' to less than 6 mm

Joint filling: none to minor clay
Wall weathering: 'SL' minor 'SO'
From Table 10.4, rating: 25.

Groundwater condition: dry
From Table 10.5, rating: 15.

Altered porphyry MBR
MBR = Intact rock strength rating + Discontinuity density rating + Discontinuity condition rating + Groundwater condition rating = 5 + 18 + 25 + 15 = 63.

Development adjustments

The application of development adjustments involves combining the engineering data with the geologic status.

Blasting damage
Expect poor to fair conventional blasting. From Table 10.6, for 'moderate damage,' rating $A_B = 0.90$.

Induced stresses
Slusher lanes are 3 m (10 ft) wide on 10.5 m (35 ft) centers. The 1.5 m × 1.5 m finger raises are on 5.3 (17.5 ft) centers so the extraction ratio

$$e_r = \frac{3 \times 5.3 + 2(1.5 \times 1.5)}{10.5 \times 5.3} = 0.37$$

From Kendorski et al. (1983), for a 3 m wide drift, a basic $e_r = 0.37$ and moderate blast damage generates an effective e_r of 0.51. This value reflects the area of rock remaining, after development, that is effective in accepting load.

   In the absence of measurements, it may be expected $\sigma_1 = \sigma_v = 1,100$ psi (7.6 MPa). The horizontal stress is assumed to be $\sigma_1(v/(1-v)) = \sigma_h = \sigma_3$, where v is assumed = 0.25 in the absence of measurements. Thus, $\sigma_v > 3\sigma_h$ and the top curve on Figure 10.12 is used.

   From Figure 10.12 induced stresses rating $A_S = 0.88$.

Fracture orientation
For altered porphyry, there are 4 fracture orientations. In order from most to least prevalent, the sets are (strike, dip, number of observations in set from Schmidt plot clusters):
   1. NE, vertical, (56 observations);
   2. WNW, steeply dipping NE, (53 observations);
   3. NE, shallow or moderate dip SE, (32 observations);
   4. NW, steeply dipping SW, (22 observations).
Slusher lane development is from NW to SE. Therefore, the sets are oriented as follows:
   Set 1.   Perpendicular
            Vertical dip
   Set 2.   Parallel
            Steep dip (45° to 90°)
   Set 3.   Perpendicular, drive with dip
            Moderate dip (20° to 45°)
   Set 4.   Parallel
            Steep dip (45° to 90°)
From Table 10.8, the set ratings are: Set 1, 1.0; Set 2, 0.8; Set 3, 0.95, Set 4, 0.80.
   Weighting these according to the number of observations of each,

$$\frac{1.0 \times (56) + 0.8(53) + 0.95(32) + 0.8(22)}{56 + 53 + 32 + 22} = A_0 = 0.90$$

Adjusted MBR computation
The adjustments are summarized as follows:
$A_b = 0.90$ $A_S = 0.88$ $A_0 = 0.90$
   Checking, $A_B \times A_S \times A_0 = 0.713$, which is greater than the 0.5 minimum value.
   Adjusted MBR $= 0.713 (63) = 45$, for altered porphyry in slusher drifts.

Production adjustments

In this step, the adjusted MBR, which is related to development support, is further adjusted to allow for dynamic and transient deformations related to caving. It should be pointed out that adequate undercutting and draw control practice is assumed, so that loads developing during routine production remain below the peak abutment levels. There is no allowance in the MBR system for incomplete blasting of pillars during undercutting in which stubs are left, or for caving difficulties such as hangups or packed drawpoints, or other influences causing excessive weight to be thrown onto the drift support.

Major structures
Since a fault zone exists in the vicinity of the cave area, this zone is considered a major structure. It is assumed that the fault zone was classified as a separate structure having an MBR $= 37$. The altered porphyry MBR is 63, as opposed to 37 for the fault zone, and this is a significant contrast. In reality, a zone of any width can be regarded as a major structure, so long as the zone is independently classifiable and of significant contrast in MBR value.
   From Table 10.10, the fault zone is along the southeast limit of Block 1, strikes generally northeast, and dips moderately northwest. The zone thickness is thought to be at least 30 m. Thus, $W = 30$ m.
   The closest point of approach, of altered porphyry to the zone boundary, within the slusher lanes, is 24 to 30 m (80 to 100 ft).
The key information is thus:
Distance to the fault zone: 24 m $= 0.8 W$
Fault strike vs. heading direction: Perpendicular
Dip direction: towards the drifts. Dip amount: moderate
From Table 10.9 the adjustment S is interpolated, $S = 0.82$.

Distance to cave line
The closest point of approach is used. The sense of the distance, for slusher lanes, will be vertical, and amounts to the level separation. For small level separations, the height of the drift is significant.
   The distance from the slusher drift crown to the undercut floor is 4.5 m $- 3$ m $= 1.5$ m (5 ft). The vertical distance adjustment curve in Fig. 10.13 considers separations only as low as 3 m, so 3 m is used.
   The adjustment $DC = 0.80$. Note that the MBR does not figure in this adjustment, where vertical distance is being considered.

Block panel size
The panel size dimension is taken perpendicular to the advancing cave line. The most unfavorable condition is selected, which in this case will be the maximum void opened up.
   For a 61 m by 61 m block, using diagonal retreat caving, the distance used will be well in excess of 61 m. Adjustment $PS = 1.0$.

Final MBR computation
The adjustments are as follows:
Major structures $S = 0.82$
Caveline distance $DC = 0.80$
Block/panel size $PS = 1.0$
The final MBR is thus:
Adjusted MBR $\times S \times DC \times PS = 45 \times 0.82 \times 0.80 \times 1.0 = 29.52 = 30$.

Support recommendations

Isolated drifts
From the support chart in Fig. 10.11, it is readily seen that an isolated drift in altered porphyry (MBR $= 63$) would require rock bolts in either a wide or medium pattern; mesh may occasionally be required.

Development support

From the same chart in Fig. 10.11 and an adjusted MBR of 45, one would recommend close pattern bolting with mesh in better sections. Elsewhere, bolts and shotcrete, or occasional light steel, will be needed to stabilize the opening prior to final lining.

Production support

The final MBR is 30. For slusher lanes, repair is fairly routine because of brow damage. The recommended support from Fig. 10.15, corresponds to reinforced concrete over bolts or over bolts and mesh. A short planned service life may lead to the selection of lighter support.

For intersections, additional concrete reinforcement should be provided.

ROOF SUPPORT DESIGN IN COAL MINING

The design of roof support for coal mines requires different procedures than those used in civil engineering tunneling and in hard rock mining. There are a number of reasons for this: different strata conditions (horizontally bedded rock formations), the shape of the entries (rectangular openings in the USA because of optimization of extraction), type of support (almost exclusively rock-bolting), method of construction (mainly machine cutting by 'continuous miners') and mining regulations. Currently, the U.S. mining industry uses some 120 million rockbolts per year, the majority of them in coal mining. In 1980, about 27,500 km of tunnels were constructed in U.S. coal mines, with coal production per kilometer of tunnel being 10,500 metric tons (USNCTT, 1981). As stated before, over 90% of underground coal production is by the room-and-pillar method which is the most economical for an average depth of coal mining of 150 m below the surface.

Title 30 of the Code of Federal Regulations (1977) states that openings should not exceed 6.1 meters in width, where roof-bolting is the sole means of support, nor should they exceed 9.2 m when roof-bolts and other support, such as wood posts, are used. Section 75 of CFR 30 stipulates that in no case should the length of roof-bolts be less than 0.76 m plus 0.3 m if anchored in the stronger strata to suspend the immediate roof. The bolt spacing and the distance between the bolt and the rib or the face should not be more than 1.5 m. Mechanical bolts should be tensioned to 50% of the yield point of the bolt or the anchorage capacity. Miners may not work under an unsupported roof.

Principles of roof support

The aim of any rock reinforcement is to enable the rock strata to support itself, that is, to utilize the inherent strength of the rock mass as much as possible. The purpose of the support is thus to increase the competance of the roof strata to achieve full stability after an opening has been made.

The commonly accepted modes of roof support are: suspension (of the weaker layers from a competent layer), beam building (by bonding and friction effect in the layers of the roof) and the keying effect (by bolting the planes of weakness). In the suspension principle it is assumed that the rock bolts are so spaced that their combined bolt-capacity is equal to the dead weight of the strata that would tend to fall into the opening. In beam building, the purpose of rock bolting is to reinforce the rock so that it will become a part of the total structure supporting the opening. The reinforced layers act as a single beam capable of supporting itself and the overlying rock.

In stratified and jointed rock the bolts create a principal compressive stress normal to the free surface of the opening. This, in turn, creates a zone of rock which acts as a structural membrane capable of providing its own support (Lang, 1961). Although the rock bolts form a beam, the basic action is still essentially that of an arch (Lang and Bischoff, 1981).

Mechanical bolts

Mechanical bolts today account for approximately 75% of the 120 million bolts installed annually in U.S. mines (Scott, 1980). Although there are several types of mechanical bolts, all have in common a mechanical device that anchors the bolt at the back of the borehole.

The non-anchored end of the bolt protrudes from the hole and is attached to a bearing plate that is flush against the roof. As the mechanical anchor is activated, the bolt is stretched between the bearing plate and the anchor point.

Mechanical bolts are always 'pre-tensioned' at the time of installation to a load level of at least 50 percent of the yield strength of the bolt (CFR 30, 1977). With mechanical bolts, any differential bed sag stretches the bolt, introducing a tensile stress in the bolt and a compressive force on the rock countering the direction of movement. The magnitude of this force depends upon the length of the bolt, and without pre-tensioning a large deformation would occure before the bolt mobilized sufficient support resistance. The purpose of pre-tensioning is to prevent rock movement rather than inhibit it and because of pre-tensioning, mechanical bolts are an active method of roof support.

It is generally accepted that mechanical bolts support the roof by suspension (Snyder et al., 1979) and particularly by beam building through a friction effect (Panek, 1964). Lamination of the roof in coal mines requires that the individual layers slide across one another as they deform. This sliding action is opposed by friction, and the mechanical bolts act to increase the friction resistance by applying a compressive force normal to the friction surface.

The effectiveness of mechanical bolts is determined by the quality of their anchorage in the rock. In many instances of bolt failure, the strength of the bolt is not approached but the anchor fails. Even where complete failure does not occur anchor slippage can be a very serious problem. Anchor slippage allows bed separation, which reduces the frictional shear strength of the bedding planes. The basic cause of the anchorage problem with mechanical bolts is the stress concentration at the anchorage point.

Resin bolts

With the introduction of fast-setting high-strength resins in the early 1970s, it became possible to integrate fully-grouted bolting into the high-speed mining cycle of U.S. coal mines. Today approximately one-quarter of all roof-bolts installed are resin bolts (Mahyara et al., 1981). Two other types of fully-grouted non-tensioned bolts are cement-grouted bolts and 'pumpable' bolts (Zink and Wang, 1977, Serbousek and Bolstad, 1981).

Resin bolting is simple in concept – a hole is drilled in the roof and a rebar is inserted in it and grouted. Resin bolts are a passive support since they apply little load to the rock unless movement occurs.

An advantage of resin bolts is their resistance to transverse shear (Fairhurst and Singh, 1974, Pells, 1974). The bonded bolt acts only where a crack in the rock tends to dilate, and all stretching in the bolt is confined to a very short section. Thus, high unit stresses are developed in response to movement (Reed, 1974). In addition, resin bolts are effective in maintaining the initial friction between layers. Nevertheless, resin bolts are thought to support the roof primarily through suspension (Snyder et al., 1979). Resin bolts achieve good anchorage even in weak rock which brings in a suspension aspect. Hoek and Brown (1980) liken the support effect of grouted bolts to steel-reinforcing in concrete – the bolts increase the internal strength of the rock mass.

Determination of design parameters for roof-bolting in coal mines

Design charts have been developed (Unal, 1983) for mechanical and resin grouted bolts for application in U.S. coal mines. The following equations are used for calculations:

Mechanical bolts
  1. Rock-load height:

$$h_t = \left[\frac{100 - \text{RMR}}{100} \right] B$$

  2. Bolt length (assumed that the bolt anchor is in the compression zone for suspension effect):

$$L_b = \frac{h_t}{2}$$

where
  h_t is the rock-load height;
  B is the roof span;
  RMR is the rock mass rating for the Geomechanics Classification.

  3. Bolt capacity (determined from pull-out tests in the field):

$$C_b = L_y \text{ or } L_f \text{ whichever is smaller}$$

where
  L_y = yield-load of steel;
  L_f = anchorage failure-load.

  4. Bolt spacing (includes a safety factor of 1.5 corresponding to a reduction of the anchorage capacity by 67%, equivalent to bolt tension $T = C_b/1.5$, to meet mining regulations):

$$S_b = \frac{C_b}{1.5 \, \gamma \, h_t}$$

Resin bolts
  1. Rock-load height:

$$h_t = \left[\frac{100 - \text{RMR}}{100} \right] B$$

2. Bolt length = resin length:

$$L_r = \sqrt{\frac{\gamma B^2 h_t}{2\sigma_h}} \quad \text{or} \quad \sqrt{\frac{B^2 h_t}{300}}$$

where σ_h is the horizontal stress acting on the roof arch and γ is the unit weight of the rock. The lower limit of the lateral stress necessary for maintaining a roof arch is assumed to be 1.15 MPa (167 psi) for a depth of 150 m (500 ft) corresponding to one-third of the vertical stress. For $\gamma = 25.1$ kN/m³ (160 lb/ft³) the simplified expression is obtained.

3. Bolt capacity and spacing: As for mechanical bolts.

Bolts and posts

Total rock pressure (rock-load):

$$P_t = \gamma h_t$$

Pressure on posts:

$$P_p = \gamma h_p$$

Pressure on bolts:

$$P_b = \gamma h_b$$

Rock-load capacity by posts:

$$C_p^* = \frac{C_p}{A_p}$$

where

C_p is load capacity of each post (tons);
A_p is the area supported by each post.

Rock-load height carried by bolts:

$$h_b = \frac{\gamma h_t - C_p^*}{\gamma}$$

Design charts

A series of design charts (Unal, 1983) for entries and intersections is available, as depicted. A guided design example demonstrates the use of the step-by-step design procedure.

GUIDED DESIGN PROBLEM

A roof support system is to be designed for a 6.1 m wide coal mine entry. Consider the use of mechanical and resin grouted bolts. The following figure illustrates the coal seam, the overlying and underlying strata.
Depth of coal seam below surface: 152 m

Roof-support design chart for coal mining – Entry width: 20-ft

ROOF ROCK CLASS	ROCK MASS RATING (RMR)	ROCK LOAD HEIGHT HT (FT)	SUPPORT SPECIFICATIONS		ALTERNATE SUPPORT PATTERNS		SPECIFICATIONS FOR POSTS
			MECHANICAL BOLTS	RESIN BOLTS	MECHANICAL BOLTS/POSTS	RESIN BOLTS/POSTS	
I VERY GOOD	90	2.0	L : 2.5' S : 5' x 5' G : 40 φ : 5/8" C : 6.2 tons			Not economical	
	80	4.0	L : 2.5' S : 5' x 4.5' G : 60 (40) φ : 3/4" (7/8") C : 11 tons	L : 2.5' S : 5' x 5' G : 60 φ : 3/4" C : 12 tons			
II GOOD	70	6.0	L : 3.0' S : 4' x 4' G : 60 φ : 3/4" C : 10 tons	L : 3.0' S : 5' x 5' G : 60 φ : 3/4" C : 18 tons			
	60	8.0	L : 4.0' S : 5' x 5' G : 60 φ : 5/8" C : 9 tons	L : 4.0' S : 5' x 5' G : 60 φ : 1" C : 23.7 tons			φp = 5.5" Sp = 10'
III	50	10.0	L : 5.0' S : 5' x 5' G : 40 φ : 3/4" C : 8 tons	L : 4.0' S : 5' x 4' G : 60 φ : 1" C : 23.7 tons			φp = 6.5" Sp = 10'
FAIR	40	12.0	L : 6.0' S : 4' x 5' G : 40 φ : 3/4" C : 7 tons	L : 4.0' S : 4' x 4' G : 60 φ : 1" C : 23.7 tons			φp = 6.5" Sp = 7.5'
IV	30	14.0	L : 7.0' S : 5' x 5' G : 40 φ : 5/8" C : 6 tons	L : 5' S : 5' x 5' G : 60 φ : 3/4" C : 12 tons		Sp = 4.5'	φp = 5.5" Sp = 5'
POOR	20	16.0	L : 8.0' S : 4' x 4.5' G : 40 φ : 5/8" C : 5 tons	L : 5' S : 5' x 5' G : 60 φ : 3/4" C : 12 tons		Sp = 5'	φp = 6.0"

L = bolt length
S = bolt spacing
G = grade of steel
φ = bolt diameter
c = bolt capacity
φp = post diameter
Sp = post spacing

Roof-support design chart for coal mining–Entry width: 18-ft

ROCK CLASS	ROCK MASS RATING (RMR)	ROCK LOAD HEIGHT HT (FT)	SUPPORT SPECIFICATIONS		ENTRY / ALTERNATE SUPPORT PATTERNS		SPECIFICATIONS FOR POSTS
			MECHANICAL BOLTS	RESIN BOLTS	MECHANICAL BOLTS/POSTS	RESIN BOLTS/POSTS	
I VERY GOOD	90	1.8	L : 2.5' S : 5' x 5' G : 40 φ : 5/8" C : 6.2 tons				
	80	3.6	L : 2.5' S : 5' x 5' G : 60 (40) φ : 3/4" (7/8") C : 11 tons				
II GOOD	70	5.4	L : 3.0' S : 4.5' x 4' G : 60 φ : 3/4" C : 10 tons	L : 2.5' S : 4.5' x 5' G : 40 φ : 1" C : 15 tons			
	60	7.2	L : 4.0' S : 4.5' x 5' G : 60 φ : 5/8" C : 9 tons	L : 3.0' S : 4.5' x 4.5' G : 60 φ : 1" C : 18 tons			φ$_p$ = 4.0" s$_p$ = 7.5'
III FAIR	50	9.0	L : 5.0' S : 4.5' x 5' G : 40 φ : 3/4" C : 8 tons	L : 4.0' S : 4.5' x 5' G : 60 φ : 1" C : 23.7 tons			φ$_p$ = 5.5" s$_p$ = 10.0'
	40	10.8	L : 6.0' S : 4.5' x 5' G : 40 φ : 3/4" C : 7 tons	L : 4.0' S : 4.5' x 4' G : 60 φ : 1" C : 23.7 tons			φ$_p$ = 5.0" s$_p$ = 5.0'
IV POOR	30	12.6	L : 7.0' S : 4.5' x 4.5' G : 40 φ : 5/8" C : 6 tons	L : 4.0' S : 4' x 4' G : 60 φ : 1" C : 23.7 tons			φ$_p$ = 5.0" s$_p$ = 4.5'
	20	14.4	L : 8.0' S : 4.5' x 4' G : 40 φ : 5/8" C : 5 tons	L : 4.0' S : 4' x 4' G : 60 φ : 1-1/4" C : 28.74 tons			φ$_p$ = 5.0" s$_p$ = 4.0'

Roof-support design chart for coal mining – Entry width: 16-ft

ROCK CLASS	ROCK MASS RATING (RMR)	ROCK LOAD HEIGHT (RMR) (FT)	SUPPORT SPECIFICATIONS		ALTERNATE SUPPORT - PATTERNS		SPECIFICATIONS FOR POSTS
			MECHANICAL BOLTS	RESIN BOLTS	MECHANICAL BOLTS/POSTS	RESIN BOLTS/POSTS	
I VERY GOOD	90	1.6	L : 2.5' S : 6' × 5' G : 40 φ : 5/8" C : 6.2 tons			Not economical	
	80	3.2	L¹: 2.5' S²: 6'×5' G : 60 (40) φ : 3/4" C : 11 tons			Not economical	
II GOOD	70	4.8	L : 3.0' S : 4'× 4.5' G : 60 (40) φ : 3/4" C : 10 tons	L : 2.5' S : 4' × 5' G : 60 φ : 3/4" C : 12 tons			
	60	6.4	L : 4.0' S : 4'× 5' G : 60 φ : 5/8" C : 9 tons	L : 3.0' S : 4'× 5' G : 40 φ : 1" C : 15.8 tons			φp = 4.0" Sp = 10'
III FAIR	50	8.0	L : 4.0' S : 4'× 5' G : 40 φ : 3/4" C : 8 tons	L : 3.0' S : 4'× 4.5' G : 60 φ : 1" C : 18 tons			φp = 5.0" Sp = 10'
	40	9.6	L : 5.0' S : 4'× 5' G : 40 φ : 3/4" C : 7 tons	L : 4.0' S : 4'× 5' G : 60 φ : 1" C : 23.7 tons			φp = 5.5" Sp = 10'
IV POOR	30	11.2	L : 6.0' S : 4'× 5' G : 40 φ : 5/8" C : 6 tons	L : 4.0' S : 4'× 4.5' G : 60 φ : 1" C : 23.7 tons			φp = 4.5" Sp = 5'
	20	12.8	L : 7.0' S : 4'× 5' G : 40 φ : 5/8" C : 5 tons	L : 4.0' S : 4'× 4' G : 60 φ : 1" C : 23.7 tons			φp = 5.0" Sp = 5'

Roof-support design chart for coal mining – Intersection of two entries, Entry width: 20-ft

ROCK CLASS	ROCK MASS RATING RMR	ROCK LOAD HEIGHT H_R (FT)	SUPPORT SPECIFICATIONS		ALTERNATE SUPPORT – PATTERNS	
			MECHANICAL BOLTS/POSTS	RESIN BOLTS/POSTS	MECHANICAL BOLTS/POSTS	RESIN BOLTS/POSTS
I VERY GOOD	90	2.8	L : 2.5' S : 5' x 5' G : 40 φ : 3/4" C : 8.8 tons	L* : 3.0'/3.0' S : 5' x 5' G : 40 φ : 3/4" C : 8.8 tons		
	80	5.7	L : 3.0' S : 5' x 5' G : 40 φ : 5/8" C : 6.2 tons $φ_p$: 4"	L* : 4.0'/4.0' S : 5' x 5' G : 60 φ : 1" C : 23.7 tons		
II GOOD	70	8.5	L : 5.0' S : 5' x 5' G : 40 φ : 3/4" C : 8.8 tons $φ_p$: 5"	L* : 3.0'/5.0' S : 5' x 5' G : 60 φ : 3/4" C : 13.2 tons $φ_p$: 4.5"		
	60	11.3	L : 6.0' S : 5' x 5' G : 40 φ : 3/4" C : 8.8 tons $φ_p$: 6"	L* : 3.5'/6.0' S : 5' x 5' G : 60 φ : 3/4" C : 13.2 tons $φ_p$: 5.5"		

$L*$: Resin Length/Bolt Length

Roof-support design chart for coal mining–Intersection of two entries, Entry width: 20-ft

ROCK CLASS	ROCK MASS RATING RMR	ROCK LOAD HEIGHT H_R (FT)	SUPPORT SPECIFICATIONS		ALTERNATE SUPPORT – PATTERNS	
			MECHANICAL BOLTS/POSTS	RESIN BOLTS/POSTS	MECHANICAL BOLTS/POSTS	RESIN BOLTS/POSTS
III FAIR	50	14.2	L : 7.0' S : 5' x 5' G : 40 φ : 5/8" C : 6.2 tons $φ_p$: 7"	L*: 3.5'/6.0' S : 5' x 5' G : 60 φ : 3/4" C : 13.2 tons $φ_p$: 6.5"		
	40	17.0	L : 9.0' S : 5' x 5' G : 40 φ : 5/8" C : 6.2 tons $φ_p$: 5.5"	L*: 3.5'/7.0' S : 5' x 5' G : 40 φ : 1" C : 15.8 tons $φ_p$: 7"		
IV POOR	30	19.8	L : 10.0' S : 5' x 5' G : 40 φ : 5/8" C : 6.0 tons $φ_p$: 6.0"	L*: 4.5'/8.0' S : 5' x 5' G : 60 φ : 1" C : 23.7 tons $φ_p$: 7"		
	20	22.6	L : 12.0' S : 5' x 4' G : 40 φ : 5/8" C : 5.0 tons $φ_p$: 6.5"	L*: 5.0'/8.0' S : 5' x 4' G : 60 φ : 1" C : 23.7 tons $φ_p$: 7"		

Stratigraphic column

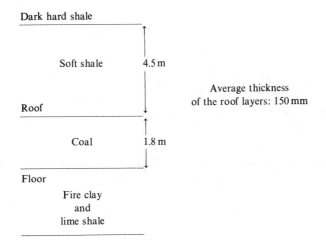

Tests have been carried out in the roof strata and the coal seam yielding the following property data.

Data	Coal	Soft shale	Dark shale
Thickness (m)	1.8	4.5	27.5
Unit weight kN/m³	12.5	25.1	26.7
Young's modulus (GPa)	3.2	10.3	14.5
Uniaxial compressive strength (MPa)	17	40	81
Rock strata conditions	NA	Separation < 1 mm; slightly weathered, slightly rough surfaces; no infilling	
Ground water conditions	Damp	Damp	Damp
In situ stresses	Horizontal stress = Vertical stress		

SOLUTION

Step 1: Determine the rock mass rating (RMR) for roof strata and summarize all input parameters for design

In accordance with the Geomechanics Classification, the following ratings are obtained for the classification parameters:

Strength of intact rock (soft shale): 40 MPa	rating = 4
Spacing of discontinuities: 150 mm	rating = 8
Rock quality designation RQD: 60% for 150 mm spacing (see chart)	rating = 13
Condition of strata: separation < 1 mm, slightly weathered and slightly rough (see Table A)	rating = 25
Groundwater conditions: damp throughout	rating = 10
	Basic RMR = 60
Adjustments: orientation of discontinuities: horizontal = fair;	rating = −5

in situ stresses: multiplier $A_s = 1.0$ for $\sigma_h = \sigma_v$
machine excavation: multiplier $A_B = 1.0$

Adjusted RMR = 55

Stand-up time: $\sim$ 5 weeks

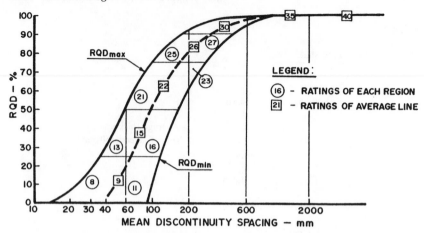

Chart for correlation between RQD and discontinuity spacing

Table A. Assessment of discontinuity conditions in coal mines for the Geomechanics Classification (RMR)

Separation of bedding	None	Hairline	< 1 mm	1–5 mm	> 5 mm
Roughness of surfaces	Very rough	Rough	Smooth	Slickensided	Slickensided
Weathering of surfaces	Fresh, hard	Slightly weathered	Highly weathered	Highly weathered	Completely weathered
Infilling (gouge)	None	None	Minor clay	Stiff clay, gouge	Soft clay, gouge
Continuity	All bedding planes continuous across entry				
Rating	30	25	20	10	0

Summary of input parameters for design:

$RMR = 55$ Depth $H = 152$ m   Roof thickness $h_i = 4.5$ m
Entry width $B = 6.1$ m   Seam height $h = 1.8$ m   Stress ratio $\sigma_h/\sigma_v = 1.0$

Step 2: Determine the practical spacing-patterns for the entry-width

Make a small sketch for the purpose of having a quick and easy reference for different bolt-spacings. Logical and practical spacing-patterns should be assigned to each entry based on the number of bolts to be used across the opening. Such patterns are:

For three bolts in a 6.1 m span:

Pattern $(S_1 \times S_2)$	Average spacing $(S = \sqrt{S_1 \times S_2})$
1.5 × 1.5	1.5
1.5 × 1.37	1.4
1.5 × 1.2	1.35
1.5 × 1.0	1.27

For four bolts in a 6.1 m span:

1.2 × 1.5	1.36
1.2 × 1.37	1.3
1.2 × 1.2	1.2
1.2 × 1.0	1.1

Step 3: Calculate the rock-load height

The rock-load height (h_t) is given by:

$$h_t = \left(\frac{100 - \text{RMR}}{100}\right)B$$

$$h_t = \left(\frac{100 - 55}{100}\right)6.1$$

$$h_t = 2.75\,\text{m}\,(9\,\text{ft})$$

If the RMR value is not known, the rock-load height can be estimated from the roof-fall data by taking the roof-fall height as the rock-load height. At this point it should be noted that for coal mining purposes the options for the types of bolts are limited to mechanical and resin bolts with a possibility of additional wooden-posts for both bolt-types. The resin bolts include full-column bolting and 'combination' bolting. Other bolt-types (i.e. roof trusses and yieldable bolts) can be analyzed but are not considered in this example.

Step 4: Calculate the design parameters for mechanical bolts

a) Rock-load height $\quad h_t = 2.75\,\text{m}$ (from Step 3)

b) Bolt length $\qquad L = \dfrac{h_t}{2}$

$$L = 1.4\,\text{m}\,(4.5\,\text{ft})$$

c) Bolt capacity

Determine the anchorage failure load (L'_f) from in situ tests. If these are not performed, then Table B can be used as a rough estimate. Thus for RMR = 55, $L'_f = 8.5$ tons.

Table B. Estimated anchorage failure-loads of mechanical bolts* (after Unal, 1983)

Rock mass rating (RMR)	Anchorage failure Load L_f tons	Metric t
100	14	12.7
90	12	10.9
80	11	10.0
70	10	9.1
60	9	8.2
50	8	7.3
40	7	6.4
30	6	5.5
20	5	4.6

*During preliminary design, the values shown above are useful for making estimates of the anchorage capacity. However, anchorage strengths to provide design information must eventually be determined by conducting pull-tests at the site.

Table C. Mechanical properties of Grade 40 steel-rods (after Gerdeen et al., 1977)

Nominal Diameter		Yield load (L'_y)		Ultimate lead	
		Tons	Tonnes	Tons	Tonnes
Grade 40 steel-rod					
5/8″	16 mm	6.2	5.6	10.8	9.8
3/4″	19 mm	8.8	8.0	15.4	14.0
7/8″	22 mm	12.0	10.9	21.0	19.1
1.0″	25 mm	15.8	14.4	27.6	25.1
$1\frac{1}{8}″$	29 mm	20.0	18.2	35.0	38.8
$1\frac{3}{8}″$	35 mm	31.2	28.4	54.0	49.1
5/8″	16 mm	9.3	8.5	13.9	12.6
3/4″	19 mm	13.2	12.0	19.8	18.0
7/8″	22 mm	18.0	16.4	27.0	24.5
1.0″	25 mm	23.7	21.5	35.5	32.3
$1\frac{1}{8}″$	29 mm	30.0	27.3	45.0	40.9
$1\frac{3}{8}″$	33 mm	46.8	42.5	70.0	63.6

Determine the yield load (L'_y) of bolts: Since the anchorage failure-load should match the steel yield load, utilizing Table B and Table C, a suitable yield-load (L'_y) can be selected for bolt diameter (ϕ) and grade of steel (G):

(ϕ)	(G)	(L'_y)	
19 mm (3/4″)	40	8.8 tons (8.0 t)	From Table B
16 mm (5/8″)	60	9.3 tons (8.5 t)	From Table C

These yield loads are the closest values to the anchorage failure-load for standard sizes of bolts. The less expensive of the two should be selected. Determine the bolt capacity (C_b) as follows:

$C_b = L'_f$ or L'_y whichever is smaller:

$C_b = 8.5$ tons (7.7 t)

  d) Bolt spacing

The bolt spacing is calculated for a safety factor = 1.5 as:

$$S_b = \sqrt{\frac{C_b}{SF \, \gamma \, h_t}}$$

$S_b = 0.85$ m (2.8 ft)

A bolt spacing of 0.85 m is not practical and supporting the entry with mechanical bolts alone would not be economical. Therefore the next logical step is to consider either what additional support can supplement mechanical bolts or change the type of bolt.

Step 5: Calculate the design parameters for mechanical bolts and wood posts

Make use of rock-load height (h_t) and bolt capacity (C_b) determined in Step 4. Other parameters such as the compressive strength of the post (C_p), the effective roof-area supported by each post (A_p), the load capacity of the post (C'_b) and the rock-load height supported by post (h_b) must be determined in this step.

The roof-support pattern is directly influenced by the post diameter and the post spacing. Each post-diameter, with predetermined capacities leads to a unique bolting pattern, for a selected value of post spacing. Additional support is not required by the mining regulations if the entry width is equal to or less than 6.1 m. Therefore, if posts are used for such entries, the post spacing is not restricted by law. However, for practical purposes, a maximum post-spacing of 3 m (10 ft) is suggested.

Perform a tabulation by considering the following:

a) Try post-diameters ranging from 100 mm (4″) to 175 mm (7″), in increments of 12.7 mm (1/2″).

b) Find the relevant post capacities from Table D.

c) Try post-spacings (S_p) which are simple multiples of the commonly used bolt spacings (S_b) i.e.,

$$S_p = 1.0 S_b, 1.5 S_b, 2.0 S_b$$

where

$$S_b = 1.2 \text{ m}, 1.37 \text{ m and } 1.5 \text{ m}$$

d) Calculate the pressure on a post (rock pressure which can be carried by each post).

e) Calculate the rock-load height to be carried by the bolts (h_b).

f) Calculate the bolt spacing.

g) If possible, select a bolt spacing closest to a 1.5 m × 1.5 m pattern which is the optimum arrangement when mining regulations and economy are considered. Note that for roof-spans other than 6.1 m, the optimum bolting pattern might change.

h) To calculate the bolt length (L) and the bolt capacity (C_b) follow the procedure in Step 4 (b) and (c)

Table D. Estimated minimum capacities of standard size of mine posts (after Unal, 1983)

Post diameter (in)	ϕ_p (mm)	Minimum capacity C_p	
		tons	tonnes
4	100	20	18.2
5	127	30	27.3
6	150	50	45.5
7	178	70	63.6

One sample calculation is demonstrated for a 150 mm (6″) diameter post with a capacity of 50 tons (45.5 t) at a post spacing of 3 m (10 ft). These calculations are performed on a programmable hand calculator. Example:

ϕ_p:6.0 in (150 mm)
C_p:50 tons (45.5 t)
S_p:10 ft (3 m)
h_t:9 ft (2.75 m)
C_b:8.5 tons (7.7 t)
γ:160 lbs/ft³ (25.1 kN/m)³

$$C_p' = \frac{C_p \times 2000}{S_p \times (B/2)} = \frac{(50 \text{ tons})(2000 \text{ lbs/ton})}{(10 \text{ ft})(20/2 \text{ ft})} = 1000 \text{ lbs/ft}^2 (47.9 \text{ kPa})$$

$$h_b = h_t - \frac{C_p'}{\gamma} = (9 \text{ ft}) - \frac{(1000 \text{ lbs/ft}^2)}{(160 \text{ lbs/ft}^3)} = 2.75 \text{ ft} (0.84 \text{ m})$$

$$S_b = \sqrt{\frac{C_b \times 2000}{SF \times \gamma \times h_b}} = \sqrt{\frac{(8.5 \text{ tons})(2000 \text{ lbs/ton})}{(1.5)(160 \text{ lbs/ft}^2)(2.75 \text{ ft})}} = 5.08 \text{ ft} (1.55 \text{ m})$$

Referring to Step 2, this bolt spacing (S_b) is preferable since it provides a bolting pattern of 1.5 m × 1.5 m which is within the mining regulations and requires the least amount of bolts across the entry.

Consideration of other possibilities will show that there are five viable alternatives. The deciding parameter is the maximum bolt-spacing allowed by the mining regulations. Further, economic considerations indicate that in this particular example the maximum post-spacing, 3 m (10 ft), provides the most economical combination. Consequently, the following support specification and pattern are the final choice for the entry supported by mechanical bolts and posts:

Bolt length	L_b: 1.5 m
Bolt spacing	S_b: 1.5 × 1.5 m
Steel grade	G: 40
Bolt diameter	ϕ_b: 19 mm
Bolt capacity	C_b: 8.5 tons
Post diameter	ϕ_p: 150 mm
Post spacing	S_p: 3 m
Post capacity	C_p: 50 tons

Support pattern:

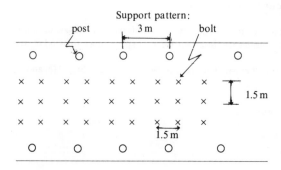

Step 6: Calculate the design parameters for resin bolts

a) Rock-load height, h_t, remains the same as in Step 3.

$$h_t = 2.75 \text{ m}$$

b) Resin length:

$$L_r = \sqrt{\frac{\gamma B^2 h_t}{2\sigma_h}}$$

If the value of the in-situ horizontal stress is not known, use the equation given below:

$$L_r = \sqrt{\frac{1}{300} B^2 h_t}$$

$L_p = 1.06$ m (3.5 ft) is the minimum resin length required.

c) Bolt length: If posts are not used as an additional support, the bolt length is equal to the resin length.

$$L_b = L_r$$

$$L_{b_{min}} = 1.1 \text{ m}$$

This is the minimum length required but the resin length (and hence the bolt length) can be increased to obtain a better spacing provided that the bolt capacity is adjusted accordingly.

d) Bolt capacity:

$$C_b = L_f' \text{ or } L_y' \text{ whichever is smaller.}$$

The anchorage failure-load (L_f') is

$$L_f' = \frac{L_r \times 12}{BF} = 16.8 \text{ tons} (15.3 \text{ t})$$

where the bond factor $BF = 2.5$ in/ton (6.99 cm/t) is selected from Table E.

Table E. Recommended data for anchorage of resin grouted bolts in rough drill-holes with 1/8 inch (3 mm) thickness annulus (after Gerdeen et al., 1977)

Compressive strength of rock	Bond factor inch/ton	cm/t	Diameter required			
			Bolt in.	mm	Hole in.	mm
3.5–7 MPa	3.75	10.48	0.75	19	1.00	25
(500–1000 psi)						
Mudstone	3.00	8.38	1.00	25	1.25	32
Silstone	2.50	6.99	1.25	32	1.50	38
10–20 MPa	2.50	6.99	0.75	19	1.00	25
(1500–3000 psi)						
Coal	2.00	5.59	1.00	25	1.25	32
Shale	1.67	4.67	1.25	32	1.50	38
25–70 MPa	1.88	5.25	0.75	19	1.00	25
(4000–10,000 psi)						
Sandstone	1.50	4.19	1.00	25	1.25	32
Limestone	1.25	3.49	1.25	32	1.50	38

The steel yield load (L_y') is obtained from Tables B and C. For $\phi = 19$ mm and $G = 60$, $L_y' = 13.2$ tons (12 t). Thus: $C_b = 13.2$ tons since $L_y' < L_f'$.
    e) Bolt spacing (S_b) is determined from:

$$S_b = \sqrt{\frac{C_b}{1.5 \times \gamma \times h_t}}$$

$$= 3.5 \text{ ft} (1.06 \text{ m})$$

With reference to Step 2, this bolt spacing is too small for practical and economical installation. Thus, other combinations of bolt diameter, bolt length and steel grade should be considered.
    Among the many combinations, there are three viable alternatives, namely:

$L_b(m)$	$\phi_b(m)$	G	$C_b(t)$	$S_b(m)$	Pattern	Remarks
1.1	32	40	25.0	1.47	1.5×1.35	Expensive
1.1	25	60	21.0	1.35	1.2×1.5	$SF < 1.5$
1.2	25	60	23.7	1.43	1.2×1.5	Best

A bolting pattern of $1.5 \text{ m} \times 1.5 \text{ m}(5' \times 5')$ is not possible due to a limitation of the maximum recommended bolt-capacity. The deciding parameter in this example is the maximum bolt-spacing that can be provided within the limitations of the mining regulations, safety factors and economy. From the values shown above, a 25 mm diameter bolt, 1.2 m long and grade 60 rebar, is the best choice. The 1.2 m length best utilizes the full strength of the bolt since the steel yield-load is only very slightly less than the anchorage yield-load. The shorter bolt provides too small a spacing pattern while the longer bolt is a waste.

The following are the recommended support specifications when resin bolts are used without additional support:

L_b: 1.2 m
S_b: 1.2 m × 1.5 m
G: 60
ϕ: 25 mm
C_b: 23.7 tons ·

Again, this pattern meets all legal requirements, offers good stability, ease of installation and an adequate factor of safety.

Step 7: Calculate the design parameters for resin bolts and posts

It is obvious from the previous step that, using posts as an additional support is not feasible. The following observations can be made:

a) The maximum allowable spacing pattern is 1.5 m × 1.5 m while a spacing of 1.2 m × 1.5 m is already achieved without using posts.

b) Using posts would reduce the resin length from 1.2 m to only 0.76 m.

c) Improvements in the number of bolts needed, might not be economically justified even with the smallest available post size (100 mm) and bolt size ($\phi = 16$ mm, $G = 40$) due to limitations imposed by the mining regulations.

Step 8: Comparison of mechanical bolting with resin bolting

The final choice between the two types of roof bolting is made on economical grounds. Below is a summary of the two alternatives.

Roof support for 6.1 m wide coal mine entry
RMR = 55   Rock-load = 2.75 m

Parameter	Mechanical bolts Bolts	Posts	Resin bolts (fully bonded)
Length	1.5 m	Entry height	1.2 m
Spacing	1.5 × 1.5 m	3 m	1.5 × 1.5 m
Steel grade	40	NA	60
Diameter	19 mm	150 mm	32 mm
Capacity	8.5 tons	50 tons	28.7 tons
Bolt tension	60% capacity	NA	NA
Material cost (1982 $)		$6.59/m	$5.37/m

Step 9: Conclusion

Resin bolts, as specified in the above table, are chosen in preference to mechanical bolts with posts. The resin bolts are selected because of the lower cost of support, i.e. $5.37 per meter of tunnel length.

Step 10 *: As an after-thought, consider the effect of worsening roof conditions*

RMR = 35   Rock-load = 3.97 m

Parameter	Mechanical bolts		Resin bolts (bond length: 1.2 m)		Resin bolts
	Bolts	Posts	Bolts	Posts	(fully bonded)
Length	2.1 m	Entry height	1.5 m	Entry height	1.5 m
Spacing	1.56 m	2.4 m	1.5 × 1.5 m	3 m	1.4 × 1.5
Steel grade	40	NA	60	NA	60
Diameter	19 mm	178 mm	32 mm	114 mm	32 mm
Capacity	6.5 tons	70 tons	28.7 tons	27.5 tons	35.9 tons
Bolt tension	60% cap.	NA	NA	NA	NA
Material cost (1982$)	$8.72/m		$7.02/m		$6.36/m
Increased cost over best option	+37.1%		+10.3%		

REFERENCES

Bieniawski, Z. T. The Geomechanics Classification in rock engineering applications. *Proc. 4th Int. Cong. on Rock Mech.*, ISRM, Montreux, A. A. Balkema, Rotterdam, 1979, Vol. 2, pp. 41–48.

Bieniawski, Z. T. *Tunnel Design by Rock Mass Classifications*, U.S. Army Engineer Waterways Experiment Station, Technical Report GL–79–19, September 1979, 131 p.

Bieniawski, Z. T. The challenges of new graduate engineering courses. *Proceedings*, 1980 *Annual Conference of the American Society for Engineering Education*, University of Massachusetts, Amherst, 1980, Vol. 1, pp. 102–106.

Bieniawski, Z. T., Banks, D. C. and Nicholson, G. A. Discussion on Park River Auxiliary Tunnel, *Journal of the Construction Div.* American Society of Civil Engineers, Vol. 106, December 1980, pp. 616–618.

Blackey, E. A. Park River Auxiliary Tunnel. *Journal of the Construction Division*, American Society of Civil Engineers, Vol. 105, No. C04, December 1979, pp. 341–349.

Code of Federal Regulations (CFR30, 1977). *Mandatory Safety Standards-Underground Coal Mines.* Vol. 30, Part 75, 1977.

Cummings, R. A., Kendorski, F. S. and Bieniawski, Z. T. *Caving mine rock mass classification and support estimation*, Engineers International, Inc., Contract #J0100103 with U.S. Bureau of Mines, September 1982, 195 p.

Eck, R. W. and Wilhelm, W. J. Guided Design: An Approach to Education for the Practice of Engineering, *Engineering Education*, American Society for Engineering Education, November 1979, pp. 191–219.

Engels, J. G., Cahill, J. T. and Blackey, E. A. Geotechnical performance of a large machine-bored precast concrete lined tunnel. *Proceedings, Rapid Excavation and Tunneling Conference*, AIME, New York, 1981, Vol. 2, pp. 1510–1533.

Fairhurst, C. and Singh, B. Roof bolting in horizontally laminated rock. *Eng. and Mining Journal*, Feb. 1974, pp. 80–90.

Gerdeen, J. C., Snyder, V. W., Wiegelahn, G. L. and Parker, J. *Design Criteria for Roof Bolting Plans using Fully Resin Grouted Non-tensioned Bolts to Reinforce Bedded Mine Roof,* Bureau of Mines OFR 46(4)–80, Michigan Tech. University, NTIS No. PB80–10060, 1977.

Hoek, E. Geotechnical design for large opening at depth. *Proc. Rapid Excavation & Tunneling Conf*, AIME, New York, 1981, Vol. 2, pp. 1171–1179.

Hoek, E. and Brown E. T. *Underground Excavations in Rock*, Institution of Mining and Metallurgy, London, 1980, pp. 244–365.

Kendorski, F. S. and Cummings, R. A. Prediction of caving mine drift deformations. *Proc., 1st Int. Conf. on Stability in Underground Mining*, University of British Columbia, Vancouver, August 1982.

Kendorski, F. S., Cummings, R. A., Bieniawski, Z. T. and Skinner, E. H. Rock mass classification for block caving mine drift support. *Proc., 5th Int. Congress on Rock Mech.*, ISRM, Melbourne, Australia, April 1983, pp. B51–63.

Lama, R. D. and Vutukuri, V. S. *Handbook on Mechanical Properties of Rock*, Trans Tech Publ., Aedermannsdorf, Switzerland, Vol. 2, 1978, 481 p.

Lang, T. A. Theory and practice of rockbolting. *Trans. Amer. Inst. Mining Engers.*, Vol. 220, 1961, pp. 333–348.

Lang, T. A. and Bischoff, J. A. Research Study of Coal Mine Rock Reinforcement, *Bureau of Mines Final Report, Contract No. J0295072*, Leads, Hill and Jewett, Inc. January 1981, 224 p.

Lang, T. A. and Bischoff, J. A. Stabilization of rock excavations using rock reinforcement. *Proc. 23rd U.S. Symp. on Rock Mechanics*, AIME, New York, 1982, pp. 935–944.

Lang, T. A., Bischoff, J. A. and Wagner, P. L. *Program Plan for Determining Optimum Bolt Tension* – Theory and Application of Rock Reinforcement Systems in Coal Mines, Bureau of Mines Final Report Contract No. J0285006, Leeds, Hill and Jewitt, Inc. March 1979, 255 p.

Laubscher, D. H. *Selection of mass underground mining methods, design and operation of caving and sublevel stopping mines*, Stewart, D. R. Editor, AIME, New York, 1981, pp. 843–851.

Littlejohn, C. S. and Bruce, D. A. Rock anchors: state of the art. *Ground Engineering*, Vol. 8, No. 3, 1965, pp. 25–32, Vol. 9, No. 4, 1976, pp. 33–44.

Mahyara, A., Brest van Kempen, C. J. H., Conwey, J. P. and Jones, A. H. Controlled thrust and torque placement of mechanical anchor bolts and their relationship to improved roof control. *Proc. 1st Conf. on Ground Control in Mining*, Morgantown, W. Va., July 1981, pp. 98–105.

Norwegian Institute of Rock Blasting. *Rock Bolting – A Practical Handbook* Pergamon Press, New York, 1979, pp. 84.

Ontario Hydro Corporation. *Design Manual for Hydraulic Tunnels in Rock*, Toronto, Canada, 1978, 259 p.

Panek, L. A. Design for bolting stratified roof. *Trans. Amer. Inst. Mining Engrs.*, Vol. 229, 1964, pp. 113–119.

Patrick, W. C. and Hass, C. J. Roof support selection: a look at total cost. *Mining Congress Journal*, March 1980, pp. 45–48.

Pells, P. The behavior of fully bonded rockbolts. *Proc. 3rd Int. Cong. Rock Mech.*, ISRM, Denver, 1974, Vol. IIB, pp. 1212–1217.

Priest, S. D. and Hudson, J. A. Discontinuity spacing in rock. *Int. J. Rock Mech. and Min. Sci.*, Vol. 13, 1976, pp. 135–198.

Reed, J. J. Rock reinforcement and stabilizing bolting alternatives. Mining Congress Journal, Vol. 60, No. 12, Dec. 1974, pp. 40–45.

Scott, J. J. Interior rock reinforcement fixtures – state of the art. *Proc. 21st U.S. Symp. on Rock Mechanics*, Univ. of Missouri, Rolla, 1980, pp. 744–756.

Serbousek, M. O. and Bolstad, D. O. Inorganic cement grouted bolt system. *Proc. 1st Conf. on Ground Control in Mining*, Morgantown, W. Va., July 1981, pp. 137–140.

Snyder, W. R., Gerdeen, J. C. and Wiezelahn, G. L. Factors governing the effectiveness of roof bolting systems using fully resin grouted and nontensioned bolts. *20th U.S. Symp. on Rock Mech.*, Austin, Texas, June 1979, pp 607–614.

Unal, E. Design Guidelines and Roof Control Standards for Coal Mine Roofs, Ph.D. Thesis, The Pennsylvania State University, 1983, 355 p.

U.S. Army Corps of Engineers. *Rock Reinforcement-Engineering and Design*. Engineer Manual EM–1110–2–2901, 1980.

U.S. National Committee on Tunneling Technology. *Demand Forecast of Underground Construction and Mining in the United States*. National Academy Press, Washington, DC, 1981, 27 p.

Voegele, M., Fairhurst, C. and Cundall, P. A. Analysis of tunnel support loads using a large displacement, disticnt block model. *Proc. 1st Int. Symp. Storage in Excavated Rock Caverns*, Rockstore, Stockholm, 1977, Vol. 2, pp. 247–252.

Wales, C. E. *Guided Design Approach*, Educational Technology Publications, Englewood Cliffs, NJ, 1978.

Wales, C. E. (Editor). *Proceedings of National Conference on Teaching Decision-Making and Guided Design*, West Virginia University, Morgantown, 1980, 198 p.

Wales, C. E. and Stager, R. A. The Design of an Educational System. *Engineering Education*, Vol. 62, No. 5, February 1972, pp. 456–459.

Wales, C. E. and Stager, R. E. *Guided Design*, West Virginia University, Morgantown, 1977, 118 p.

Zink, G. and Wang, F. D. Application of cement grout for roof bolting. Energy Resources & Excavation Technology, *Proc. 18th U.S. Symp. on Rock Mech.*, Keystone, Colorado, June 1977, pp. 3A1–1.

Author index

Subject index